Charles M. Carmichael

# МАГНИТНЫЕ ПРЕВРАЩЕНИЯ

**MAGNITNYE PREVRASHCHENIYA**
**MAGNETIC TRANSITIONS**

# MAGNETIC TRANSITIONS

by

K. P. Belov

Authorized translation from the Russian

*by W.H. Furry*

CONSULTANTS BUREAU
NEW YORK

The original Russian text
was published by
the State Publishing House
for Physicomathematical Literature
in Moscow in 1959.
The translation incorporates revisions
made by the author
subsequent to the publication
of the Russian original.

*Белов Константин Петрович*
Магнитные превращения.

*Library of Congress Catalog Card Number: 61-11208*

*227 West 17th St., New York 11, N. Y.*


*Printed in the United States of America*

# CONTENTS


Author's Preface to American Edition ................. ix
Preface ....................................... x

CHAPTER I. The Thermodynamic Theory of the Magnetic Transition .......................... 1
1. Phase transitions of the second kind ............ 1
2. The thermodynamics of the ferromagnetic transition . . 5
3. The role of fluctuations of the long-range magnetic order.......................... 11

CHAPTER II. Phenomena in the Neighborhood of the Curie Point and Model Theories of Ferromagnetism ....... 16
1. The temperature dependence of the spontaneous magnetization in the neighborhood of the Curie point . 16
2. The curve of the true magnetization (para-process) in the neighborhood of the Curie point.......... 19
3. The paramagnetism of ferromagnetic materials above the Curie point ...................... 21
4. On the temperature dependence of the molecular-field constant ......................... 23
5. Effects of short-range magnetic order ........... 25
6. Effects of s-d exchange interaction ............ 29
7. On the temperature dependence of the spontaneous magnetization in alloys ................. 32

CHAPTER III. Investigation of the Phenomena in Ferromagnetic Materials in the Neighborhood of the Curie Point . 34
1. The thermodynamic description of the true magnetization (para-process) ............... 34
2. The susceptibility of the para-process in the neighborhood of the Curie point ............ 41
3. The temperature dependence of the spontaneous magnetization ...................... 45
4. The determination of the Curie temperature ....... 48
5. The effect of structural changes in alloys on the temperature dependence of the spontaneous magnetization in the neighborhood of the Curie point . 53

6. The "discontinuity" of the specific heat at the Curie point . . . . . . . . . . . . . . . . . . . . . . . . 66
7. The effect of allotropic transitions on the temperature dependence of the magnetization . . . . . . . . . . 68
8. On the causes of the appearance of a "tail" of the spontaneous magnetization . . . . . . . . . . . . . . . 74
9. The effects of elastic stresses on the magnetization in the region of the para-process . . . . . . . . . . . . 79
10. Magnetostriction . . . . . . . . . . . . . . . . . . . . . . . . 88
11. Determination of the spontaneous deformation of the lattice in the ferromagnetic transition . . . . . . . 92
12. Displacement of the Curie point under the influence of elastic stresses . . . . . . . . . . . . . . . . . . . . . 98
13. Magnetothermal and galvanomagnetic effects . . . . 102
14. Effects of the crystallographic magnetic anisotropy and the domain structure in the neighborhood of the Curie point . . . . . . . . . . . . . . . . . . . . . 105
15. Relaxation phenomena in ferromagnetic materials in the neighborhood of the Curie point . . . . . . . . . 107
16. The temperature dependence of ferromagnetic resonance . . . . . . . . . . . . . . . . . . . . . . . . 109
17. Ferromagnetic materials in the region above the Curie point . . . . . . . . . . . . . . . . . . . . . . . 112

CHAPTER IV. The Antiferromagnetic Transition . . . . . . . . . 124
1. On the thermodynamic theory of the antiferromagnetic transition. . . . . . . . . . . . . . . . . . . . . . . . . . 124
2. Theoretical models of antiferromagnetism . . . . . . . 127
3. The temperature dependence of the magnetic susceptibility of antiferromagnetic materials . . . 130
4. "Nonmagnetic" phenomena in the neighborhood of the antiferromagnetic transition point . . . . . . . 132
5. Resonance absorption . . . . . . . . . . . . . . . . . . . . . . 138
6. Neutron-diffraction studies . . . . . . . . . . . . . . . . . . 141
7. On the thermodynamic theory of elastic and volume anomalies in antiferromagnetic materials . . . . . 143
8. On the weak "ferromagnetism" of certain antiferromagnetic materials. . . . . . . . . . . . . . 148

CHAPTER V. Magnetic Transitions in Ferrimagnetic Materials . 153
1. On the theory of the temperature dependence of the spontaneous magnetization of ferrites . . . . . . . . . 154
2. Investigation of the magnetization of ferrites in the neighborhood of the Curie point . . . . . . . . . . . . 161
3. Study of the temperature dependence of the magnetization of ferrites that have a point of compensation . . 167
4. Ferrite garnets . . . . . . . . . . . . . . . . . . . . . . . . 176
5. A study of magnetic transitions in pyrrhotite . . . . . . . 182
6. The role of magnetic anisotropy in ferrites in the neighborhood of the Curie point . . . . . . . . . . . . 189
7. The temperature dependence of ferromagnetic resonance in ferrites . . . . . . . . . . . . . . . . . . . . . 191
8. "Nonmagnetic" properties of ferrimagnetic materials in the neighborhood of the Curie point . . . . . . . . 195
9. Low-temperature transitions in magnetite and other ferrites . . . . . . . . . . . . . . . . . . . . . . . . . . . 202
10. Ferrites in the region above the Curie point . . . . . . . . 207

CHAPTER VI. On Methods for Measuring Magnetic and "Nonmagnetic" Phenomena in the Neighborhood of the Curie Point . . . . . . . . . . . . . . . . . . . . . 212
1. Methods for measuring the magnetization . . . . . . . . . 212
2. Thermal expansion and magnetostriction . . . . . . . . . 216
3. Elastic moduli and internal friction coefficient . . . . . 219
4. Galvanomagnetic effects . . . . . . . . . . . . . . . . . . . 223
5. Resonance absorption . . . . . . . . . . . . . . . . . . . . 225

Material Added in Proof . . . . . . . . . . . . . . . . . . . . . 227

Literature Cited . . . . . . . . . . . . . . . . . . . . . . . . . 233

# AUTHOR'S PREFACE TO AMERICAN EDITION

It is very pleasing to me that the book Magnetic Transitions has been translated into English, and that in this way American readers can become acquainted with it. Unlike other books on magnetism, my book emphasizes the application of the thermodynamic theory of phase transitions of the second kind, in the form in which it has been developed by Soviet theorists (primarily by L. D. Landau and E. M. Lifshits), to the interpretation of magnetic phenomena in ferromagnetic, ferrimagnetic, and antiferromagnetic substances. This method, which possesses great generality and rigor, has been very fruitful.

In the short time since the publication of the Russian edition of the book (1959), there has been a rapid development of this method in the interpretation of the phenomena of "weak ferromagnetism" in antiferromagnetic substances (hematite, the orthoferrites of rare-earth metals, etc.), and also of the so-called "helical" ("spiral") spin structure that is observed in certain substances (dysprosium, the alloy $MnAu_2$). Naturally these interesting topics could not be adequately treated in the present book.

Readers who wish to become acquainted with the work of Soviet physicists in this branch of the subject are referred to the latest literature [1-8].

K. P. Belov
May 22, 1961

---

1. I. E. Dzyaloshinskii, Zhur. Éksp. i Teor. Fiz. 37, 881 (1959).
2. D. A. Astrov, Zhur. Éksp. i Teor. Fiz. 38, 984 (1960).
3. A. S. Borovik-Romanov, Zhur. Éksp. i Teor. Fiz. 36, 75 (1959); 38, 1088 (1960).
4. A. S. Borovik-Romanov and V. I. Ozhogin, Zhur. Éksp. i Teor. Fiz. 39, 27 (1960).
5. N. M. Kreines, Zhur. Éksp. i Teor. Fiz. 40, 762 (1961).
6. E. A. Turov, Zhur. Éksp. i Teor. Fiz. 36, 1254 (1959).
7. V. E. Naish and E. A. Turov, Fiz. Met. i Metalloved. 11, 321 (1961).
8. "Abstracts of Reports at the Conference on Ferromagnetism," Academy of Sciences of the USSR Press, Leningrad, 1961.

# PREFACE

The study of all aspects of magnetic phenomena and magnetic materials has taken on great importance in connection with the rapid development of electrical and radio engineering, of automation, and of computing-machine technology. In recent years the physics of magnetism has been enriched by knowledge of new phenomena such as antiferromagnetism, uncompensated antiferromagnetism (ferrimagnetism), ferromagnetic resonance, etc. The study of these phenomena is of great scientific and practical interest. Besides this it must be pointed out that certain extremely important problems associated with phenomena "discovered long ago" have as yet, in spite of their importance, been studied very little. Among these one of primary importance is the problem of the behavior of magnetic substances in the neighborhood of magnetic phase transitions.

The study of the nature of the magnetic transition is of great importance for the physics of ferromagnetic phenomena, and also for an understanding of the nature of antiferromagnetism and of ferrimagnetism. A detailed study of the phenomena in the neighborhood of a magnetic transition temperature helps to elucidate the condition under which the appearance or disappearance of the ferromagnetic and antiferromagnetic states of matter occurs, and thus makes possible a deeper understanding of the nature of spontaneous magnetization, which is the quantity characteristic of these states of matter.

The study of the phenomena in the neighborhood of magnetic transitions is also of importance from the point of view of thermodynamics, since ferromagnetic and antiferromagnetic transitions are concrete examples of phase changes of the second kind. All of this gives rise to a constant interest in the study of magnetic transitions. Up to the present, however, relatively few systematic works on the study of magnetic transitions have been published.

The first thorough studies of the magnetic properties of iron in the region of the ferromagnetic transition were carried out in 1895 by P. Curie [1]. He established that for iron there is a critical temperature above which the ferromagnetic properties disappear; consequently this temperature has been given the name, Curie temperature, or Curie point.*

* From very ancient times it has been known that iron loses its ferromagnetic properties when it is heated to very high temperatures [2].

Extensive investigations of the magnetization and the thermal effects in nickel in the region of the Curie temperature were made by Weiss and his collaborators [3]. Weiss developed methods for determining the temperature dependence of the spontaneous magnetization. A knowledge of the temperature dependence of the spontaneous magnetization is necessary for the elucidation of the character of the magnetic transition in a given substance.

German physicists, in particular W. Gerlach, at one time devoted great attention to the study of the ferromagnetic transition. In his well-known survey, "The Problem of the Curie Temperature" [4], Gerlach systematized and generalized the experimental material on magnetic and various "nonmagnetic" phenomena in the region of the Curie point which had been described in the literature up to 1938. Other important work in the study of phenomena in the region of the ferromagnetic transition was done by Rozhanskii [5], Potter [6], Sücksmith [7], and others. Nevertheless many important questions connected with the behavior of materials in this region remain unsettled or in dispute to the present time. These include, for example, the question of the actual temperature behavior of the spontaneous magnetization near the Curie point, the causes of the "smearing out" of the magnetic transition in alloys, ferrites, and antiferromagnetic materials, the question of the existence of "residual" spontaneous magnetization above the Curie temperature, and the nature of the temperature dependence of elastic, electric, thermal, and other properties near the Curie point. It even remains unsettled what we should take to be the Curie temperature, and how to determine it. These questions are answered by the fact that the study of the nature of the magnetic transition encounters great difficulties of an experimental nature. The methods for determining the spontaneous magnetization near the Curie temperature are very complicated. This probably also explains the fact that up to the present there is very scanty information in the literature about the temperature dependence of the spontaneous magnetization of ferromagnetic substances near the Curie temperature, especially in the case of alloys and ferrites.

There has also been little development of the theory of the magnetic transition. For the theoretical treatment of phenomena near the Curie point it is customary, particularly in the foreign literature, to appeal to the Weiss-Heisenberg model of the molecular field. This model has provided an understanding of the essential nature of ferromagnetism, antiferromagnetism, and uncompensated antiferromagnetism; however, when applied to the description of phenomena in the neighborhood of the Curie point it gives results which are crudely qualitative and only of a preliminary nature; even for such a "simple" ferromagnetic substance as nickel it is not possible to "squeeze" the experimental results into the Weiss-Heisenberg theory. In order to somehow "reconcile" this theory with experiment it has been necessary to assume a temperature dependence of the constant of the molecular field, and also a volume dependence of this factor [8]. This is an artificial procedure and has no real physical foundation, because the molecular-field constant is a coefficient in an extremely crude approximate theory, and consequently the theory of Weiss and Heisenberg cannot be applied to the quantitative description of phenomena in the neighborhood of the Curie temperature. On the other hand the various modifications made for the improvement of the Weiss-Heisenberg theory on the basis of statistical and quasi-classical ideas (including effects of short-range order) have also not given any important results in this direction. They have only made it possible to explain in a qualitative way some details of ferromagnetic transitions.

Up to the present no attempts have been made to construct a rigorous microscopic (quantum) theory of magnetic phenomena near the Curie temperature, since a consistent quantum-mechanical treatment of this problem is an exceptionally complicated problem. Since the construction of a rigorous microscopic theory of the ferromagnetic transition at the present time encounters great difficulties, the problem that takes precedence is the thermodynamic treatment of the subject. In papers by Landau [9], Vonsovskii [10], Ginzburg [11], and Semenchenko [12], attention has been called to the usefulness of such a treatment. In these papers a number of relations of a thermodynamic nature are given for the description of magnetic phenomena near the Curie point; this can be regarded as a great advance in the theory of magnetic transitions. Thereafter this theory was extended by the author [20] to the description of phenomena associated with the effects of elastic stresses on magnetic transitions (magnetoelastic phenomena, magnetostriction, etc.).

The present book presents the results of investigations of various phenomena in the neighborhood of the Curie point which have been obtained by the author and his collaborators, and also the data available in the literature. Furthermore, unlike other monographs and surveys in which the Weiss-Heisenberg model is used for the interpretation of the phenomena in the neighborhood of magnetic transitions [3, 4, 5, 7, 8, 14, 15], the present treatment uses the thermodynamic method developed in the papers that have been mentioned [9, 10, 11, 20], and also new concepts based on models (the s-d exchange model of Vonsovskii). The use of these methods is due to an effort to give a more rigorous and all-encompassing explanation of the phenomena in the region of magnetic transition in various materials. Although the thermodynamic theory deals with an idealized case, a point magnetic transition, nevertheless its application to actual ferromagnetic and ferrimagnetic materials (including alloys and ferrites) is extremely fruitful. The approach to the study of magnetic transitions from the point of view of thermodynamics has made it possible to analyze the temperature dependence of the spontaneous magnetization near the Curie point in real materials, the dependence of various magnetic and "nonmagnetic" phenomena in the neighborhood of this point on the magnetic field, the elastic stresses, and the temperature. Many of the regularities that have been found here were previously unknown. These include, for example, the effect of elastic stresses on the spontaneous magnetization and the magnetostriction that accompanies the para-process etc. The thermodynamic method of treating the experimental data has also made it possible to give more precision to the concept of the Curie temperature. Another advantage of the thermodynamic method is that, unlike theories based on models, it makes it possible to analyze the experimental data for arbitrary ferromagnetic and ferrimagnetic materials.

This new approach to the study of the problem of the magnetic transition of course can not give a complete description of all the details in the behavior of ferromagnetic, ferrimagnetic and antiferromagnetic materials in the neighborhood of the Curie point, but the application of this method makes it possible to bring out the most essential and important features. Thus the thermodynamic method for treating the phenomena in the neighborhood of the Curie point marks a very important stage in the solution of the problem of magnetic transitions and can serve as a basis for the further development of a more adequate theory of the magnetic transition.

In the first chapter of the present book a brief exposition is given of the main propositions of the thermodynamic theory of the magnetic transition. The second chapter presents a brief summary of the results that are given by various theories based on models for the interpretation of the phenomena in the neighborhood of the Curie point. The third and main chapter of the book contains an analysis of the experimental material (in large part obtained by the author and his collaborators) on various magnetic and "nonmagnetic" phenomena in ferromagnetic materials. In the fourth chapter the phenomena near an antiferromagnetic transition point are considered; this chapter is almost entirely prepared from published material. The fifth chapter gives an analysis of magnetic and "nonmagnetic" phenomena in the neighborhood of the Curie point in ferrimagnetic materials. Here, just as in the third chapter, a large part of the experimental material that is described is due to the author and his collaborators. In the sixth and last chapter there is a discussion of some questions relating to methods of experimental study of the magnetic and "nonmagnetic" phenomena in the neighborhood of the Curie point.

The author expresses his deep gratitude to Corresponding Member of the USSR Academy of Sciences S. V. Vonsovskii, and to K. B. Vlasov and A. A. Gusev for valuable comments on the manuscript of the book.

Chapter I

# THE THERMODYNAMIC THEORY OF THE MAGNETIC TRANSITION

## § 1. Phase Transitions of the Second Kind

The generally accepted view at the present time is that the transitions between ferromagnetism and paramagnetism and between antiferromagnetism and paramagnetism are phase transitions of the second kind. The concept of phase transitions of the second kind was first introduced by Ehrenfest [16]. According to Ehrenfest these are transitions such that at the transition point not only the thermodynamic potentials of the two phases are equal (which is a necessary condition for any phase transition), but also the first derivatives of the thermodynamic potentials are equal; the second derivatives, however, are not equal at the transition point, and have a discontinuity.

The most general analytical form of the conditions that characterize phase transitions of the second kind is as follows.

1. The thermodynamic potential $\Phi$ and its first derivatives with respect to the temperature T and the generalized force $X_i$ (pressure, magnetic field intensity, etc.)

$$\frac{\partial \Phi}{\partial T} \text{ and } \frac{\partial \Phi}{\partial X_i}$$

are continuous at the transition point.

2. The second derivatives

$$\frac{\partial^2 \Phi}{\partial T^2}, \quad \frac{\partial^2 \Phi}{\partial X_i^2}, \quad \frac{\partial^2 \Phi}{\partial T, \partial X_i}$$

have discontinuities at the transition point.

Let us consider the meaning of these conditions in more detail. As is well known,

$$\frac{\partial \Phi}{\partial T} = -S \quad \text{and} \quad \frac{\partial \Phi}{\partial X_i} = x_i, \tag{1}$$

where S is the entropy and $x_i$ is a generalized coordinate (volume, spontaneous magnetization, electric polarization, etc.). Thus the first condition means that at the transition point the entropy and the generalized coordinate do not have any discontinuity, i.e., the changes of the entropy and the generalized coordinate are zero,

$$\Delta S = 0, \ \Delta x_i = 0. \tag{2}$$

This in turn means that

$$\left.\begin{aligned} \Delta Q &= T\,\Delta S = 0, \\ \Delta v &= 0, \\ \Delta \sigma_s &= 0, \end{aligned}\right\} \tag{3}$$

i.e., there is no latent heat $\Delta Q$ of the transition, and there is no discontinuity $\Delta v$, in the thermal expansion, no discontinuous change $\Delta \sigma_s$ of the spontaneous magnetization, etc.

The second condition means that there are discontinuities of the derivatives of S and $x_i$ at the transition point:

$$\Delta \frac{\partial S}{\partial T} \neq 0, \quad \Delta \frac{\partial x_i}{\partial X_i} \neq 0, \quad \Delta \frac{\partial x_i}{\partial T} \neq 0, \tag{4}$$

i.e., although the volume, the entropy, and the other characteristics are continuous at a point of transition of the second kind, their derivatives $\left( \frac{\partial v}{\partial T}, \frac{\partial v}{\partial P}, \frac{\partial S}{\partial T} \text{ etc.} \right)$ must have discontinuities.

Thus in transitions of the second kind there are no discontinuous changes of Q, v, and other quantities, as is the case in transitions of the first kind. This is due to the fact that at a transition point of the second kind the phases are indistinguishable, and only as we move away from the point do the properties of the phases and their temperature dependences become different; the result of this is that the physical characteristics of the substance, defined as derivatives of the entropy and volume with respect to temperature and pressure (for example, the specific heat, the expansion coefficients, and the compressibility), approach different limits as the transition point is approached from different directions, i.e., these quantities have discontinuities.

Thus the Ehrenfest theory establishes formal criteria for transitions of the second kind. A more profound theory of phase transitions of the second kind was later developed by Landau and Lifshits [9], who first discovered the physical meaning of these transitions.

As is well known, every phase transition of the first kind is characterized by the following indications. In a certain extremely narrow range of temperatures there is a rearrangement of the crystal lattice of the substance (there are changes of the interatomic distances and of the angles between the lattice planes). As a result of this rearrangement the symmetry of the substance changes discontinuously. At the same time there is also a change of state of the crystal; the internal energy changes and there are changes of other thermodynamic quantities, which lead to a discontinuous change of the volume and to the evolution or absorption of a latent heat of the transition.

There is also the possibility, however, of transitions of a different type, in which although a change of the symmetry of the substance occurs discontinuously, the state of the substance changes gradually. This means that the interatomic distances and the angles between the planes remain practically unchanged at the transition point. Since the state of the substance remains almost unchanged at such a phase transition point, the transition is not accompanied by the evolution or absorption of a latent heat, although $\partial S/\partial T$, $\partial v/\partial T$, and other derivatives have discontinuities (anomalous temperature dependence of S and $\underline{v}$ near the transition point). Such transitions were called by Landau phase transitions of the second kind.

As the characteristics of the state of a substance at a phase transition of the second kind Landau introduces, in addition to the usual parameters (e.g., P, T, H), a further parameter $\eta$, which is called the ordering parameter. Thus, according to Landau, the thermodynamic potential of a system near a phase transition of the second kind can be represented as a function of not only the thermodynamic variables, but also the ordering parameter $\eta$. The parameter $\eta$ serves to take into account in a quantitative way those changes of the potential $\Phi$ near a phase transition point of the second kind which are due to the appearance in the system (as a result of the phase transition of the second kind) of an ordered distribution of the atoms of different types in an alloy, of a spontaneous magnetization, of an electric polarization, etc.

The parameter $\eta$ varies from $\eta = 0$ (absolute disorder) to $\eta = 1$ (absolute order). When the substance is cooled below a certain temperature $T = \theta$ the substance begins to change from the disordered state into a partially ordered state. As the temperature is lowered further the state of complete order is finally reached. Figure 1 shows in a schematic way the temperature dependence of the ordering parameter. Whereas in a phase transition of the first kind the parameter $\eta$ changes discontinuously with change of the temperature (Fig. 1a), in a transition of the second it changes smoothly (Fig. 1b).

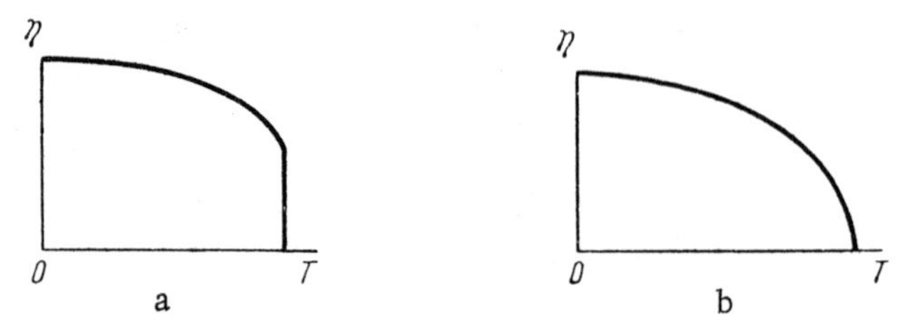


Fig. 1. Dependence of the ordering parameter on the temperature. a) Transition of the first kind; b) transition of the second kind.

It must be noted that in a certain sense the variable $\eta$ is not on the same footing as the variables T and P. Whereas T and P can be prescribed arbitrarily, the value of $\eta$ must be determined from the condition that $\Phi$ be a minimum for given P and T.

Near a phase transition point of the second kind, where $\eta$ takes small values, the function $\Phi$ can be expanded [9] in a series of even powers of $\eta$:

$$\Phi(T, P, \eta) = \Phi_0 + a\eta^2 + b\eta^4 + \ldots, \tag{5}$$

where the coefficients a and b are functions of the pressure P and the temperature T.

An equilibrium state is one for which $\partial\Phi/\partial\eta = 0$. Differentiating Eq. (5) with respect to the parameter $\eta$, equating the derivative to zero, and neglecting terms containing $\eta$ to degrees higher than the fourth, we find two solutions:

$$\eta = 0; \quad \eta = \sqrt{-\frac{a}{2b}}. \tag{6}$$

The first solution $\eta = 0$ corresponds to the stable state above the transition point, and the second $\left(\eta = \sqrt{-\frac{a}{2b}}\right)$ corresponds to the stable state below the transition point. Since the value $\eta = 0$ corresponds to the disordered state and $\eta = 1$ to the ordered state, to obtain agreement with experiment we must postulate that for each given value of P there is a certain temperature T = $\theta$ (the Curie point) at which a (T, P) = = 0 [9, 10].

A thermodynamic analysis of the coefficients a and b gives the following values:

$$T < \theta, \quad T = \theta, \quad T > \theta,$$
$$a < 0, \quad a = 0, \quad a > 0,$$
$$b > 0, \quad b > 0, \quad b > 0.$$

The method of expanding the thermodynamic function near a phase transition point of the second kind in a power series in the ordering parameter $\eta$ has been extremely fruitful. It has made it possible to give a thermodynamic description of various phenomena, for example, atomic ordering in alloys [9], the behavior of ferromagnetic materials [10, 11, 20] and of ferroelectric materials [17, 18] near the Curie point, etc.

It must be remarked that at present the question of the convergence of the expansion of the function $\Phi$ has not been settled, because up to now there has not been a complete study of the properties of the thermodynamic potential in the immediate neighborhood of a phase transition point of the second kind ([9], [19]).

The fundamental assumption in the Landau theory is that near a phase transition point of the second kind, where $\eta$ takes arbitrarily small values, the function $\Phi$ (P, T, $\eta$) can be expanded in a power series in $\eta$. As Landau remarked, however, the possibility of such an expansion is not obvious. This is because a phase transition point of the second kind is a singular point on the curve of the thermodynamic potential, and therefore such an expansion cannot be carried to terms of arbitrary order, and the coefficients of the expansion can have singularities as functions of P and T. In this connection it is interesting to examine concrete examples of phase transitions of the second kind, in particular ferromagnetic and antiferromagnetic transitions. In a given case the validity of the expansion (5) can be tested experimentally.

## § 2. The Thermodynamics of the Ferromagnetic Transition

Vonsovskii [10] and Ginzburg [11] have applied the theory of phase transitions of the second kind proposed by Landau to the description of the phenomena near the Curie point in ferromagnetic materials.

The ferromagnetic material is regarded as a single domain, that is, the fact that it is broken up into domains is not taken into account. The quantity chosen as the ordering parameter ($\eta$) is $J = \sigma_s/\sigma_0$, where $\sigma_s$ is the specific spontaneous magnetization (per gram of substance) at the temperature in question, and $\sigma_0$ is the specific magnetization at 0°K. The quantity J is the fractional magnetization or the degree of long-range magnetic order. With increase of the temperature the magnetic state of the ferromagnetic substance gradually changes; its ordering parameter, or, what is the same thing, the spontaneous magnetization, decreases continuously. Precisely at the Curie point J becomes zero. This, however, does not cause a discontinuity in the first derivative of the thermodynamic potential (the entropy, the spontaneous magnetization, etc.), but the second derivatives must change discontinuously at this point (for example, the specific heat and the temperature coefficient of the spontaneous magnetization).

Near the Curie temperature the quantity J is small, and therefore the function $\Phi$ can be expanded in a power series in J *:

$$\Phi = \Phi_0 + aJ^2 + bJ^4 + \ldots \qquad (7)$$

(terms in odd powers of J are not included, since the expansion of a scalar function ($\Phi$) in powers of a vector function (J) can contain only terms of even degrees). Near $\theta$ the coefficient $a(P, T)$ is small in magnitude, and therefore by expanding it in powers of the difference $T - \theta$ we can write

$$a = a_0'(T - \theta) + \ldots$$

Substituting this expression in Eq. (7), we get:

$$\Phi = \Phi_0 + a_0'(T - \theta) J^2 + bJ^4 + \ldots \qquad (8)$$

Below the Curie point we find the equilibrium value of J from the condition $\partial\Phi/\partial J = 0$ (we neglect terms containing J to powers higher than

* $\Phi$ can be expanded not only in powers of J (cf. [10]), but also in powers of the volume magnetization [11] and in powers of the specific magnetization [20]; the final formulas are identical, but the coefficients can differ by factors $\rho$ (the density) and $\sigma_0$ (or $J_0$).

the fourth):

$$\frac{\partial\Phi}{\partial J}=2a_\theta'(T-\theta)J+4bJ^3=0,$$

and from this we have for the variation of the spontaneous magnetization with the temperature near the Curie point

$$J^2=\left(\frac{\sigma_s}{\sigma_0}\right)^2=\frac{a_\theta'}{2b}(\theta-T). \tag{9}$$

This formula, which was first obtained by Vonsovskii [10], agrees with the analogous formula obtained from the Weiss-Heisenberg model [5, 8, 13]. Unlike the latter formula, however, Eq. (9) has been obtained from very general thermodynamic considerations.

By using the thermodynamic method we can proceed further to find the change of the specific heat on passage through the Curie temperature. The entropy of the ferromagnetic material is given by

$$S=-\frac{\partial\Phi}{\partial T}=-\frac{\partial\Phi_0}{\partial T}-a_\theta'J^2,$$

where $\frac{\partial\Phi_0}{\partial T}=S_0=S_{T>\theta}$ is the entropy in the disordered state (for $T>\theta$, $J=0$). Differentiating the expression for S with respect to T and multiplying the result by T, we get

$$C_p=T\frac{\partial S}{\partial T}=C_0-a_\theta'T\frac{\partial J^2}{\partial T}, \tag{10}$$

where $C_p$ is the specific heat at the given pressure P and $C_0$ is the specific heat for $T>\theta$.

Differentiating Eq. (9) with respect to T, we have

$$\frac{\partial J^2}{\partial T}=-\frac{a_\theta'}{2b}.$$

Substituting this expression in Eq. (10) at $T=\theta$, we get

$$C_p=\theta\frac{\left(a_\theta'\right)^2}{2b}+C_0. \tag{11}$$

For $T>\theta$, where the ferromagnetic part $\theta\frac{\left(a_\theta'\right)^2}{2b}$ of the specific heat is absent, we have $C_p=C_0$.

Thus the change of the specific heat on passage through the Curie point is given by

$$\Delta C_p = \theta \frac{(a'_\theta)^2}{2b}. \qquad (12)$$

The quantities $a'_\theta$, b, and $\theta$ can be found from the magnetization curves near the Curie point, and consequently the discontinuity of the specific heat can be calculated from the magnetic characteristics (see Chapter III).

Combining the relations that have been given, we can also write

$$S = S_{T>\theta} + \frac{\Delta C_p}{\theta}(\theta - T). \qquad (13)$$

At $T = \theta$, $S = S_{T} > \theta$, i.e., in the passage through the Curie temperature there is in fact no change of the entropy and no latent heat is given out ($T\ \Delta S = \Delta Q = 0$), as it is in transitions of the first kind.

Thus a thermodynamic analysis of the ferromagnetic transition confirms that such a transition is to be regarded as a transition of the second kind.

Ginzburg [11] has included in the expression for the thermodynamic potential the magnetic-field energy JH:

$$\Phi = \Phi_0 + aJ^2 + bJ^4 - JH. \qquad (14)$$

From the condition for equilibrium, $\partial\Phi/\partial J = 0$, we get an equation for the description of the true magnetization (the para-process) of a ferromagnetic material* near the Curie point

$$\alpha\sigma + \beta\sigma^3 = H. \qquad (15)$$

In this equation $\sigma$ is the specific magnetization that is measured experimentally and is equal to $\sigma_s + \sigma_i$, where $\sigma_i$ is the specific true magnetization caused by the application of the field H; $\alpha$ and $\beta$ are thermodynamic coefficients that depend on P and T. Their values are given, in terms of the coefficients a and b already introduced, by the following expressions:

$$\alpha = \frac{2a}{\sigma_0}, \qquad (16)$$

* The application of a magnetic field changes only the magnitude of the magnetic moment of a domain.

$$\beta = \frac{4b}{\sigma_0^3}. \quad (17)$$

The values of $\alpha$ and $\beta$ are found experimentally from curves of the magnetization taken close to the Curie point (see Chapter III).

We note that because of the para-process, when there is an applied magnetic field, the ordering parameter $\eta = J$ does not go to zero in the neighborhood of the Curie point. This result follows from Eq. (15). Even at the Curie point itself, where the spontaneous magnetization $\sigma_s$ goes to zero, the ferromagnetic substance retains the magnetization $\sigma_i$ (the true magnetization). Vonsovskii [10] has shown that the Curie points do not form a line in the (H, T) plane, because in the presence of a field the phase transition point vanishes altogether and the concept of the Curie point loses its meaning. Therefore in the (H, T) plane the Curie point is an isolated point that lies on the T axis (H = 0).

The method of series expansion of the thermodynamic potential can be used for the description of magnetic transitions in antiferromagnetic materials, and also in uncompensated antiferromagnetic materials (ferrimagnetic materials).

Near the transition point in an antiferromagnetic material the thermodynamic potential $\Phi$ can be expanded in series in terms of the parameters that characterize the magnetic moments of the magnetic sublattices. Just as in the case of a ferromagnetic material, as we approach the Curie point these parameters always go to zero according to the law $\sim \sqrt{\theta - T}$. In the case of a ferrimagnetic material the series expansion of $\Phi$ must be made in terms of the difference of the magnetizations of the sublattices. When this is done the relations obtained for the description of the phenomena in the neighborhood of the Curie point of a ferrimagnetic material do not differ from the relations given above for ordinary ferromagnetic materials.

As has been stated, the parameter $\eta = J$ is the so-called long-range magnetic order. The physical meaning of this concept follows. At low temperatures, for which the ferromagnetic (or ferrimagnetic) material is almost completely in the ordered state, the destruction of the ordered arrangement of the spins with rising temperature occurs very slowly (see Fig. 1, b). As the temperature increases further, however, and $\eta$ decreases, the destruction of the ordered state becomes easier, because the larger the regions in the ferromagnetic material with $\eta \neq 1$ become, the less energy is required for further destruction of the ordering. Thus the growth of the disordered state begins to develop like an avalanche, and at a definite temperature (the Curie point) this leads to complete disappearance of the order. The avalanche-like decrease of the ordered arrangement of the spins is due to the fact that this order depends on the coupling of a very large number of spins. According to Samoilovich [21], a peculiar mechanism of "relay transmission" acts under these conditions.

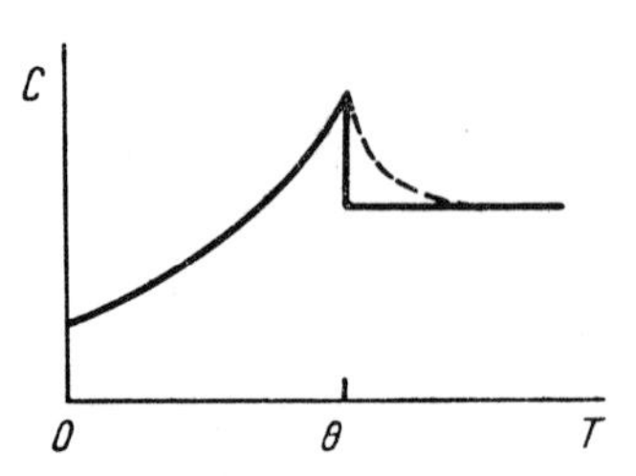


Fig. 2. Schematic representation of the temperature dependence of the specific heat of a ferromagnetic substance near the Curie point.

Let us consider some single spin which is at a definite place in the lattice of a ferromagnetic material. This spin directly influences only its neighbors. But these neighbors transmit its influence to more distant spins. Thus a certain correlation is established between spins that are remote from each other, although they do not directly interact with each other. As the temperature is increased the thermal motion forces certain spins to take antiparallel positions, but the relay coupling still exists and the magnetic long-range order is preserved. As the temperature is raised further, the number of antiparallel spins increases and the correlation in the positions of spins remote from each other becomes weaker and weaker. A time finally comes when all of the "relay" couplings go out of action and the long-range magnetic order disappears. The temperature at which this happens is the Curie point.

If only the long-range order existed, there would be a sharp break in the temperature dependence of the specific heat (Fig. 2). Experiment shows, however, that the anomaly in the specific heat does not disappear immediately above the Curie point; after a sharp drop of the specific heat there is an asymptotic approach to the normal value (dashed curve in Fig. 2).

There are analogous anomalies in other "nonmagnetic" properties of ferromagnetic materials (for example, the coefficient of thermal expansion, the temperature coefficient of the electric resistance, etc). The gradual disappearance of the anomalies of the "nonmagnetic" properties is due to the fact that although there is no long-range order above the

Curie point, an ordered position of the spins is still preserved in small volumes that contain relatively small numbers of spins (short-range order of fluctuations of the long-range magnetic order).*

## § 3. The Role of Fluctuations of the Long-Range Magnetic Order

The necessity of taking into account statistical fluctuations in the study of phase transitions of the second kind has been repeatedly emphasized in the literature [12, 22, 23, 24]. Vonsovskii [10], who based his work on that of Landau [22], was the first to deal with this problem for the ferromagnetic transition. The magnitude of the fluctuation of the long-range magnetic order can be calculated by means of general methods. According to statistical physics the probability of a fluctuation of the quantity J (for constant P and T) is proportional to $e^{-\frac{\Delta\Phi v}{kT}}$, where $v$ is the volume of the fluctuation and $\Delta\Phi$ is the increase of the thermodynamic potential caused by the fluctuation $\Delta J$. In the immediate neighborhood of the Curie point the fluctuation of the long-range magnetic order reaches its maximum value, in accordance with the general propositions of statistical physics.

Since above the Curie point J = 0, the degree of magnetic order changes from the value J to zero, i.e., the quantity $\Delta J$ is equal to the quantity J itself:

$$\Delta J = J.$$

Neglecting the term $bJ^4$ in Eq. (8), we get

$$\Delta\Phi = \Phi - \Phi_0 = a_\theta'(T-\theta)\,J^2 = a_\theta'(T-\theta)\,(\Delta J)^2.$$

The probability of such a fluctuation is given by

$$W(\Delta J) = Ae^{-\frac{a_\theta'(T-\theta)(\Delta J)^2 v}{kT}},$$

where A is determined from the normalization condition

$$\int_{-\infty}^{+\infty} W(\Delta J)\, d(\Delta J) = 1.$$

* It will be shown in Chapter III that in real ferromagnetic materials anomalies of the "nonmagnetic" properties above the Curie point can also be caused by structural inhomogeneities.

After a simple calculation we get

$$A = \sqrt{\frac{a_0'(T-\theta)}{\pi k T}}.$$

For the mean-square fluctuation of the long-range magnetic order (or the fractional magnetization) in the neighborhood of the Curie point we find

$$\overline{(\Delta J)^2} = A \int_{-\infty}^{+\infty} (\Delta J)^2 e^{-\frac{a_0'(T-\theta)(\Delta J)^2 v}{kT}} d(\Delta J) = \frac{kT}{2a_0'(T-\theta)v}. \quad (18)$$

Thus, as we approach the Curie temperature the quantity $\overline{(\Delta J)^2} \to \infty$; that is, it must increase very sharply.

Having found the fluctuation of the long-range magnetic order, we can determine the fluctuation of other thermodynamic quantities. For the specific heat, for example, we get

$$\overline{\Delta C_p} = \frac{k\theta}{2v} \frac{T}{(T-\theta)^2}.$$

The calculations given above relate to the fluctuation in each small region of the body, where there is spontaneous formation of ordered groups of magnetic spins under the action of the thermal fluctuations. These fluctuations are inhomogeneous and are functions of the position of the point inside the body, so that we must take into account not only the dependence of $\Phi$ on the quantity J itself, but also, in general, its dependence on the gradient $\nabla J$.

Assuming that $\nabla J$ is a small quantity, we can expand $\Phi$ in even powers of J and $\nabla J$:

$$\Delta\Phi = \Phi - \Phi_0 = a_0'(T-\theta)J^2 + bJ^4 + c(\nabla J)^2 + \ldots$$

If we take into account the term in $(\nabla J)^2$, then at $T = \theta$ the fluctuations are finite, because the denominator contains not only the term $(T - \theta)^2$ but also a term that does not depend on the temperature difference; this also makes the value of $\Delta C_p$ finite.

Fluctuation "nuclei" of the ordered phase appear not only at $T = \theta$, but also above the Curie point; as we approach $\theta$ through higher temperatures they become larger and larger. It is possible that these "nuclei" are very unstable. At a given instant they may be appearing in one part of the body and disappearing in another part, and so on. Since the fluctuation of the magnetic moment of the ferromagnetic body as a whole must be composed of the fluctuations of the moments in the individual parts of the volume of the body, this total moment is evidently close to zero.

It is important to take into account the fluctuations of the long-range order in the description of the various "nonmagnetic" phenomena in the region of the ferromagnetic transition.

If we do not take into account the fluctuation, the curve E(T) of the dependence of the energy of the ferromagnetic substance on the temperature has a sharp break at $T = \theta$ and does not change with the temperature for $T > \theta$; when, however, we take into account the fluctuations of the long-range order the dependence of the energy on the temperature is very smooth. This in turn leads to a smoothing of the curve $C_p(T)$ of the specific heat (Fig. 2), and of the curve of the electric conductivity $\rho(T)$ and of other "nonmagnetic" properties. It is hard to detect the effect of the fluctuations experimentally since the "smearing-out" of the curve of $C_p(T)$ and $\rho(T)$ in the region $T = \theta$ is to a large extent caused by inhomogeneities of the structure of the material (see Chapter III).

According to Vonsovskii a general qualitative description of the course of a ferromagnetic transition is as follows. In the region of very high temperatures $T \gg \theta$ the thermal motion is so intense that it destroys every ordered orientation of the magnetic spins even in very small volumes of the body. At temperatures that are not extremely high ($T > \theta$), as we approach the Curie point from the high-temperature side, exchange forces begin to play an important role and become sufficient to establish order at short distances; "swarms" of parallel spins appear, which are essentially local fluctuations of the magnetic order. When averaged over the whole body, however, the number of "swarms" is the same for the two orientations to the right and to the left, and therefore the body as a whole does not have any spontaneous magnetization in the usual sense of this word. The orientation of the local magnetization of the "swarms" depends strongly on the thermal motion, and therefore the fields required for their parallel orientation are very much larger than are required for the magnetization of the ferromagnetic material for $T < \theta$.

As we approach $T = \theta$ the exchange energy becomes comparable with the thermal energy; in this case the exchange interaction can establish not only an ordered position of the spins at short distances but also a correlation between the "swarms"; that is, there are now regions of spontaneous magnetization whose magnetic moments can be oriented along the field even in a comparatively weak field.

Owing to the intense development of fluctuations near a point of phase transition of the second kind there is a certain relaxation time required for the establishment of a state of thermodynamic equilibrium in the magnetic spin system. The value of the relaxation time characterizes the rate of reestablishment of a disturbed thermodynamic equilibrium (the rate of "dissolving" of the fluctuations). This problem has been treated theoretically by Landau and Khalatnikov [25]. According to their theory the relaxation time must increase as the system approaches the phase transition point of the second kind (the problem of the relaxation time for the case of a magnetic transition is treated in Chapter III). In conclusion we remark that there are attempts in the literature to treat "smearing-out" of the transitions near the Curie temperature from a somewhat different point of view. Semenchenko [12] sets up a correspondence between phase transitions of the second kind and critical phenomena. He assumes that near the temperature of a ferromagnetic transition the development of fluctuations (because the thermodynamic potentials of the two phases are almost equal) brings about a stratification of the homogeneous phase into a large number of "groups" of spins which form a dispersed magnetic system. As we get farther from the Curie point, either above it or below it, this dispersed structure decreases, and the system becomes homogeneous. The existence of this dispersed structure in the region of the Curie point causes the "smearing-out" of the maximum in the curve of the specific heat against temperature. Semenchenko's point of view agrees essentially with the Vonsovskii theoretical arguments, because Semenchenko is using a vague form of the idea of fluctuations of the long-range magnetic order. The situation is similar in studies which bring heterophase fluctuations into the discussions [23].

From the papers on the thermodynamic interpretation of the magnetic transition we can draw the conclusion that the treatment to be preferred is that developed by Vonsovskii and Ginzburg on the basis of Landau's theory of phase transitions of the second kind. The advantage of this treatment is that it operates with the ordering parameter; the introduction of this parameter makes possible a quantitative description of the behavior of ferromagnetic and ferrimagnetic substances in the region of the Curie point. The formal thermodynamic theory of the magnetic transition can be made more precise by introducing the fluctuations of the long-range order into the discussion. This makes it possible to explain in a qualitative way the peculiar character of the variation of the phenomena in the region of the Curie temperature and thus to make more accurate the conclusions drawn from the formal thermodynamic theory. It must be remarked that the conclusions of the thermodynamic theory of the magnetic transition and the relations deduced from this theory have up to the present not been subjected to a systematic and extensive comparison with the experimental data.

Chapter II

# PHENOMENA IN THE NEIGHBORHOOD OF THE CURIE POINT AND MODEL THEORIES OF FERROMAGNETISM

The Weiss model and its quantum-mechanical foundation given by Frenkel [26] and Heisenberg [27] have played an outstanding part in the development of our ideas about the nature of ferromagnetism. This model, which subsequently came to be called the Weiss-Heisenberg model, was made the foundation of the theory of the spontaneous magnetization of a substance. It helped in the general understanding of the nature of ferromagnetism and helped to explain in a qualitative way many ferromagnetic phenomena; in some cases this model made it possible to give also a rather satisfactory qualitative description of phenomena, for example, of the temperature dependence of the spontaneous magnetization of iron and nickel at temperatures not too close to absolute zero or to the Curie temperature.

Without expounding the Weiss-Heisenberg theory itself, which is explained in detail in many monographs and textbooks, we shall consider in this chapter the question of what the Weiss-Heisenberg model contributes to the description of magnetic phenomena in the neighborhood of the Curie point. In other words we shall here be interested in the question of how the experimental data that relates to the region of a ferromagnetic transition fit into the magnetic equation of state that follows from the Weiss-Heisenberg model.

## § 1. The Temperature Dependence of the Spontaneous Magnetization in the Neighborhood of the Curie Point

Both the original Weiss theory and the Heisenberg theory lead to essentially the same magnetic equation of state, which we shall write in the following form:

$$\frac{\sigma}{\sigma_0} = L_j(a). \tag{19}$$

Here $\sigma/\sigma_0$ is the ratio of the specific magnetizations taken respectively at an arbitrary temperature and at the absolute zero, $L_j$ is the generalized Langevin function, j is the quantum number that fixes the orientation of the magnetic moment $\mu$ of an atom, and the quantity a is given by

$$a = \frac{\sigma\mu N\rho + \mu H}{kT}, \tag{20}$$

where N is the molecular-field constant (proportional to the exchange integral), $\rho$ is the density, and k is Boltzmann's constant. For our further purposes it is more convenient to write the equation (20) in the form

$$\frac{\sigma}{\sigma_0} = \frac{kT}{\sigma_0\mu N\rho}\, a - \frac{H}{\sigma_0 N\rho}\,. \tag{21}$$

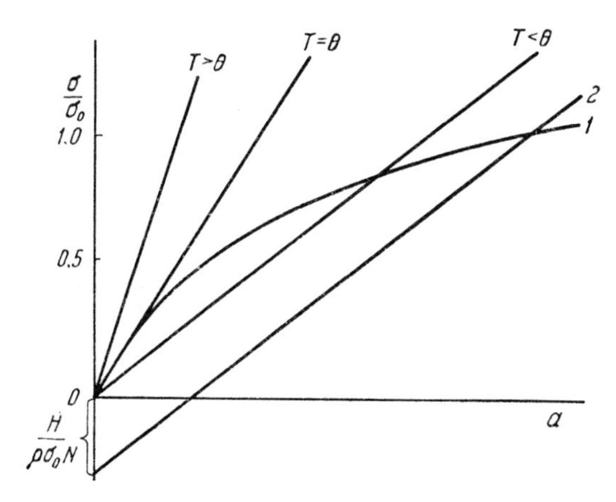


Fig. 3. Dependence of the magnetization on the parameter a. 1) Curve of Eq. (19); 2) curve of Eq. (21).

The first consequence that follows from the equations (19) and (21) is that there is a sharp temperature boundary between ferromagnetism and paramagnetism. In fact, it is seen from Fig. 3, which shows plots of Eqs. (19) and (21), that the intersection of curve 2 and curve 1 corresponds to the presence of a spontaneous magnetization in the substance; if there is no spontaneous magnetization, then curve 2 and curve 1 do not intersect and the substance is in the paramagnetic state. It can also be seen from Fig. 3 that the tangent to curve 1 at the point $a = 0$ (i.e., for H = 0) fixes a boundary, on one side of which there is ferromagnetism (below the tangent), and on the other side, paramagnetism. According to Weiss the temperature at which curve 2 becomes the tangent to curve 1 is the Curie temperature $\theta$. Quantitatively, we get the value of $\theta$ from the condition for equality of the slope of the tangent to the curve $L_j(a)$ at the point where $a = 0$ to the slope of the straight line 2, i.e.,

$$L_j'(0) = \frac{k\theta}{\mu N \rho \sigma_0},$$

from which it follows that

$$\theta = \frac{\mu N \rho \sigma_0 L_j'(0)}{k}. \quad (22)$$

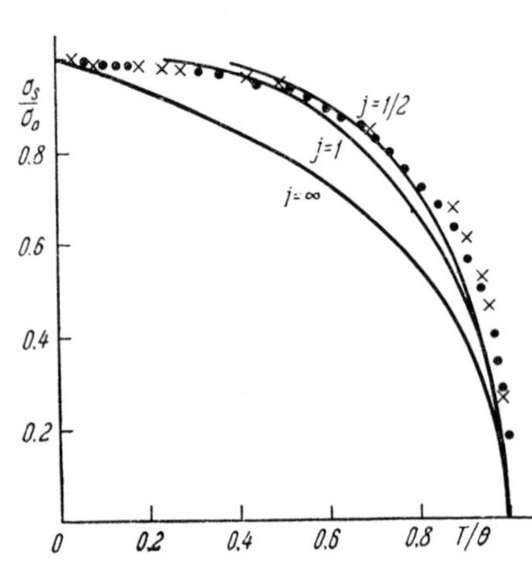


Fig. 4. Temperature dependence of the spontaneous magnetization for Ni and Fe. The solid lines are the theoretical curves; ●) Experimental points for Ni; ×) experimental points for Fe.

Let us now see what Eq. (19) gives for the description of the spontaneous magnetization. From Eqs. (19) and (20), for $H = 0$ we have

$$\frac{\sigma_s}{\sigma_0} = L_j\left(\frac{\mu N \rho \sigma_s}{kT}\right), \quad (23)$$

where $\sigma_s$ is the spontaneous magnetization (at $H = 0$). Using Eq. (22), we get

$$\frac{\sigma_s}{\sigma_0} = L_j\left(\frac{1}{L_j'(0)} \frac{\theta}{T} \frac{\sigma_s}{\sigma_0}\right). \quad (24)$$

Let us examine how the equation (24) describes the experimental data at temperatures that are not too close to the Curie point. In Fig. 4 there are theoretical curves $L_{\frac{1}{2}}$, $L_1$, and $L_\infty$, which correspond to the values $j = \frac{1}{2}$ (the magnetic moments can have two possible orientations: parallel or antiparallel), $j = 1$ (the magnetic moments are paired), and $j = \infty$ (the magnetic moments can have all possible orientations). The last case corresponds to the Weiss theory in its original form. This same diagram shows the experimental results for Ni and Fe. As can be seen from the diagram, in the range of values $T/\theta = 0.5$-$0.8$ the experimental data are adequately described by the equation

$$\frac{\sigma_s}{\sigma_0} = L_{1/2}\left(\frac{\sigma_s/\sigma_0 \; \theta/T}{L_{1/2}'(0)}\right). \quad (25)$$

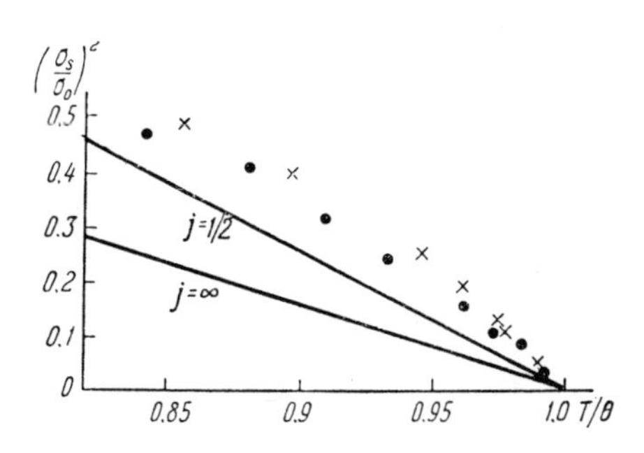


Fig. 5. Temperature dependence of the spontaneous magnetization near the Cure point according to the data of Potter. The solid lines are theoretical curves; ●) Experimental points for Ni; ×) experimental points for Fe.

At lower temperatures the experimental data for Ni and Fe are in better agreement with the equation

$$\frac{\sigma_s}{\sigma_0} = L_1\left(\frac{\sigma_s/\sigma_0\ \theta/T}{L_1'(0)}\right). \tag{26}$$

In the temperature range $T/\theta = 0.8-1$ there are large deviations of the experimental data from both of the curves $L_{\frac{1}{2}}$ and $L_1$.

The problem of the temperature dependence of the spontaneous magnetization in the immediate neighborhood of the Curie temperature has been treated in detail from the point of view of the Weiss theory by Rozhanskii [5]. In the region $T \to \infty$ the quantity $\sigma_s/\sigma_0$ is very small. Expanding the expression (24) in powers of $\sigma_s/\sigma_0$, we have

$$\frac{\sigma_s}{\sigma_0} = \frac{\sigma_s}{\sigma_0}\left(\frac{T}{\theta}\right) - \frac{3}{10}\left(\frac{\sigma_s}{\sigma_0}\right)^3\left(\frac{\theta}{T}\right)^3\frac{(j+1)^2+j^2}{(j+1)^2} + \ldots \tag{27}$$

From this we get

$$\left(\frac{\sigma_s}{\sigma_0}\right)^2 = \left(1-\frac{T}{\theta}\right)\left(\frac{T}{\theta}\right)^2\frac{10}{3}\,\frac{(j+1)^2}{j^2+(j+1)^2}.$$

Figure 5 shows the theoretical dependence of $(\sigma_s/\sigma_0)^2$ on $T/\theta$ for the two extreme cases: $j = \frac{1}{2}$ and $j = \infty$; this same figure shows the results of the measurements of Potter for Ni and Fe. It can be seen that the experimental data are in strong disagreement with the theory.

## § 2. The Curve of the True Magnetization (Para-process) in the Neighborhood of the Curie Point

Expanding the function (19) in a power series in the small parameter a, we can get an equation for the curve of the true magnetization (para-process) in the immediate neighborhood of the Curie point [14, 28]. We here consider this expansion for the two limiting cases, $j = \frac{1}{2}$ and $j = \infty$.

For these cases the equation (19) can be written in the following form:

$$\frac{\sigma}{\sigma_0} = \operatorname{th} a \qquad \left(j = \frac{1}{2}\right), \tag{28}$$

$$\frac{\sigma}{\sigma_0} = \left(\operatorname{cth} a - \frac{1}{a}\right) \qquad (j = \infty). \tag{29}$$

Stopping after the second terms in the series, we have

$$\frac{\sigma}{\sigma_0} = a - \frac{a^3}{3} \qquad \left(j = \frac{1}{2}\right),$$

$$\frac{\sigma}{\sigma_0} = \frac{a}{3} - \frac{a^3}{45} \qquad (j = \infty).$$

Taking into account the relations (20) and (22), and also using the fact that $L'_{\frac{1}{2}}(0) = 1$ and $L'_{\infty}(0) = {}^1\!/_3$ (see [8]), we get

$$\frac{\sigma}{\sigma_0} = \frac{\mu H}{kT} + \frac{\sigma}{\sigma_0}\frac{\theta}{T} - \frac{1}{3}\left(\frac{\mu H}{kT} + \frac{\sigma}{\sigma_0}\frac{\theta}{T}\right)^3 \qquad \left(j = \frac{1}{2}\right),$$

$$\frac{\sigma}{\sigma_0} = \frac{1}{3}\frac{\mu H}{kT} + \frac{\sigma}{\sigma_0}\frac{\theta}{T} - \frac{1}{45}\left(\frac{\mu H}{kT} + 3\,\frac{\sigma}{\sigma_0}\frac{\theta}{T}\right)^3 \qquad (j = \infty).$$

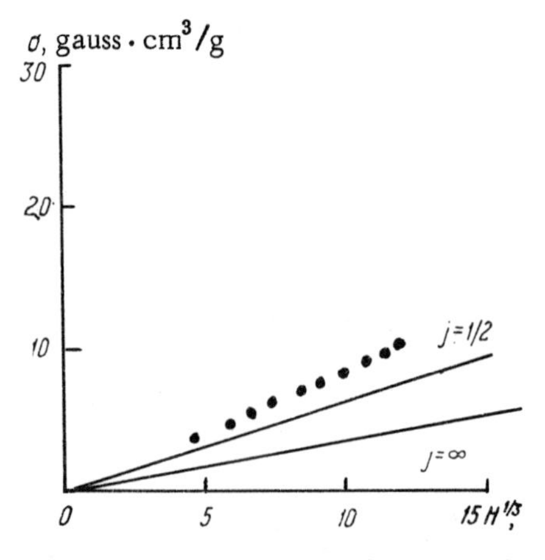


Fig. 6. The dependence of the specific magnetization $\sigma$ on $H^{1/3}$ at the Curie point for nickel. The solid lines are the theoretical curves; the solid circles are the experimental points.

In the immediate neighborhood of the Curie point ($T = \theta$) we have the following equations for the curve of the true magnetization:

$$\sigma = \sigma_0 \sqrt[3]{\frac{3\mu}{k\theta}}\, H^{1/3} \qquad \left(j = \frac{1}{2}\right), \tag{30}$$

$$\sigma = \sigma_0 \sqrt[3]{\frac{45}{81}\frac{\mu}{k\theta}}\, H^{1/3} \qquad (j = \infty). \tag{31}$$

In Fig. 6 the solid lines are the theoretical straight lines and the points are the results of the measurements for nickel. It can be seen that the formulas (30) and (31) give a description of the results of the measurements which is qualitatively satisfactory; there is, however, no quantitative agreement. In calculating the theoretical curves from the formulas (30) and (31) we have assumed that $\mu$ is equal to one Bohr magneton (in accordance with the Heisenberg theory). If, however, we substitute into these formulas the average value of $\mu$ for Ni, the disagreement between the theoretical curves and the experimental data is still not removed.

## § 3. The Paramagnetism of Ferromagnetic Materials above the Curie Point

The Weiss-Heisenberg theory is also used to describe the magnetization above the Curie point, where the ferromagnetic material goes over into the paramagnetic state. Here, just as in the preceding case, we expand the functions (28) and (29) in power series in the quantity $a$. Confining ourselves to the first term of the expansions, we can write

$$\frac{\sigma}{\sigma_0} = a \qquad \left(j = \frac{1}{2}\right),$$

$$\frac{\sigma}{\sigma_0} = \frac{a}{3} \qquad (j = \infty).$$

Substituting Eq. (20), we have

$$\frac{\sigma}{\sigma_0} = \frac{\mu H}{kT} + \frac{N\rho\sigma\mu}{kT} \qquad \left(j = \frac{1}{2}\right),$$

$$\frac{\sigma}{\sigma_0} = \frac{1}{3}\frac{\mu H}{kT} + \frac{1}{3}\frac{N\rho\sigma\mu}{kT} \qquad (j = \infty).$$

Differentiating with respect to H, we get the specific susceptibility

$$\chi = \frac{\dfrac{\sigma_0\mu}{kT}}{1 - \dfrac{\sigma_0 N\rho\mu}{kT}} \qquad \left(j = \frac{1}{2}\right), \tag{32}$$

$$\chi = \frac{\frac{1}{3}\frac{\sigma_0\mu}{kT}}{1 - \frac{1}{3}\frac{\sigma_0 N\rho\mu}{kT}} \qquad (j = \infty). \tag{33}$$

Next, using the relation (22) and also the values $L'_{\frac{1}{2}}(0) = 1$ and $L'_{\infty}(0) = 1/3$, we get from the last two formulas (independent of the value of $j$) the relation

$$\frac{1}{\chi} = \frac{N\rho}{\theta}(T - \theta). \tag{34}$$

This shows that above the Curie point the reciprocal of the specific susceptibility must be a linear function of T, which is in qualitative agreement with experiment. Experiment (measurements of Weiss and Forrer, Potter, and Sucksmith) shows, however, that in the immediate neighborhood of the Curie point, as we approach it from the high-temperature side, the dependence of $1/\chi$ on T is not linear. It can be seen from Fig. 7 that both for nickel (Fig. 7, a) and also for iron (Fig. 7, b) the curves have a strong curvature near the Curie point, i.e., in this region there is not even qualitative agreement between the theory and the experimental results. Agreement is found only when we go sufficiently far from the Curie point toward higher temperatures.

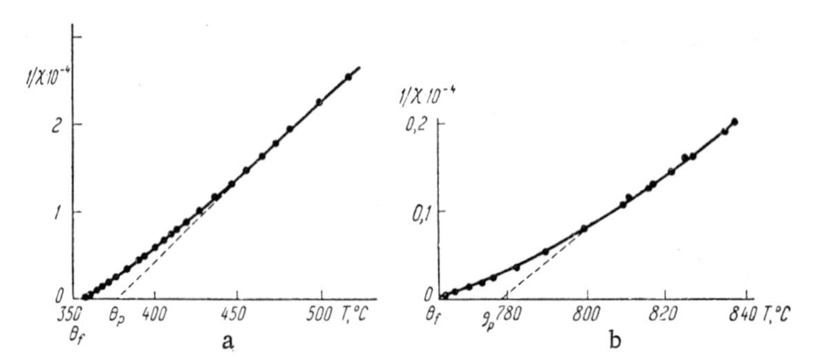


Fig. 7. Temperature dependence of the reciprocal of the susceptibility in the region above the Curie point.

For the description of the phenomena in the region above the Curie point one uses the so-called paramagnetic Curie point $\theta_p$, which is introduced by extrapolating the linear part of the curve of $1/\chi(T)$ until it intersects with the temperature axis (see the dashed lines in Fig. 7). The paramagnetic Curie point $\theta_p$ is higher than the ferromagnetic Curie point $\theta_f$. The existence of the paramagnetic Curie point does not follow from the Weiss-Heisenberg model; its introduction is a purely arbitrary procedure used to simplify the description of the temperature dependence of the susceptibility in the immediate neighborhood of the ferromagnetic Curie point, which the Weiss-Heisenberg theory is unable to describe. We note that in the temperature range above the Curie point in which the relation (34) is qualitatively satisfied there is a quantitative disagreement between the experimental data and the theory.

## § 4. On the Temperature Dependence of the Molecular-Field Constant

Potter [6], Kornetzki [29], Gerlach [4], and others have tried to get a better agreement between Eq. (19) and experiment in the neighborhood of the Curie temperature by introducing a temperature dependence of the molecular-field constant N. According to Potter, the molecular-field constant for nickel increases by a factor of almost three on passage through the Curie temperature. The change of N with the temperature can be interpreted physically only as a dependence of the exchange interaction energy on the interatomic distances, which are changed by the thermal expansion of the material. According to the calculations in [29], however, the effect of the thermal expansion of nickel in the passage through the Curie temperature can lead only to an extremely small change of N. Nevertheless later papers [30, 31, 32] have also considered a temperature dependence of the molecular-field constant in discussing the peculiar features of the temperature dependence of ferromagnetic phenomena.

Vonsovskii [13] has pointed out the incorrectness and the metaphysical nature of this sort of argument. The concept of the molecular field has no real physical meaning in the Weiss theory. As Vonsovskii points out, this concept would possibly not appear at all in a theory based on consistent and exact quantum calculations. From a methodological point of view the study of the temperature dependence of N is inconsistent, since N is a coefficient that appears in theories which are inexact, and are simply untrue in the neighborhood of the Curie point. The consideration of such a dependence can lead to dubious and unfounded conclusions. There is also no meaning in a consideration of the dependence of the constant N on the volume or on the interatomic distance. This latter dependence is commonly introduced in the discussion of the experimental data on the magnetostriction of the para-process [8], on the influence of pressure on the Curie point (see the more detailed discussion in Chapter III), etc. For the same reason there is not much meaning in a consideration of the temperature dependence of the exchange integral A in the Heisenberg theory, since this theory is a very approximate one, although in themselves the exchange forces have a real physical meaning because they cause the existence of ferromagnetism.

In this connection it is also necessary to point out the lack of foundation for deductions about the behavior of the magnetic moment of an atom in a ferromagnetic substance on passage through the Curie point [4]. These conclusions are drawn on the basis of the following arguments. It follows from Eq. (34) that

$$\chi = \frac{C}{T - \theta},$$

where $C = \theta / N\rho$ is the Weiss constant for the temperature range $T \gg \theta$. By using the relations (22), we can write

$$C = \frac{\theta}{N} = \frac{\mu \sigma_0 L_j'(0) \rho}{k}.$$

Substituting the values (see [8])

$$L_j'(0) = \frac{j+1}{3j}, \quad \mu = 2j\mu_B, \quad \frac{\mu_B}{k} = \frac{1}{14\,900},$$

we get for the value of C for one gram of the substance

$$C = \sigma_0 \frac{2}{3} \frac{j+1}{14\,900}. \tag{35}$$

Table 1 gives values of C calculated from Eq. (35) and the experimental values obtained by Sücksmith and Pearse [33].

TABLE 1. Values of the Coefficient C for Iron and Nickel

| Ferromagnetic material | $\sigma_0$ | $j$ | C calculated | C experimental |
|---|---|---|---|---|
| Ni | 57.6 | $^1/_2$ | 0.00387 | 0.00548 |
| | | 1 | 0.00516 | |
| | | $^3/_2$ | 0.00647 | |
| Fe | 222 | $^1/_2$ | 0.0149 | 0.0227 |
| | | 1 | 0.0199 | |
| | | $^3/_2$ | 0.0249 | |

It can be seen that for nickel in the paramagnetic region the best agreement of the theory with experiment is given for the case in which the spins are paired (j = 1), whereas in the ferromagnetic region the best agreement is obtained when the spins are isolated (because we then have $j = \frac{1}{2}$). We see from Table 1 that for iron the best agreement of the values of C is obtained for $j = {}^3/_2$.

For iron the theory gives deviation from the values of the quantum numbers, and consequently from the values of the magnetic moment of elementary magnets.

Thus in the paramagnetic region the Weiss theory leads to implausible values of the magnetic moments of the atoms (the elementary "magnets" in ferromagnetic materials).

Is there a change of the magnetic moment of an atom in a ferromagnetic material in the ferromagnetic transition? This question cannot be settled within the framework of the crude Weiss-Heisenberg model. Every attempt to settle it by means of the Weiss-Heisenberg theory must be regarded as artificial. The question of the change of the magnetic moment of an atom on passage through the Curie point can be elucidated primarily from studies of the temperature dependence of the magnetization in ultrahigh fields (at which there is absolute saturation) and from measurements of the gyromagnetic effect below and above the Curie point. The first method would be the more direct and correct, but it is impossible to accomplish such studies with present experimental techniques. The second method makes it possible to estimate the part played by the orbital moments in ferromagnetism above and below the Curie point.

## § 5. Effects of Short-Range Magnetic Order

The Weiss-Heisenberg theory enables us to understand the main regularities in the temperature dependence of the spontaneous magnetization and the true magnetization in ferromagnetic metals near the Curie point. Other features in the behavior of magnetic phenomena in this temperature range cannot be understood from the Weiss-Heisenberg theory even in a qualitative way (for example the temperature dependence of the specific heat). As we have seen, the quantitative predictions of this theory also cannot withstand criticism. This is natural, because the Weiss-Heisenberg model is an extremely crude one.

In the original Weiss theory the interaction forces that lead to the spontaneous magnetization were taken into account by the introduction of a certain hypothetical molecular field. The molecular field is the analogue of the self-consistent field in a crystal, which is often introduced in physical theories to simplify the calculation of the complex interactions of a system of electrons and ions.

The method of description of the interaction in a ferromagnetic material by means of a self-consistent field is based on the fact that each elementary moment interacts with any other moment in the body in just the same way (long-range order in the positions of the magnetic moments).

In the Heisenberg theory, which gives a quantum-mechanical foundation for the Weiss model, a similar simplification is introduced, namely the true energy spectrum of the system of electrons in the ferromagnetic body is replaced by the spectrum of the centers of gravity of the energy bands, and this is also equivalent to the introduction of a certain self-consistent field. Therefore the Heisenberg theory could not give more than is given by the Weiss theory. The more exact calculation of the energy spectrum of the electrons that has been made by Bloch, Holstein, and Primakoff [34], and in particular that made by Bogolyubov and Tyablikov [35], have made it possible to give a more exact description of the temperature dependence of the spontaneous magnetization of ferromagnetic materials [36]. Because of mathematical difficulties, however, the calculation is possible essentially only for temperatures near 0°K. Dyson [37] has made a further attempt to improve the calculation of the energy spectrum of the electrons in ferromagnetic materials. This has not only improved the temperature dependence of the spontaneous magnetization, but has also considerably widened the range of temperatures for which the quantum theory of ferromagnetism can be used (up to $\theta/4$).

The problem of constructing an exact quantum-mechanical theory of the magnetic phenomena in the neighborhood of the Curie point is still unsolved. Therefore the developments of the theory have taken a different path. In order to give an explanation of certain details in the temperature dependence of the spontaneous magnetization near the Curie point, and of associated phenomena (for example, the temperature dependence of the specific heat), attempts have been made to "perfect" the Weiss-Heisenberg theory by taking into account the short-range order in the positions of the spins. These attempts are based on the following considerations.

According to the ideas of quantum mechanics, the exchange forces act at very short distances and each spin interacts with the nearest spin in the lattice. For this reason it is necessary to include in the argument the short-range order in the positions of the spins. For this same reason the energy of a ferromagnetic material must depend on the short-range magnetic order.

The application of classical statistics to the calculation of the short-range order in the positions of the spins (the "quasi-classical" treatment of ferromagnetism) can give only a qualitative picture of the phenomena in the neighborhood of the Curie point. In the literature there are many theoretical papers on the quasi-classical calculations of the short-range magnetic order in ferromagnetic materials, which often involve the use of extremely complicated mathematical apparatus [38-41], the use of which, however, is completely unjustified, as has already been remarked, because of the purely illustrative nature of this way of describing ferromagnetism.

In order to show the possibilities of the quasi-classical method for describing the phenomena near the Curie point, we shall present a decidedly abbreviated account of the calculation made by Stil'bans [42]. This calculation is the simplest and clearest one.

To calculate the short-range magnetic order in the positions of the spins Stil'bans uses the so-called "quasi-chemical" method. If the energy is measured from the states of complete order, then we can with an expression for the energy of the ferromagnetic body in the form

$$E = 2An_{rl}, \tag{36}$$

where A is the exchange integral for nearest-neighbor spins, and $n_{rl}$ is the number of antiparallel neighbors. In order to find a value of the energy for each temperature, it is necessary to determine the equilibrium values of three coupled quantities: $n_{rl}$, $n_{rr}$, and $n_{ll}$ (where $n_{rr}$ and $n_{ll}$ are the numbers of parallel neighbor-pairs of spins pointing to the right and to the left, respectively). The numbers of parallel and antiparallel neighbor-pairs can be regarded as the concentration of component (rr), (ll), and (rl), between which there is a reaction analogous to a chemical reaction

$$(rr) + (ll) \rightleftarrows 2(rl).$$

It can be shown that this reaction occurs in any regrouping of the spins that does not change the total numbers $N_r$ and $N_l$ of spins pointing to the right and to the left. In carrying through the analogy between a chemical reaction and the "reaction" between parallel and antiparallel spin neighbor-pairs, Stil'bans uses for the determination of the equilibrium values of the "concentrations" of parallel and antiparallel neighbor pairs the so-called law of mass action

$$\frac{n_{rr}n_{ll}}{n_{rl}^2} = \frac{Z_{rr}Z_{ll}}{Z_{rl}^2} = \frac{e^{\frac{4A}{kT}}}{4}, \tag{37}$$

where $Z_{rr}$, $Z_{ll}$, and $Z_{rl}$ are the partition functions for parallel and antiparallel neighbor-pairs. Substituting in Eq. (37) the ratios

$$n_{rr} = \frac{N_r Z - n_{rl}}{2} \quad \text{and} \quad n_{ll} = \frac{N_l Z - n_{rl}}{2},$$

where Z is the number of nearest neighbors in the lattice (the coordination number), we have

$$n_{rl} = \frac{NZ}{2} \frac{\sqrt{1 + 4\frac{N_r N_l}{N}(4C - 1)} - 1}{4C - 1}. \tag{38}$$

Here the symbol C has been used to denote the expression $C = e^{4A/kT}/4$. The relative magnetization $J = \sigma_s/\sigma_0$ can be expressed in the following way:

$$J = \frac{N_r - N_l}{N}.$$

Here J determines the long-range magnetic order. Substituting this ratio into Eq. (38), we get

$$n_{rl} = \frac{NZ}{2} \frac{\sqrt{1 + (1 - J^2)(4C - 1)} - 1}{4C - 1}. \tag{39}$$

The expression (39) connects the short-range order and the long-range order at any given temperature. Substituting Eq. (39) into the expression for the energy, Eq. (36), and using the condition that the energy be a minimum, Stil'bans arrives at the following magnetic equation of state:

$$J = \operatorname{th} \frac{ZA}{kT} \frac{J}{\sqrt{1 + (1 - J^2)(4C - 1)}}. \tag{40}$$

This equation differs in form from the Weiss-Heisenberg equation only by the presence of the irrational expression in the denominator (whose value, by the way, does not differ much from unity). The inclusion of the short-range order thus does not produce any large changes in the shape of the theoretical curve for the temperature dependence of the spontaneous magnetization. For the energy at $T < \theta$ one gets the expression

$$E \approx \frac{NZA}{2}(1 - J^2),$$

but at $T > \theta$

$$E = \frac{NZA}{1 - e^{\frac{2A}{kT}}},$$

i.e., the energy of the ferromagnetic body does not vanish at the Curie point; it approaches zero for $T \to \infty$. This provides a possibility for a qualitative explanation of the existence of "remnants" of the ferromagnetic anomalies of the specific heat and of other "nonmagnetic" properties in the region above the Curie point. The result obtained here also follows, however, from more general thermodynamic considerations when one takes into account the fluctuations of the long-range magnetic order (cf. Chapter I). In this sense the inclusion of the short-range order is equivalent to inclusion of the fluctuations of the long-range magnetic order.

## § 6. Effects of s-d Exchange Interaction

It follows from the relation (27) that the temperature dependence of the spontaneous magnetization in the immediate neighborhood of the Curie point can be described by the formula

$$J^2 = \left(\frac{\sigma_s}{\sigma_0}\right)^2 = \xi\left(1 - \frac{T}{\theta}\right), \tag{41}$$

where $\xi$ is a constant. If we set $j = \frac{1}{2}$ in Eq. (27), then $\xi \approx 3$; this value gives the best agreement with experiment for pure ferromagnetic metals. Nevertheless, even in this case the deviation of the experimental data from the theoretical values is very large. For nickel and iron the quantity $\xi$ always has values larger than three.

Vonsovskii and Vlasov have shown [43] that the quantitative agreement between the formula (41) and experiment can be improved if one takes into account the exchange interaction of the inner 3d electrons with the outer 4s electrons in the metal. Unlike the Frenkel-Heisenberg model, in which one effectively takes into account only the interaction between the d electrons of neighboring atoms, it is assumed in the Vonsovskii-Vlasov treatment that in addition to the strong d-d interaction there is an exchange interaction between the s and d electrons, with the s electrons forming a free-electron gas in the metal. In this case the total free energy can be written in the form

$$F = F_s + F_d. \tag{42}$$

Here $F_s$ is the free energy of the s electrons; the authors give an expression for this quantity in the following form:

$$F_s = n[-\alpha' J_d J_s + \lambda(\beta + \beta' J_d)(1 + J_s)^{5/3} + \lambda(\beta - \beta' J_d)(1 - J_s)^{5/3}], \tag{43}$$

where n is the number of s electrons per unit volume, $J_d$ and $J_s$ are the relative magnetizations of the d and s electrons, and $\lambda$ is a coefficient of the order of three. The expressions for the constants $\alpha'$, $\beta$, $\beta'$ are

$$\alpha' = \frac{1}{2}(A^0_{sd} + 6A_{sd}); \quad \beta = -I_s + \frac{1}{2}A_{sd}; \quad \beta' = \frac{1}{2}A_{sd},$$

where $A^0_{sd}$ is the exchange integral between s and d electrons at the same site; $A_{sd}$ is the corresponding exchange integral for neighboring sites; and $I_s$ is the transfer integral of the s electrons.

For temperatures close to the Curie point one can write as the expression for the free energy $F_d$:

$$F_d = -NkT \ln \operatorname{ch} \frac{b}{2kT} J_d + \frac{1}{4} NbJ_d^2, \tag{44}$$

where N is the number of d electrons per cubic centimeter and b is a quantity proportional to the exchange integral of d electrons at neighboring sites.

The equilibrium values of $J_s$ and $J_d$ are found from the condition that the total energy be a minimum. Differentiating Eq. (42) with respect to $J_s$ and $J_d$ and equating the derivatives to zero, we get

$$J_s = \frac{9}{20\lambda}\frac{\gamma}{\beta} J_d,$$

$$J_d = \frac{\theta}{\theta_d}\sqrt{3\left(1 - \frac{T}{\theta}\right)}, \tag{45}$$

where

$$\gamma = \alpha' - \frac{10}{3}\lambda\beta' = \frac{1}{2}A^0_{sd} - 2A_{sd},$$

$\theta_d$ is the Curie temperature found by including only the interaction of the d electrons ($\theta_d = b/2k$), and $\theta$ is the Curie temperature when one takes into account the s-d exchange interaction, with the value

$$\theta = \frac{\theta_d}{1 - \frac{9}{10}\frac{n}{\lambda N}\frac{\gamma^2}{\beta b}}. \tag{46}$$

The resultant magnetization of the ferromagnetic material is given by

$$\sigma_s = (NJ_d + nJ_s)\,\mu_e = \left(N + \frac{9}{20}\frac{\gamma}{\lambda\beta}\,n\right)\mu_e \frac{\theta}{\theta_d}\sqrt{3\left(1 - \frac{T}{\theta}\right)}. \quad (47)$$

If $N = N_{at}N_d$ and $n = N_{at}n_s$, where $N_{at}$ is the number of atoms per cubic centimeter, then

$$\sigma_s = N_{at}\mu_e\left(N_d + \frac{9}{20}\frac{\gamma}{\lambda\beta}\,n\right)\frac{\theta}{\theta_d}\sqrt{3\left(1 - \frac{T}{\theta}\right)}.$$

For low temperatures near 0° K we can write

$$\sigma_0 = N_{at}\mu_e\left(N_d + \frac{9}{20}\frac{\gamma}{\lambda\beta}\,n_s\right). \quad (48)$$

Substituting Eq. (48) in Eq. (47), we get for the relative magnetization

$$J = \left(\frac{\sigma_s}{\sigma_0}\right)^2 = \left(\frac{\theta}{\theta_d}\right)^2 3\left(1 - \frac{T}{\theta}\right).$$

Comparing this result with Eq. (41), we have

$$\xi = 3\left(\frac{\theta}{\theta_d}\right)^2. \quad (49)$$

For $\gamma = 0$ or $n = 0$, that is, for cases in which the s electrons do not play any part in producing the ferromagnetism, it follows from Eq. (46) that $\theta = \theta_d$, and for this case we get $\xi = 3$. This agrees with the results of the Weiss-Heisenberg theory. If the s electrons contribute to the ferromagnetism, then according to Eq. (47) we have $\theta > \theta_d$, and the coefficient $\xi$ given by Eq. (49) will be larger than three. Thus the theory of Vonsovskii and Vlasov indicates the possibility of improving the quantitative agreement between the formula (41) and experiment by taking into account the s-d exchange interaction in a ferromagnetic metal. The work of Vonsovskii and Vlasov is essentially the first use of the quantum theory to explain the temperature behavior of the spontaneous magnetization near the ferromagnetic transition point. Recently these same authors have shown [44] that inclusion of the s-d exchange interaction makes it possible to explain the features of the temperature dependence of the magnetic susceptibility of ferromagnetic materials above the Curie point which had not found any explanation in the Weiss-Heisenberg theory (Chapter III).

## § 7. On the Temperature Dependence of the Spontaneous Magnetization in Alloys

It can scarcely be expected that the magnetic equation of state (19) derived from simple and approximate assumptions would also hold for ferromagnetic alloys. First of all it can be said that since the phenomenon of ferromagnetism is caused by the specific locations of the atoms in the lattice and the nature of the neighborhood of an atom, the curves for the temperature dependence of the spontaneous magnetization in alloys should be different from the curves for pure ferromagnetic metals. For alloys the curves of $\frac{\sigma_s}{\sigma_0}(T/\theta)$ have a flatter shape than for metals. There has been very little theory developed for the temperature dependence of the spontaneous magnetization of alloys; two attempts that have been made in this direction are of a qualitative nature [45, 46].

In 1938 Bitter [45] first raised the question of the possibility of extending the equation of state of Weiss and Heisenberg to the case of binary ferromagnetic alloys. He introduced the idea of two sublattices in the ferromagnetic material, which had the property that the magnetic moment of the atoms that are in a particular sublattice interact only with the magnetic moments of the atoms of the other sublattice. By means of these ideas Bitter tried to explain the dependence of $\sigma_s/\sigma_0$ on $T/\theta$ and the dependence of the Curie temperature on the composition of an alloy and on the positions of the atoms in the sublattices. Another attempt in this direction is due to Vonsovskii [46]. He showed that for a lattice consisting of atoms of types a and b it is necessary to take into account exchange integrals of the forms $A_{aa}$, $A_{bb}$, and $A_{ab}$. By extending the Frenkel-Heisenberg theory of ferromagnetism to this more complicated case, Vonsovskii obtained a formula for the temperature dependence of the spontaneous magnetization of a binary alloy,

$$\sigma_s = \sigma_0 \operatorname{th} \frac{z\sigma_s}{2\sigma_0 kT}\left[n_a(n_a - n_b P)A_{aa} + 2n_a n_b(1+P)A_{ab} + n_b(n_b - n_a P)A_{bb}\right], \tag{50}$$

where $n_a$ and $n_b$ are the relative concentrations of the atoms a and b in the alloy, z is the coordination number of the lattice, and P is the degree of atomic ordering. For a completely disordered alloy (P = 0) the expression (50) takes the usual form:

$$\sigma_s = \sigma_0 \operatorname{th} \frac{\sigma_s}{\sigma_0}\frac{\theta}{T}, \tag{50}$$

where $\theta = \frac{z}{2k}\left(n_a^2 A_{aa} + 2n_a n_b + n_b^2 A_{bb}\right)$ is the Curie temperature of the alloy.

Thus, according to Vonsovskii the temperature dependence of the spontaneous magnetization of an alloy has the same form as for a pure metal. The difference reduces to the use of a different expression for the Curie temperature (it is to this last problem that Vonsovskii's paper is mainly devoted; cf. also [47]). Up to the present there has been no theoretical treatment of the effect of the composition and of the degree of atomic ordering on the temperature dependence of the spontaneous magnetization of an alloy. It must be noted that the formula (50), which was derived from extremely crude and approximate quantum-mechanical assumptions, is of an extremely qualitative nature. At low temperatures one can find the exact temperature behavior of $\sigma_s(T)$ if one starts from more consistent quantum-mechanical calculations. For example, Vonsovskii [46] and later Kondorskii and Pakhomov [48] have used a method of approximate second quantization to obtain formulas for the temperature dependence of the spontaneous magnetization in the form of a 3/2 power law for binary ordered alloys of various crystal structures and various compositions.

Chapter III

# INVESTIGATION OF THE PHENOMENA IN FERROMAGNETIC MATERIALS IN THE NEIGHBORHOOD OF THE CURIE POINT

## § 1. The Thermodynamic Description of the True Magnetization (Para-process)

Near the Curie temperature, because of the small values of the constants of magnetic anisotropy and magnetostriction, the processes of displacement and rotation are stopped even for comparatively weak magnetic fields. In stronger fields the magnetization of a ferromagnetic material near the Curie temperature occurs because of the true magnetization (para-process), which is very large in this case and almost completely determines the ferromagnetic behavior of the substance.

Figure 8 shows the isotherms of the magnetization of pure nickel. As can be seen from the diagram, as the temperature is increased magnetic saturation sets in at weaker fields than at room temperature; this indicates that as the Curie temperature is approached the processes of displacement and rotation come to an end in very weak fields (a few tenths of an oersted). In the temperature range 350-360° the magnetization is of a sharply nonlinear character and occurs mainly because of the para-process.

For the thermodynamic description of the true magnetization near the Curie point it is more convenient to put Eq. (15) in the form

$$\alpha(\sigma_s + \sigma_i) + \beta(\sigma_s + \sigma_i)^3 = H, \qquad (51)$$

where $\alpha = 2a/\sigma_0$, $\beta = 4b/\sigma_0^3$, and $\sigma_i$ is the true magnetization produced by the field.

Figures 9 to 11 show the dependence of $H/\sigma$ on $\sigma^2$ for pure nickel and for alloys according to the data of [49] and [53] ($\sigma = \sigma_s + \sigma_i$ is the experimentally measured magnetization). Equation (51) is in fairly good agreement with experiment both for pure nickel and for alloys. Deviations from the straight line are found only in weak fields, where processes of rotation and displacement that are not taken into account in the relation (51) are still occurring.

In the immediate neighborhood of the Curie point Eq. (51) should be in particularly good agreement with experiment, because it is here that the expansion (7) of the thermodynamic potential $\Phi$ in power series gives the most exact results. Furthermore it is here that the effect of processes of rotation and displacement should be the smallest. We find the equation for the magnetization curve at the Curie point if in Eq. (51) we set $\sigma_s = 0$ and $\alpha = 0$ (condition for the Curie point):

$$\sigma_i = \frac{\sigma_0}{(4b)^{1/3}} H^{1/3}. \tag{52}$$

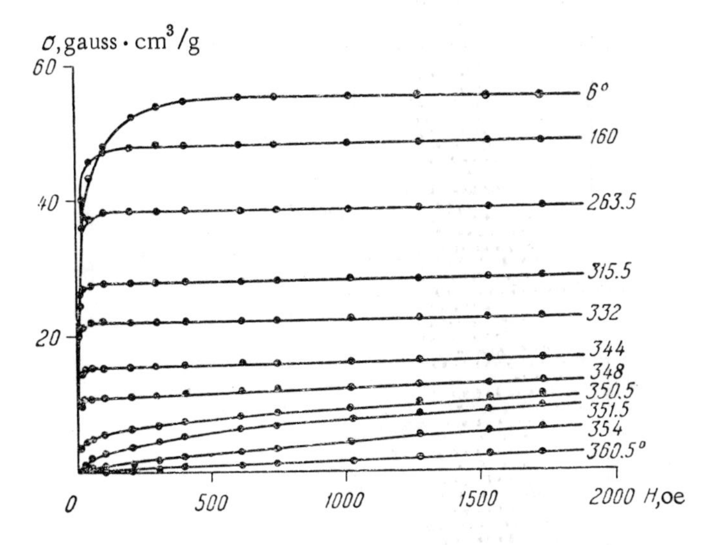


Fig. 8. Isotherms of the magnetization of electrolytic nickel.

This relation is well confirmed by experiment not only for pure nickel but also for various alloys.

Thus the theory of phase transitions of the second kind gives a good description of the true magnetization near the Curie point. It must be noted that in the derivation of the equations (5) and (52) the only assumption made is that the thermodynamic potential can be expanded in a series of even powers of the relative magnetization.

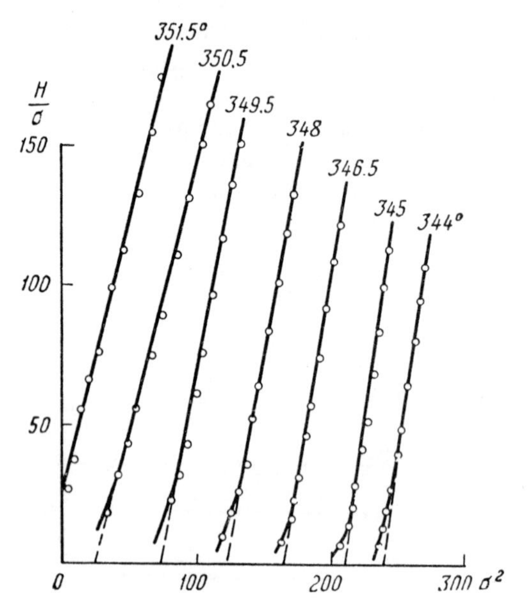


Fig. 9. Dependence of H/σ on $\sigma^2$ for electrolytic nickel.

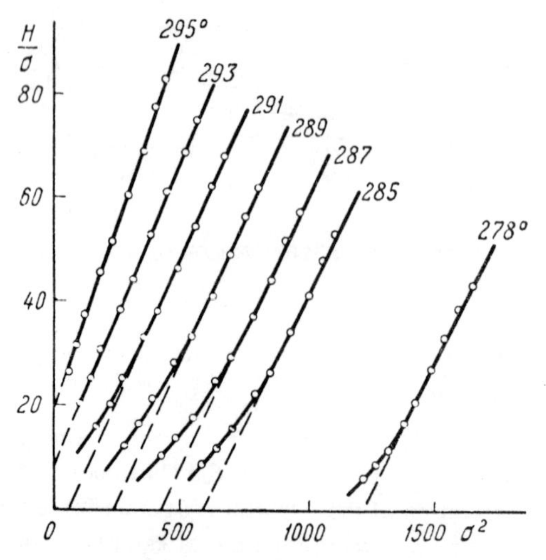


Fig. 10. Dependence of H/σ on $\sigma^2$ for an alloy of 36% nickel and 64% iron.

It is very important from the theoretical point of view to determine the temperature dependence of the thermodynamic coefficients $\alpha$ and $\beta$. The thermodynamic theory of the quantities $\alpha$ and $\beta$ and of their temperature dependence gives incomplete information, and therefore this dependence must be found experimentally. It follows from Figures 9 to 11 that one can determine the values of $\alpha$ from the intercepts of the straight line $H/\sigma$ ($\sigma^2$) on the axis of ordinates. The values of the coefficient $\beta$ can be determined by measuring the slopes of the straight lines.

Figures 12 and 13 show the dependence of $\alpha$ and $\beta$ on the temperature for various materials. It is seen that for $T < \theta$, $\alpha$ is negative; at $T = \theta$, $\alpha = 0$; and for $T > \theta$, $\alpha > 0$. The coefficient $\beta$ is positive at all temperatures. The change of sign of the coefficient $\alpha$ with changing temperature and the fact that the coefficient $\beta$ keeps the same sign are in agreement with the results of the thermodynamic theory. It can be seen from Figs. 12 and 13, however, that the curves $\alpha(T)$ and $\beta(T)$ are different for different materials: the quantities $\alpha$ and $\beta$ and the nature of their temperature dependences are determined by the structural peculiarities of the ferromagnetic material. In the immediate neighborhood of the Curie point the temperature dependence of the coefficient $\alpha$ is linear to a first approximation for all materials,

$$\alpha = \alpha'_{\theta} (T - \theta), \tag{53}$$

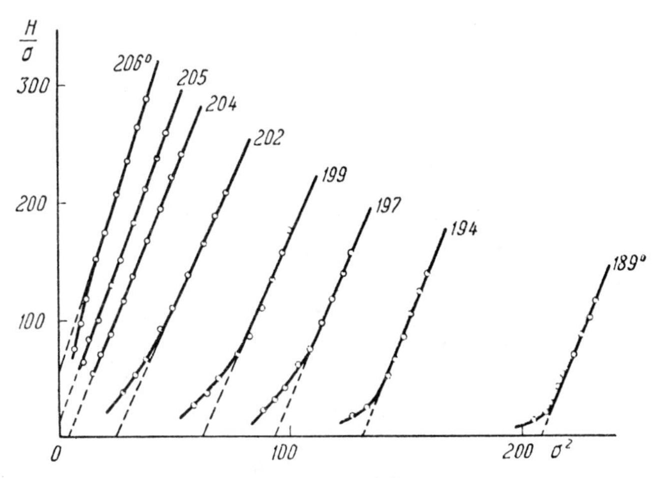


Fig. 11. Dependence of $H/\sigma$ on $\sigma^2$ for an alloy of 15% copper and 85% nickel.

where $\alpha'_\theta$ is a coefficient that gives the slope of the tangent to the curve $\alpha(T)$ at $T = \theta$. In the case of the coefficient $\beta$ the situation is more complicated; here the influence of structural factors is so great that even in the immediate neighborhood of the Curie point the nature of the dependence $\beta(T)$ can be very different for different materials.

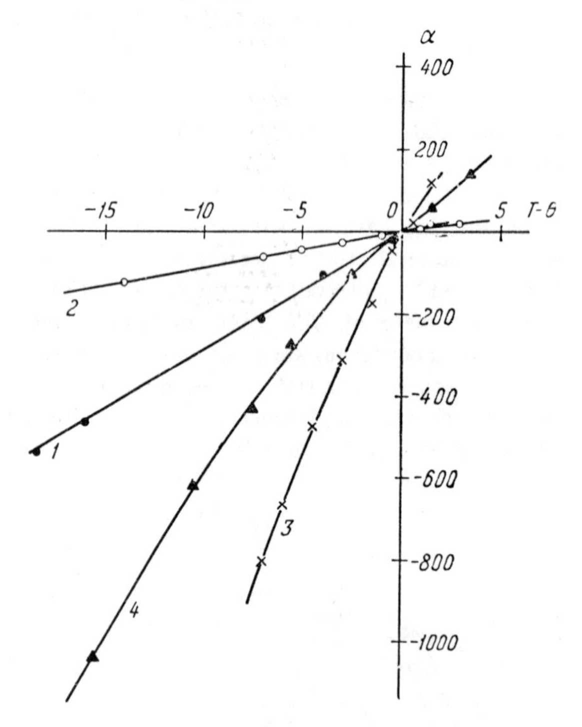


Fig. 12. Curves of the temperature dependence of the thermodynamic coefficient $\alpha$. 1) Fe; 2) 36% Ni, 64% Fe; 3) Ni; 4) 15% Cu, 85% Ni.

We note that a cubic equation of the type of Eq. (51) can also be obtained from a theory based on a model, by expanding the Weiss function or some modified form of this function (for example, the Brillouin function) in a series of powers of the parameter

$$a = \frac{\mu H}{kT} + \frac{\theta}{T}\frac{\sigma}{\sigma_0}.$$

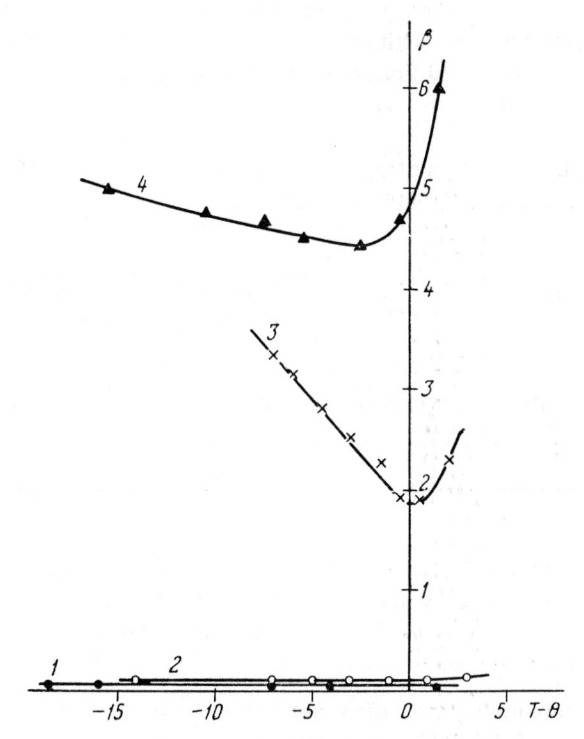


Fig. 13. Curves of the temperature dependence of the thermodynamic coefficient β. 1) Fe; 2) 36% Ni, 64% Fe; 3) Ni; 4) 15% Cu, 85% Ni.

If we neglect the small terms of this expansion, then we can obtain relations that are identical in form with Eqs. (51) and (52):

$$\frac{k}{\mu\sigma_0}(T-\theta)\sigma+\frac{1}{3}\left(\frac{k}{\mu}\frac{\theta^3}{\sigma_0^3}\frac{1}{T^2}\right)\sigma^3=H, \tag{54}$$

$$\sigma_\theta=\sigma_0\left(\frac{3\mu}{k\theta}\right)^{1/3}H^{1/3}. \tag{55}$$

It can be seen from a comparison of the relations (54) and (55) with Eqs. (51) and (52) that the Weiss theory is not in contradiction with the thermodynamic theory of the ferromagnetic transition. The formulas

(54) and (55) are, however, unsuitable for a quantitative description of the experimental results, because the coefficients of $\sigma$ and $\sigma^3$ in these equations do not agree with the experimental values. Table 2 shows the values of $\sigma_0$ calculated from the formula (55) and the values found at helium temperatures.

TABLE 2. Values of $\sigma_0$ Calculated from the Formula (55) and Obtained from Measurements near 0°K

| Material | $\theta$, °K | $\sigma_0$ | | $1/\theta^{1/3}$, $deg^{-1/3}$ |
|---|---|---|---|---|
| | | calculated from (55) | obtained from measurements near 0°K | |
| Ni | 624 | 119.7 | 56.8 | 0.117 |
| Fe | 1036 | 432 | 222 | 0.1 |
| 15% Cu, 85% Ni | 478 | 78.5 | 42 | — |
| 36% Ni, 64% Fe | 565 | 292 | 184.4 | 0.12 |

It is seen that in all cases the calculated values of $\sigma_0$ are approximately twice as large as the experimental values, which means that the Weiss theory cannot be used for the quantitative description of the magnetization near the Curie point.

The only useful conclusion that can be drawn from the formula (55) which follows from the "microscopic" theory is that regarding the dependence of the para-process on the value of the ratio $\sigma_0/\theta^{1/3}$; the larger the value of $\sigma_0$ is for a given ferromagnetic material, and the smaller the value of $\theta$, the larger the slope of the curve $\sigma(H^{1/3})$ at the Curie point, i.e., the more intense is the course of the para-process; this result is understandable because the larger the number of spins in the ferromagnetic material and the smaller the exchange interaction between them, the larger will be the effect of the "perturbing" action of the magnetic field near the Curie point.

It must be noted, however, that the quantity $1/\theta^{1/3}$ does not change much as we go from one material to another [it varies over the range 0.10 to 0.12 $deg^{-1}$ (see Table 2)], and consequently the intensity of the para-process near the Curie point practically depends only on the quantity $\sigma_0$. This last conclusion, however, also follows from Eq. (52); i.e., the fact that the true magnetization $\sigma_i$ is proportional to the quantity $\sigma_0$ also follows from the most general thermodynamic considerations.

## § 2. The Susceptibility of the Para-process in the Neighborhood of the Curie Point

It is usually supposed that the para-process is characteristic only of strong magnetic fields; therefore there has been almost no consideration of the para-process in weak fields. In actual fact it is precisely in weak fields that the para-process is most intense. In the low-temperature region the observation of the para-process in weak fields is impossible, since it is "hindered" by the processes of displacement and rotation. Near the Curie temperature one can study the para-process even in weak fields.

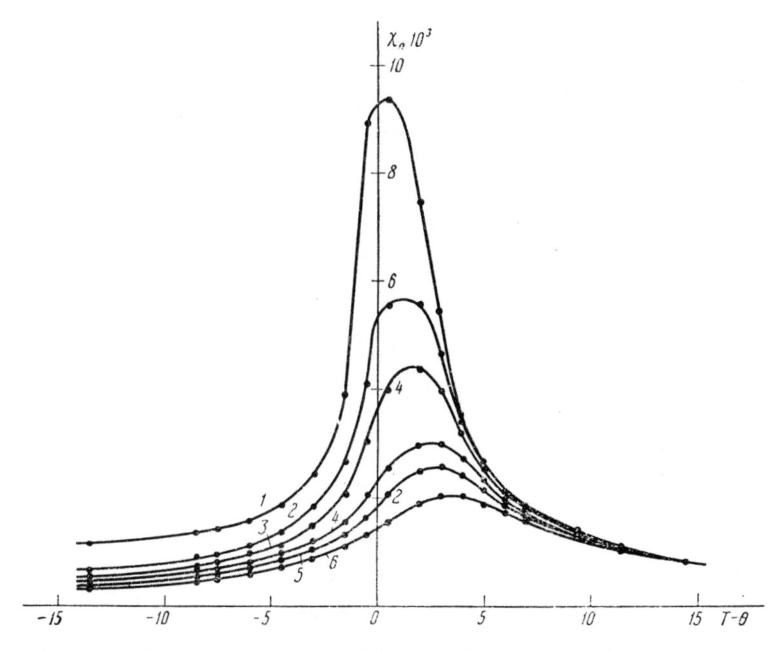


Fig. 14. The temperature dependence of the susceptibility of the para-process for nickel. 1) H = 206 oe; 2) H = 413 oe; 3) H = 619 oe; 4) H = 1032 oe; 5) H = 1290 oe; 6) H = 1755 oe.

To elucidate the dependence of the para-process on the fields near the Curie point let us find the susceptibility of the para-process, $\chi_n = d\sigma_i/dH$. Differentiating Eq. (51) with respect to H, we have

$$\chi_n = \frac{1}{\alpha + 3\beta(\sigma_s + \sigma_i)^2}. \tag{56}$$

For the initial susceptibility of the para-process (at $H \to \infty$) we get from Eq. (56) by substituting $\sigma_i = 0$ and $\sigma_s^2 = -\alpha/\beta$ (see Chapter III, Section 3) the result

$$(\chi_n)_{H \to 0} = -\frac{1}{2\alpha}. \tag{57}$$

Equation (57) indicates that as we approach the Curie point, where $\alpha = 0$, the quantity $(\chi_n)_{H \to 0}$ must increase without limit. In practice, however, since $\chi_n$ is always measured in some finite field, the susceptibility follows the formula (56), which gives a finite value of $\chi_n$ at the Curie point. Figures 14 and 15 show the results of measurements of the temperature dependence of the susceptibility of the para-process for nickel and an alloy of 36% nickel and 64% iron. It can be seen that near the Curie point $\chi_n$ reaches a maximum; this result is in agreement with the formulas (56) and (57), because for $T = \theta$ we have $\alpha \to 0$.

Substituting the relation (53) in Eq. (57), we get for the temperature range $T < \theta$:

$$(\chi_n)_{\substack{H \to 0 \\ T < \theta}} = -\frac{1}{2\alpha'_\theta (T - \theta)}. \tag{58}$$

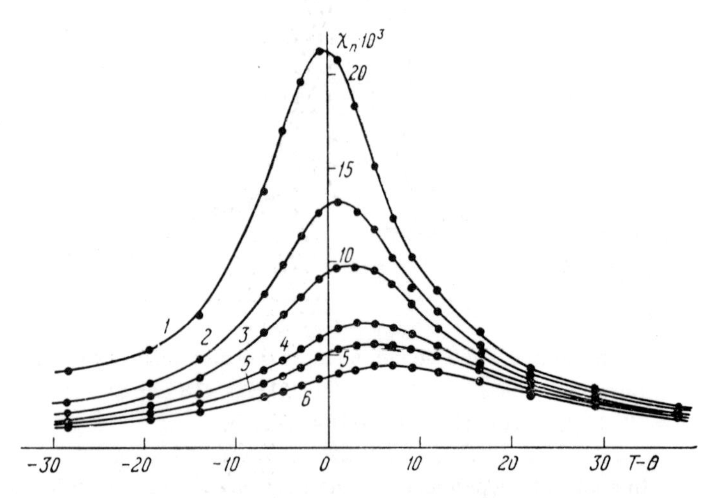


Fig. 15. Temperature dependence of the susceptibility of the para-process for an alloy of 36% nickel and 64% iron. 1) H = 206 oe; 2) H = 413 oe; 3) H = 619 oe; 4) H = 1032 oe; 5) H = 1290 oe; 6) H = 1755 oe.

For the range $T > \theta$, neglecting the cubic terms in Eq. (51) and setting $\sigma_s = 0$, we have after differentiating with respect to H:

$$(\chi_n)_{\substack{H \to 0 \\ T > \theta}} = \frac{1}{\alpha'_\theta (T - \theta)}. \qquad (59)$$

Dividing Eq. (59) by Eq. (58), we get the so-called "rule of two" [11]

$$\frac{(\chi_n)_{\substack{H \to 0 \\ T > \theta}}}{(\chi_n)_{\substack{H \to 0 \\ T < \theta}}} = -2. \qquad (60)$$

According to this rule the initial susceptibility of the para-process near the Curie point (on the side of higher temperatures) must be twice as large as the initial susceptibility that corresponds to temperatures below the Curie point (the maximum of the curve of the initial susceptibility $(\chi_n)_{H \to 0}(T)$ lies at the Curie point).

It must be noted that the "rule of two" also follows from the series expansion of the function of the Weiss-Heisenberg type (cf., e.g., [14]). The experimental verification of this rule is difficult, however, since in an experiment it is impossible to determine the value of $(\chi_n)_{\substack{H \to 0 \\ T < \theta}}$ in a pure form. The test of the "rule of two" by using in Eq.(60), instead of the value of the initial susceptibility of the para-process, the value of the susceptibility of the para-process measured in strong fields [14] cannot be regarded as correct.

Measurements have provided evidence that the susceptibility of the para-process near the Curie temperature depends strongly on the field. Figure 16 shows curves of the reciprocal of the susceptibility of the para-process for electrolytic nickel in the neighborhood of the Curie temperature, obtained in various fields. It can be seen that in the region $T < \theta$ the slope of the straight line for $1/\chi_n(T)$ depends on the field strength. It must also be pointed out that for the verification of the rule one cannot take the values of $1/\chi_n$ shown in Fig. 16 for the region $T > \theta$. The reason is that in the temperature region immediately adjacent to the Curie point the value of the paramagnetic susceptibility which one should substitute in the relation (60) according to the thermodynamic theory is decidedly distorted by the "remnants" of the spontaneous magnetization (cf. Section 17). The dependence of $\chi_n$ on H is easiest to interpret in the immediate vicinity of the Curie point. Differentiating Eq. (52) with respect to H, we have

$$(\chi_n)_\theta = \frac{\sigma_0}{3\sqrt[3]{4b}} H^{-2/3}. \tag{61}$$

It follows from Eq. (61) that the height of the maximum of the susceptibility of the para-process in the neighborhood of the Curie point must decrease as the field is increased. This conclusion from the theory is in agreement with experiment. It can be seen from Fig. 14 and 15 that the larger the field, the smaller is the value of $(\chi_n)_\theta$. It can also be seen that the field produces a very strong "smearing out" of the curve of $\chi_n(T)$. It is probable that there exists a field so strong that with this field the curve of $\chi_n(T)$ would be completely "smoothed out" and that the maximum of the susceptibility curve would disappear. It can be shown that the position of the maximum of the susceptibility of the para-process is displaced toward higher temperatures as the field is increased. This can also be seen easily from the curves shown in Figs. 14 and 15.

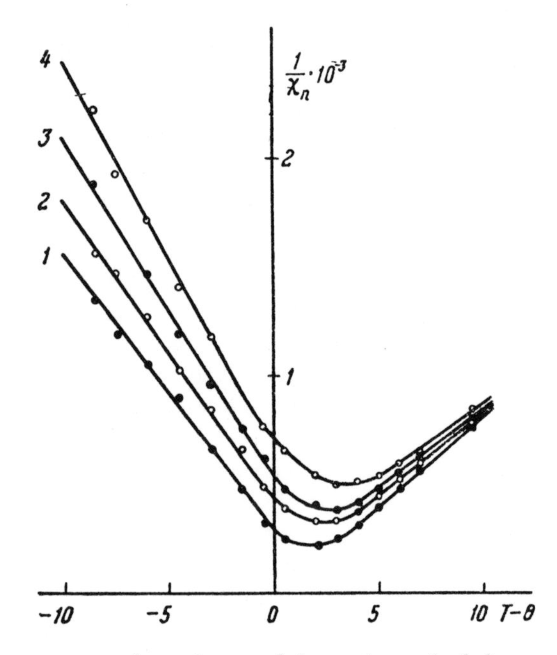


Fig. 16. Temperature dependence of the reciprocal of the susceptibility of electromagnetic nickel in the neighborhood of the Curie point. 1) H = = 619 oe; 2) H = 1032 oe; 3) H ) 1290 oe; 4) H = 1755 oe.

The temperature dependence of the initial susceptibility of the para-process in the region $T < \theta$, like the temperature dependence of the spontaneous magnetization, could serve as a quantity characteristic of the magnetic transition in a ferromagnetic material. On the other hand the curve of the temperature dependence of the susceptibility of the para-process measured in some particular field cannot serve for this purpose. Such a curve will differ from the curve $(\chi_n)_{H \to 0}(T)$ both quantitatively and qualitatively. With increase of the magnetic field the quantity $\chi_n$ decreases (see Figs. 14 and 15), and the "width" of the curve increases; in addition, the maxima of the curve are displaced toward higher temperatures. Thus, strictly speaking, the determination of the Curie temperature from the maxima of curves of $\chi_n(T)$ is also impossible. Only the position of the maximum of the initial susceptibility of the para-process gives the exact value of the Curie temperature.

Everything that has been said about the effect of the field on the susceptibility of the para-process is in agreement with the very general thermodynamic considerations which were given in Chapter I. According to these arguments, in the (H, T) plane the Curie point is an isolated point and must lie on the T axis only for $H = 0$. It follows from this that in the presence of a field one cannot determine the value of $\theta$ and draw conclusions about the character of the magnetic transition from the curve of $\chi_n(T)$.

## § 3. The Temperature Dependence of the Spontaneous Magnetization

The procuedure of determining the spontaneous magnetization by linear extrapolation of the curves of the true magnetization to zero field, which is usually used at low temperatures, cannot be used near the Curie point, because here the curve of $\sigma_i(H)$ is decidedly nonlinear. The following methods exist for determining the temperature behavior of the spontaneous magnetization near the Curie point:

1. The method of lines of equal magnetization proposed by Weiss and Forrer [3], in which the results of measurements of the true magnetization at various temperatures are used to construct curves $H(T)_{\sigma_i} =$ const. In the region of the para-process these curves are straight lines. By carrying out an extrapolation to $H = 0$, one finds the temperature at which $\sigma_i$ is numerically equal to $\sigma_s$.

2. The method of the "magnetocaloric effect" [3] employs an extrapolation of the curves of $\Delta T(\sigma^2)$, which are straight lines in the region of the para-process, to the value $\Delta T = 0$, or, in other words to $H = 0$; the lines cut off segments $\sigma^2 = \sigma_s^2$ on the axis of abscissas. This method has a rigorous thermodynamic justification (cf., e.g., [8]).

In an analogous way one can determine the quantity $\sigma_s$ by using the data from measurements of the magnetostriction of the para-process [50], or of the galvanomagnetic effect [51], if the contributions to these effects from processes of displacement and rotation are sufficiently small, as is usually the case near the Curie point.

It has been shown experimentally that these two methods give approximately the same results.

3. Using Eq. (51), one can determine the temperature behavior of $\sigma_s$ near the Curie point by a third method [49]. In fact, we have from Eq. (51) for $H = 0$ and $\sigma_i = 0$.

$$\sigma_s^2 = -\frac{\alpha}{\beta}. \tag{62}$$

By substituting experimental values of $\alpha$ and $\beta$ one can calculate the temperature behavior of $\sigma_s$ near the Curie point.

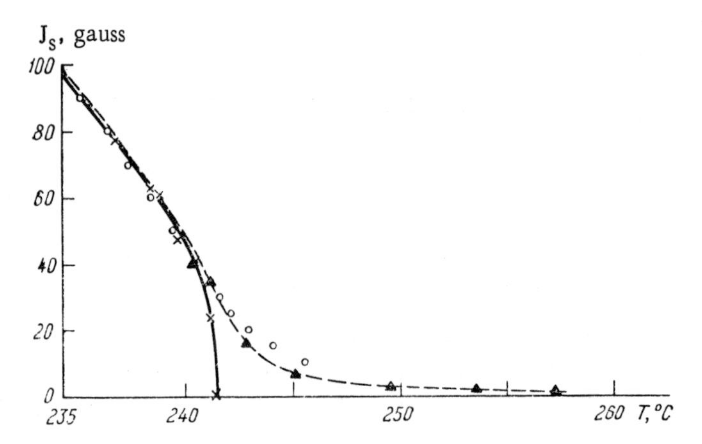


Fig. 17. Temperature dependence of the spontaneous magnetization of an alloy of 97% nickel and 3% silicon, determined by three different methods. ×) Method of thermodynamic coefficients; ▲) method of the galvanomagnetic effect; O) method of lines of equal magnetization.

Hereafter we shall call this method for determining $\sigma_s(T)$ the method of thermodynamic coefficients.

Figure 17 shows the temperature dependence near the Curie point of the spontaneous magnetization per cubic centimeter for an alloy of 97% nickel and 3% silicon, as determined by Paches [52] by three different methods: the method of lines of equal magnetization, the method of the galvanomagnetic effect, and the method of thermodynamic coefficients. At some distance from the Curie point all three methods give the same results. The curves depart from each other, however, as we approach the Curie point. The curve determined by the method of thermodynamic coefficients turns sharply downward and breaks off at the temperature axis. The curves determined by the other two methods approach the temperature axis gradually, forming the so-called "tails" of the spontaneous magnetization. These "tails" arise because of the "remnants" of the spontaneous magnetization above the Curie temperature.

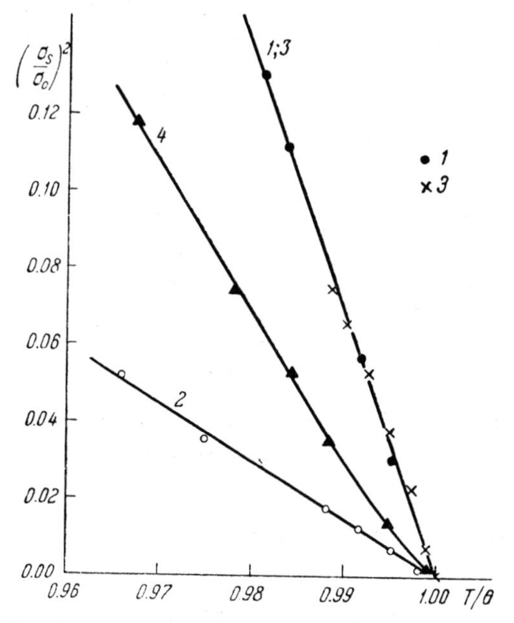


Fig. 18. Dependence of $(\sigma_s/\sigma_0)^2$ on $T/\theta$ near the Curie point. 1) Fe; 2) 36% Ni, 64% Fe; 3) Ni; 4) 15% Cu, 85% Ni.

Because of the properties of Eq. (51) the method of thermodynamic coefficients provides no possibility for determining the "remnants," since according to the thermodynamic theory of the ferromagnetic transition $\sigma_s = 0$ in the region above the Curie point. The use of the method of thermodynamic coefficients for the determination of $\sigma_s(T)$ is nevertheless of interest for the following reasons.

A comparison of the curves of $\sigma_s(T)$ determined by the method of thermodynamic coefficients with the curves determined by the methods 1 and 2 provides a correct separation of the "remnants" of the spontaneous magnetization from the main curve of $\sigma_s(T)$. It is possible in this way to construct curves of the dependence of $(\sigma_s/\sigma_0)^2$ on $T/\theta$ which according to the thermodynamic theory of the ferromagnetic transition [10] (and also according to model theories [8]) should be straight lines (cf. Eqs. (9) and (27)]. An analysis of this relation makes it possible to compare the temperature behavior of $\sigma_s$ in various materials and to determine the influence of structural factors on this dependence (this point will be discussed later). Figure 18 shows the dependence of $(\sigma_s/\sigma_0)^2$ on $T/\theta$ for several (well annealed) ferromagnetic materials according to the data given in [53], as calculated by the method of thermodynamic coefficients. It is seen that the linear relations between $(\sigma_s/\sigma_0)^2$ and $T/\theta$ hold very well not only for pure metals but also for alloys.

## § 4. The Determination of the Curie Temperature

The Curie temperatures of ferromagnetic materials are at present determined by several methods. Owing to the presence of "tails" of the spontaneous magnetization and to the influence of the para-process there can be considerable differences between the values of the Curie temperature determined by different methods, in particular for alloys.

To establish the most correct method for determining the Curie temperature, an analysis has been made in [52] of four different methods for determining this temperature:

1) From the maximum of the temperature coefficient of the resistance $(1/R_0)(\Delta R/\Delta T)$;

2) From the maximum of the negative galvanomagnetic effect (caused by the para-process) $-(\Delta R/R)_n$;

3. From the vanishing of the spontaneous magnetization ($\sigma_s$ or $I_s$) determined by the method of thermodynamic coefficients or, what is the same thing, from the vanishing of the coefficient $\alpha$;

4) From the vanishing of the initial permeability.

The results of the measurements are given in Table 3. The error in the temperature determinations was ± 0.3°. The measurements of the magnetic and electric characteristics were made with the same specimen under the same temperature conditions and practically simultaneously.

TABLE 3. Values of the Curie Temperature Determined by Various Methods

| Material | Values of the Curie temperature determined | | | | |
|---|---|---|---|---|---|
| | from the max. of the temp. coefficient of resistance | from the max. of the negative galvanomagnetic effect | by the method of thermodynamic coefficients | from the initial permeability | difference $\theta_{\alpha=0}-\theta_{\frac{1}{R}\frac{\Delta R}{\Delta T}}$ |
| 100% Ni | 346.5 | 347.7 | 348.2 | 347.8 | 1.7 |
| 96.9% Ni, 3.1% Si | 237.3 | 240.5 | 241.5 | 243.3 | 4.2 |
| 95.1% Ni, 4.9% Si | 155.2 | 158.5 | 160.5 | 160.7 | 5.3 |
| 95.1% Ni, 4.9% Si * | 155.2 | 157.5 | 158.5 | – | 3.3 |
| 97.5% Ni, 2.5% Mn | 310.2 | 311.8 | 313.0 | 315.0 | 2.8 |
| 80% Ni, 20% Mn | 87.1 | 92.5 | 94.7 | 97.0 | 7.6 |
| 38% Ni, 62% Fe | 293.8 | 296.0 | 303.5 | 299.8 | 9.7 |

*After annealing.

It can be seen from the table that for all materials the maximum of $(1/R_0)(\Delta R/\Delta T)$ occurs at a lower temperature than the maximum of $(-\Delta R/R)_n$ and the latter occurs at a temperature lower than that at which the quantities $\sigma_s$, $I_s$, or $\alpha$ go to zero.

There is some disagreement between the values of the Curie temperature determined from the initial permeability and those determined by other methods. This is explained by the fact that because of the side effects the measurement of the Curie temperature from the initial permeability is less exact than the measurements by the first three methods.

The difference between the determinations of the Curie point by the various methods (see Table 3) increases with increase of the concentration of the nonmagnetic element in an alloy, which leads to an increase of the "tail" of the spontaneous magnetization. Thus the more the magnetic transition is spread out, the larger the difference in the values of the Curie point determined by the methods that have been enumerated.

In order to estimate which method gives the most correct determination of the Curie temperature it is necessary to establish the values of the spontaneous magnetization at the Curie point measured by the various methods.

Figures 19, 20, and 21 show curves of the temperature dependence of the spontaneous magnetization determined by the method of thermodynamic coefficients (dashed curve) and by the method of the galvanomagnetic effect, and also of the temperature dependence of the quantities $(1/R_0)(\Delta R/\Delta T)$, $(\Delta R/R)_n$ and $\alpha$ for nickel, an alloy of 97% nickel and 3% silicon, and an alloy of 38% nickel and 62% iron. It can be seen that the maximum of $(1/R_0)(\Delta R/\Delta T)$ (or, in the case of the alloy of 38% Ni and 62% Fe, the place where the derivative is discontinuous) lies in the range of temperatures where there is still a rather large spontaneous magnetization. The same can be said about the position of the maximum of the negative galvanomagnetic effect, although it is indeed located at a higher temperature.

Both of these points are in a range of temperatures where the curve of $\sigma_s(T)$ is still falling steeply. It follows from this that there is no basis for taking the position of the maximum of the anomaly of a "nonmagnetic" property as the true Curie point, as is sometimes done in the literature (for example, [4]). A more correct method for determining the Curie point is the method of thermodynamic coefficients (finding the temperature at which $\alpha = 0$). At this temperature an overwhelmingly large part of the volume of the specimen is in the paramagnetic state, and there remain in the ferromagnetic state only very small regions, the "remnants" of the spontaneous magnetization. This temperature always lies above the temperature of the maxima of the anomalies of the "nonmagnetic" properties. It must be noted that these two points coincide only in the ideal case in which the ferromagnetic transition is not "smeared out." We note also that in inhomogeneous materials, where this "smearing out" is large, the method of thermodynamic coefficients gives a temperature which is an "average" Curie temperature for the given material.

Because of the effects of the para-process, which can be important even in weak fields, and the presence of "tails" of the spontaneous magnetization (especially in alloys), the determination of the Curie temperature from the temperature dependence of the initial permeability is not an exact method.

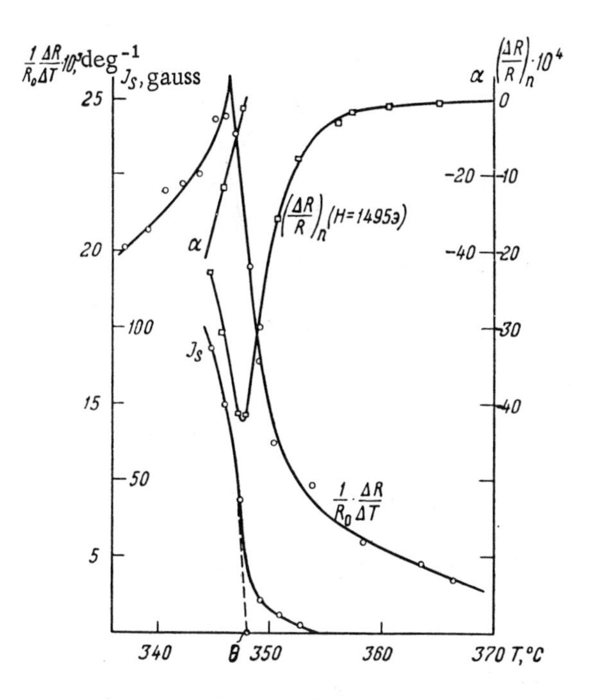


Fig. 19. Determination of the Curie temperature in nickel. $J_s$ is the spontaneous magnetization determined by the method of thermodynamic coefficients (dashed line) and the galvanomagnetic effect; $(1/R_0)(\Delta R/\Delta T)$ is the temperature coefficient of the electric resistance; $(\Delta R/R)_n$ is the galvanomagnetic effect caused by the para-process; $\alpha$ is the thermodynamic coefficient.

Attempts have been made to determine the Curie temperature from the temperature dependence of the residual magnetization and the coercive force. This method is unacceptable, however, because these magnetic characteristics of a ferromagnetic specimen can have finite values even above the Curie point, where there still exist "remnants" of the

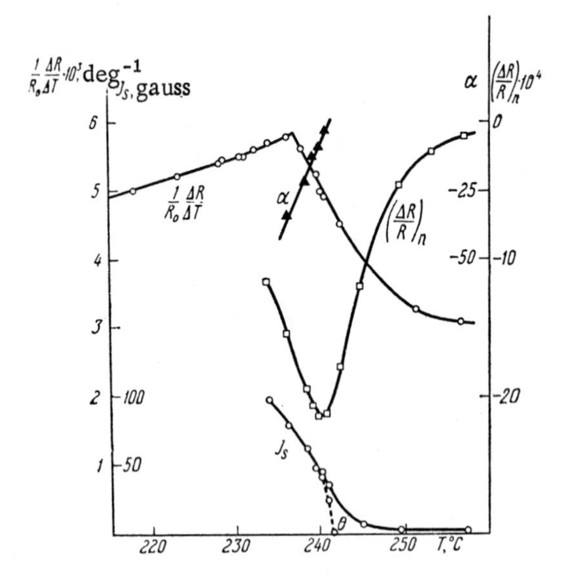


Fig. 20. Determination of the Curie temperature in an alloy of 97% Ni and 3% Si (the notations are the same as in Fig. 19).

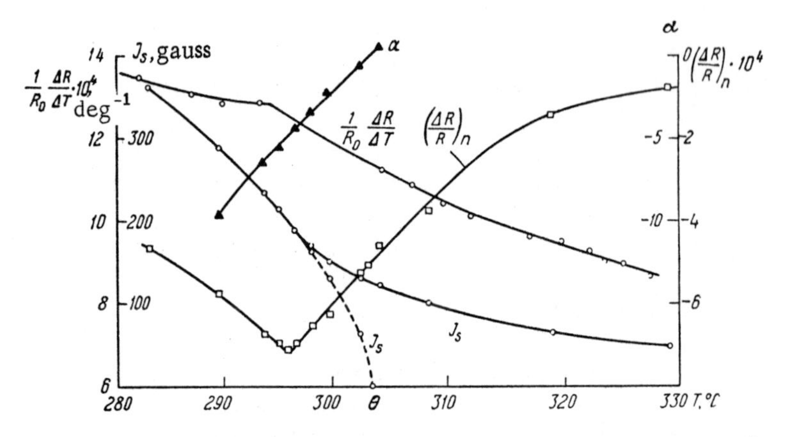


Fig. 21. Determination of the Curie temperature in an alloy of 38% Ni and 62% Fe (the notations are the same as in Fig. 19).

spontaneous magnetization. These effects go to zero only when the "remnants" of the spontaneous magnetization completely disappear. In fact, Forrer [54] has shown that the coercive force goes to zero only far beyond the ferromagnetic Curie point (at the so-called paramagnetic Curie point).

## § 5. The Effect of Structural Changes in Alloys on the Temperature Dependence of the Spontaneous Magnetization in the Neighborhood of the Curie Point

Structural characteristics of the material must have a strong effect on the character of the ferromagnetic transition. This is clear because ferromagnetism depends on the relative distances and locations of the atoms in the lattice and on the configuration of the lattice itself. Theories of ferromagnetism even take this into account in an approximate way and lead to formulas for the temperature dependence of the spontaneous magnetization which contain parameters that characterize the type of crystal lattice and the location of the atoms in the lattice [46]. The effects on the temperature dependence of the spontaneous magnetization that are produced by structural changes caused by heat treatment of alloys have been discussed in quite a number of papers [55, 56, 57, 58]. It is shown in these papers that the general form of the curve $\frac{\sigma_s}{\sigma_0}\left(\frac{T}{\theta}\right)$ (far from the Curie point) is changed somewhat by heat treatment. A really strong effect of structural changes in alloys on the shape of the curve $\frac{\sigma_s}{\sigma_0}$ $(T/\theta)$ is, however, to be expected only in the immediate neighborhood of the Curie point, where the spontaneous magnetization is extremely sensitive to these structural changes. The effect of these changes can be taken into account quantitatively by the use of a coefficient $\xi$ in the formula

$$\left(\frac{\sigma_s}{\sigma_0}\right)^2 = \xi\left(1 - \frac{T}{\theta}\right). \tag{63}$$

According to (9), (16), (17) it follows that

$$\xi = \frac{\alpha'_\theta \theta}{2b} = \frac{\alpha'_\theta \theta}{\beta\sigma_0^2}.$$

We present here the results of measurements of the curves of $\left(\frac{\sigma_s}{\sigma_0}\right)^2$ $(T/\theta)$ for several alloys [59].

Ni-Cu Alloys. Figure 22 shows curves of the dependence of $(\sigma_s/\sigma_0)^2$ on $T/\theta$ for a series of copper-nickel alloys. It is seen that the curves for pure nickel and for alloys with a small proportion of copper

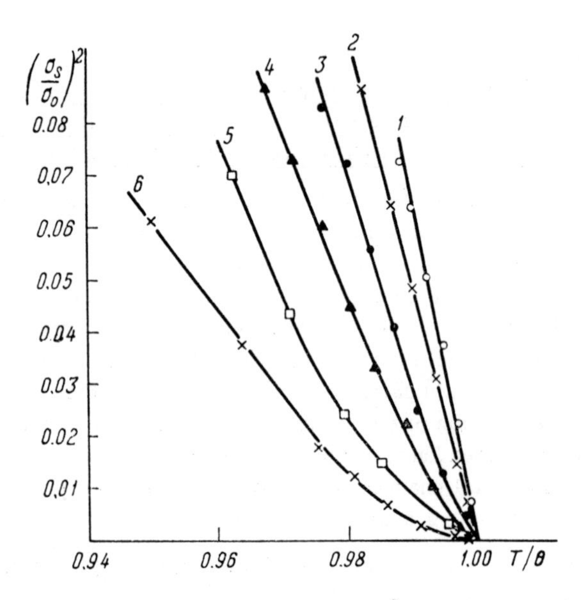


Fig. 22. Dependence of $(\sigma_s/\sigma_0)^2$ on $T/\theta$ near the Curie temperature for Ni and Ni–Cu alloys after annealing for 20 hours at 1000°C. 1) Ni; 2) 95% Ni, 5% Cu; 3) 92% Ni, 8% Cu; 4) 85% Ni, 15% Cu; 5) 80% Ni, 20% Cu; 6) 75% Ni, 25% Cu.

have a straight-line shape in accordance with Eq. (63), whereas for alloys with a larger copper content the curves are not described by the relation (63). The reason for this is as follows. Copper-nickel alloys are subject to the phenomenon of eliquation; in these alloys there is produced in the melt an inhomogeneous distribution of the copper atoms through the volume of the specimen, so that there is a fluctuation of the exchange interaction. This in turn has the consequence that the alloy will have not a single Curie point, but a whole set of somewhat different Curie points, and the ferromagnetic transition will be strongly smeared out (especially in alloys with a large content of Cu).

Prolonged annealing of the alloys must lead to diffusion of the copper atoms and consequently to equalizing of the concentration of copper through the volume of the specimen. Figure 23 shows curves of the dependence of $(\sigma_s/\sigma_0)^2$ on $T/\theta$ that were obtained for the same alloys after prolonged annealing. It is seen that the nonlinearity of the curves has disappeared for all the alloys with the exception of that containing 25% Cu, for which longer annealing is probably required to remove the eliquation. Moreover, one sees from a comparison of Figs. 22 and 23 that the slope of the straight line is increased by the annealing.

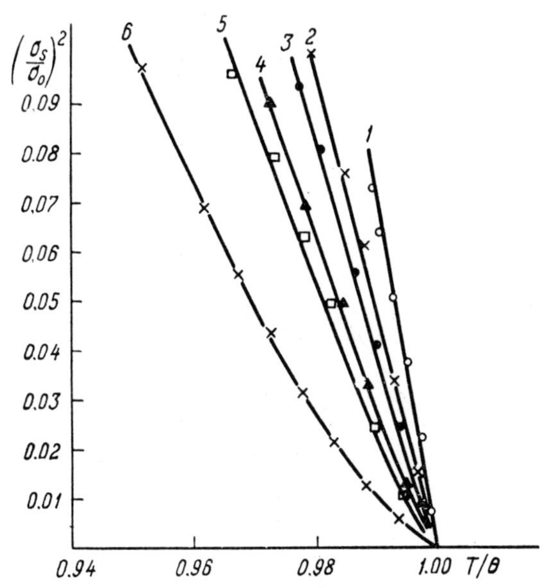


Fig. 23. Dependence of $(\sigma_s/\sigma_0)^2$ on $T/\theta$ for Ni and Ni–Cu alloys after annealing for 90 hours at 1000°C [the notations are the same as in Fig. 22].

Heat treatment has a very strong effect on the values and the temperature dependence of the thermodynamic coefficients $\alpha$ and $\beta$ (Figs. 24 and 25). These coefficients can be used to take into account in a quantitative way the effects of structural changes in alloys on the magnetic transition.

Inhomogeneities in an alloy also have a strong effect on the length of the "tail" of the spontaneous magnetization (Fig. 26). For pure metals the "tail" is always shorter than for alloys. With increase of the duration of the annealing the length of the "tail" becomes smaller. A similar shortening of the "tails" as an effect of annealing has also been observed in curves of the initial permeability and of the electric resistance [60], and also in curves of the magnetostriction [61], taken for Ni-Cu alloys near the Curie point.

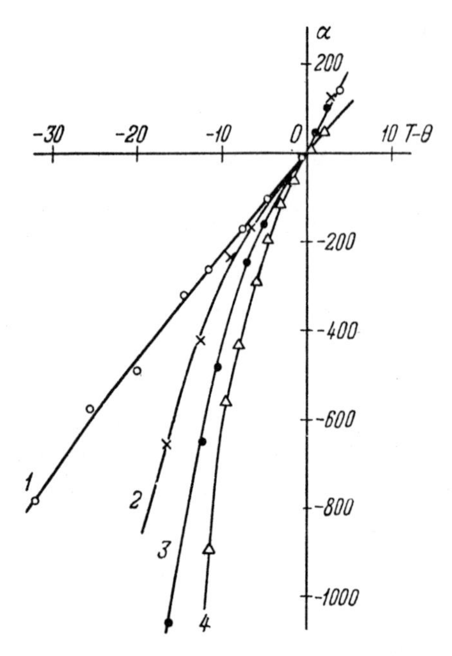


Fig. 24. Temperature dependence of the coefficient α for an alloy of 20% Cu and 80% Ni for various types of annealing. 1) 10 hours, 1000° C; 2) 20 hours, 1000°C; 3) 20 hours, 1000° C and 10 hours, 1200°C; 4) 20 hours, 1000°C and 20 hours, 1200°C.

Owing to inhomogeneities of the concentration in alloys, to non-uniform distribution of impurities, to lattice defects, and to other causes, real ferromagnetic materials always have "tails" of the spontaneous mag-

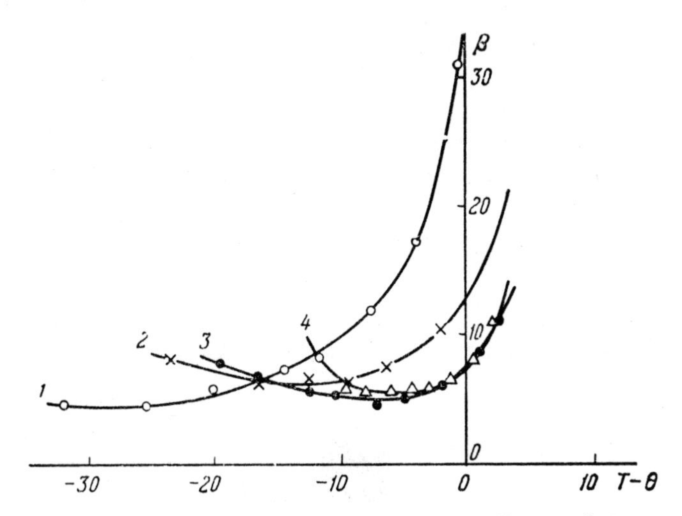


Fig. 25. Temperature dependence of the coefficient β for an alloy of 20% Cu and 80% Ni for various types of annealing (the notations are the same as in Fig. 24).

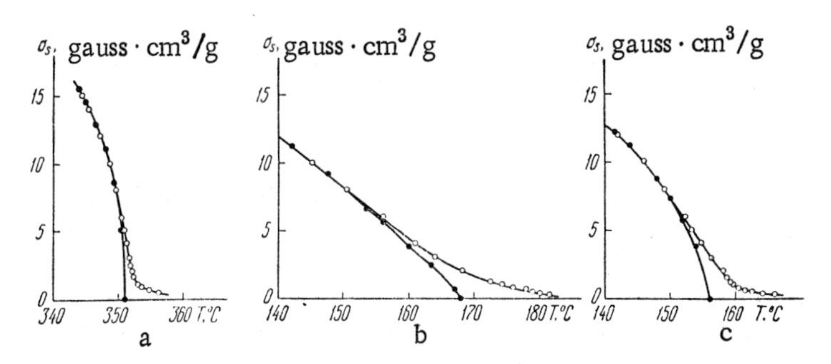


Fig. 26. "Tails" of the spontaneous magnetization. a) pure nickel; b) alloy of 80% Ni, 20% Cu, annealed 10 hours at 1000°C; c) alloy of 80% Ni and 20% Cu, annealed 20 hours at 1000°C and 20 hours at 1200°C.

netization (even in single crystals). This fact makes more difficult the study of the short-range order of the spins, for which the theory was developed by Vonsovskii [62].

A comparison of the values of the coefficient $\xi$ which determines the "steepness" of the approach of the curves of spontaneous magnetization to the Curie point for various alloys is possible only for well-annealed materials, in which the fluctuations of the exchange interaction have been reduced to a minimum. Table 4 shows the values for $\xi$ for nickel and copper-nickel alloys. As was pointed out in Chapter II, according to Vonsovskii and Vlasov

$$\xi = 3\left(\frac{\theta}{\theta_{dd}}\right)^2.$$

It follows from the theory that $\theta / \theta_{dd} > 1$, i.e., $\xi > 3$, which is confirmed by experiment not only for nickel but also for Ni-Cu alloys.

TABLE 4. Values of the Coefficient $\xi$ in Copper-Nickel Alloys

| % Ni | $\xi$ |
|---|---|
| 100.0 | 6.75 |
| 95.4 | 5.34 |
| 92.6 | 4.69 |
| 86.0 | 3.76 |
| 81.2 | 3.44 |

We note that with increase of the concentration of Cu in Ni-Cu alloys the quantity $\xi$ decreases, whereas according to the theory based on a model this quantity should remain constant and equal to 3 (cf., e.g., [15]). From the point of view of the theory of Vonsovskii and Vlasov this fact must be explained by saying that with increase of the concentration of copper in the alloy there is a change of the ratio between s-d and d-d exchange interactions.

Nickel-Iron Alloys of Invar Composition. Nickel-iron alloys of invar composition are characterized by extremely peculiar anomalies of their physical properties, which manifest themselves particularly strongly near the Curie point [63], and therefore a detailed study of the temperature dependence of the spontaneous magnetization in these alloys is of great interest. Measurements have shown that the temperature dependence of the spontaneous magnetization near the Curie point in alloys of this kind depends rather strongly on the heat treatment. This is probably to the explained by the effect of inhomogeneities of the concentration throughout the volume, which, just as in Ni-Cu alloys, can occur in invar alloys in the melt. There is, however, a type of heat treatment which makes the curve of $\sigma_s(T)$ more "normal." Figures 27, 28, and 29 show the temperature dependences of $\alpha$, $\beta$, and $(\sigma_s/\sigma_0)^2$ for an alloy of 36% nickel and 64% iron after annealing. Depending on the time of annealing, a minimum can appear in the

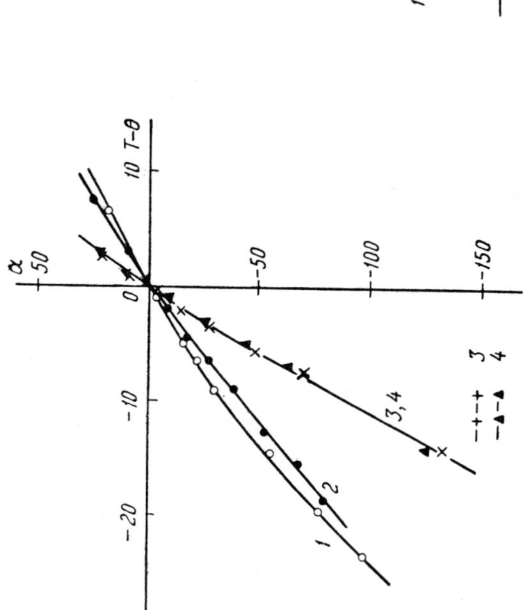


Fig. 27. Temperature dependence of the coefficient α for an alloy of 36% nickel and 64% iron with various amounts of annealing. 1) 10 hours, 1000°C; 2) 20 hours, 1000°C; 3) 20 hours, 1000°C + 10 hours, 1200° C; 4) 20 hours, 1000°C + 20 hours, 1200°C.

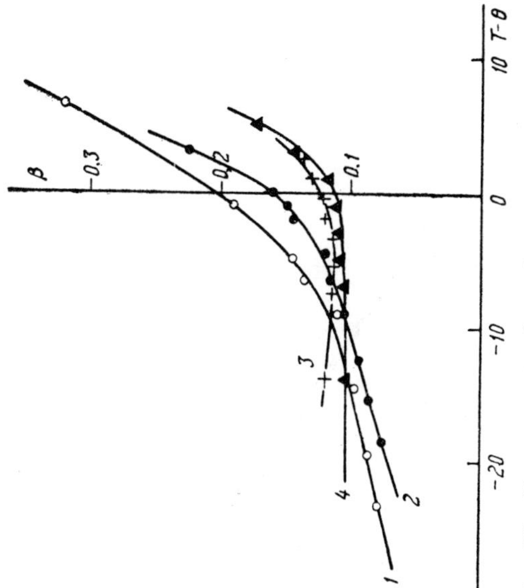


Fig. 28. Temperature dependence of the coefficient β for an alloy of 36% nickel and 64% iron with various amounts of annealing. (The notations are the same as in Fig. 27.)

curve of $\beta$ (T), as is seen in Fig. 28, and the curves $(\sigma_s/\sigma_0)^2(T)$ become straight. With further annealing there is not much change in the shape of these curves.

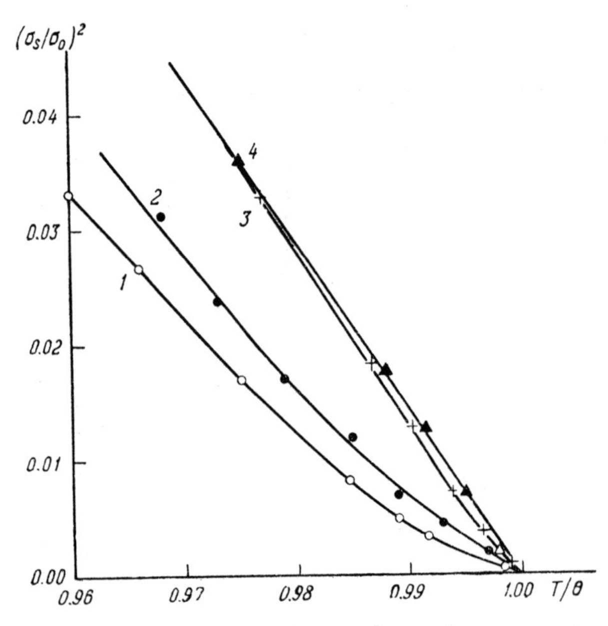


Fig. 29. Dependence of $(\sigma_s/\sigma_0)^2$ on $T/\theta$ for an alloy of 36% nickel and 64% iron with various amounts of annealing. (Notations the same as in Fig. 27.)

It has been found that nevertheless the coefficient $\xi$ for invar alloys has a value considerably smaller than three, as is illustrated in Table 5. This indicates that for an unknown reason the ferromagnetic transitions in nickel-iron alloys of invar compositions is spread over an unusually wide temperature range.

Figure 30 shows the curve of $(\sigma_s/\sigma_0)(T/\theta)$ for an alloy of 36% nickel and 64% iron after prolonged annealing. For comparison this diagram also shows the corresponding curves for nickel and for an alloy of 20% copper and 80% nickel. It can be seen that the curve for invar has an exceptionally flat shape.

TABLE 5. Values of the Coefficient $\xi$ in Invar Alloys

| Alloy | $\xi$ | $\theta$, °C |
|---|---|---|
| 36 Ni, 64 Fe | 1.44 | 298 |
| 35 Ni, 65 Fe | 1.42 | 237 |

It is possible that the cause of the anomalous shape of the curve of the the spontaneous magnetization in invar alloys is that in these alloys ferromagnetism is due not only to the exchange interaction between atoms in the first coordination sphere but also between atoms in following coordination spheres. Thus these alloys are more complicated in their magnetic behavior, and for them the temperature dependence of the spontaneous magnetization is of a different sort from that found in the majority of other alloys.

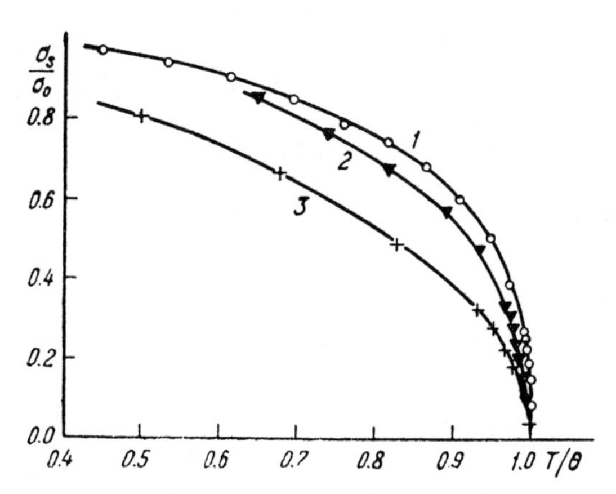


Fig. 30. Dependence of $\sigma_s/\sigma_0$ on $T/\theta$. 1) Ni; 2) 20% Cu, 80% Ni, 3) 36% Ni, 64% Fe.

The possibility is not excluded that the flat shape of the curve of the spontaneous magnetization can also be due to a colloidal distribution of the ferromagnetic $\alpha$ phase in the matrix of the $\gamma$ phase, which causes fluctuations of the exchange interaction in the alloy. The suggestion that there may be a colloidal distribution of the $\alpha$ phase in an invar alloy has been made in a paper by Zakharova and Khatanova [64] on studies of alloys of this type by x-ray and electron-optical methods.

Ni-Mn Alloys. As is well known, in nickel-manganese alloys that are close to the composition $Ni_3Mn$ a suitable heat treatment leads to an atomic ordering with the result that there is a sharp change of the magnetic and "nonmagnetic" properties of the alloy [65]. Therefore it is interesting to find out how the atomic ordering effects the temperature dependence of the spontaneous magnetization near the Curie point. A specimen of an alloy of 21 atomic percent Mn and 79 atomic percent Ni was subjected to quenching (the disordered state was established), and then to annealing at 380°C for various periods of time.

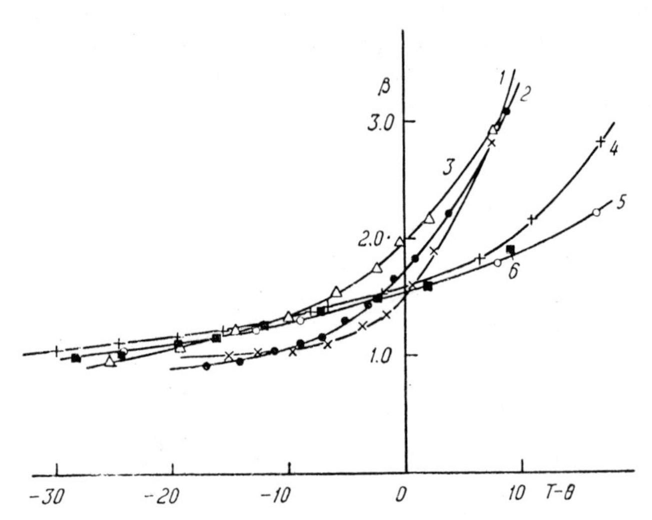


Fig. 31. Temperature dependence of the coefficient $\beta$ for an alloy of 21 atomic percent Mn and 79 atomic percent Ni with various amounts of annealing: 1) 1 hour; 2) 2 hours; 3) 6 hours; 4) 16 hours; 5) 36 hours; 6) 84 hours.

Figure 31 shows curves of the temperature dependence of the coefficient $\beta$ for anneals of different durations. It can be seen that none of these curves has a minimum that would indicate that the curve was becoming "normalized." It can be seen from Fig. 32, which shows the

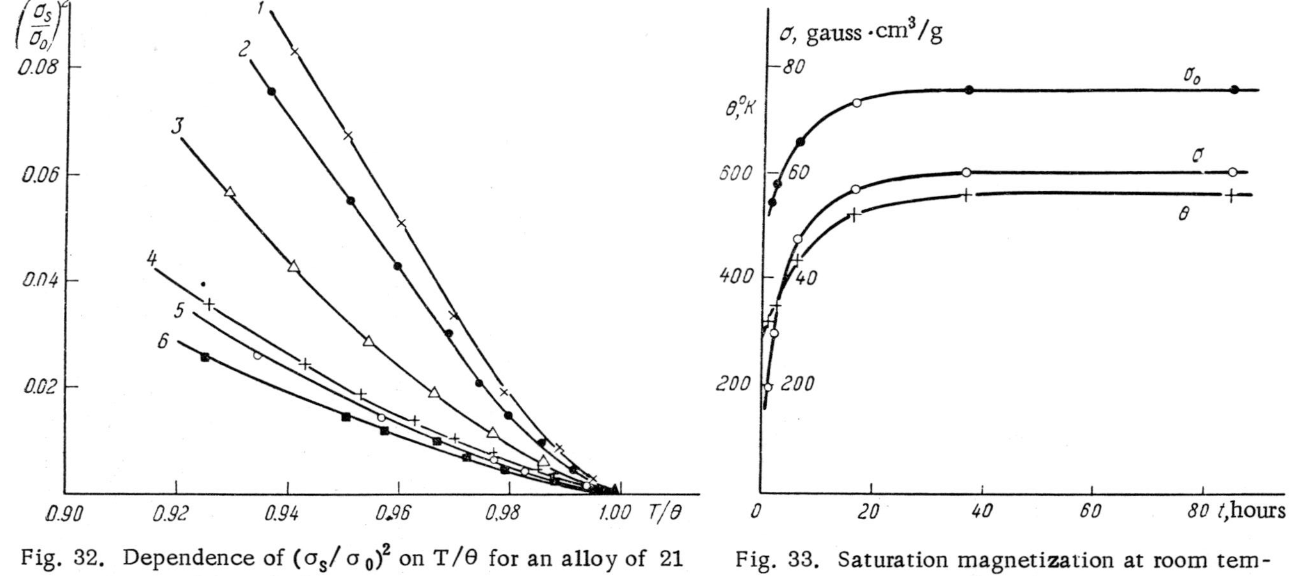


Fig. 32. Dependence of $(\sigma_s/\sigma_0)^2$ on $T/\theta$ for an alloy of 21 atomic percent Mn and 79 atomic percent Ni. (Notations the same as for Fig. 31.)

Fig. 33. Saturation magnetization at room temperature ($\sigma_r$) and at 0°K ($\sigma_0$), and the Curie temperature $\theta$, for an alloy of 21 atomic percent Mn and 79 atomic percent Ni, as function of the duration of annealing.

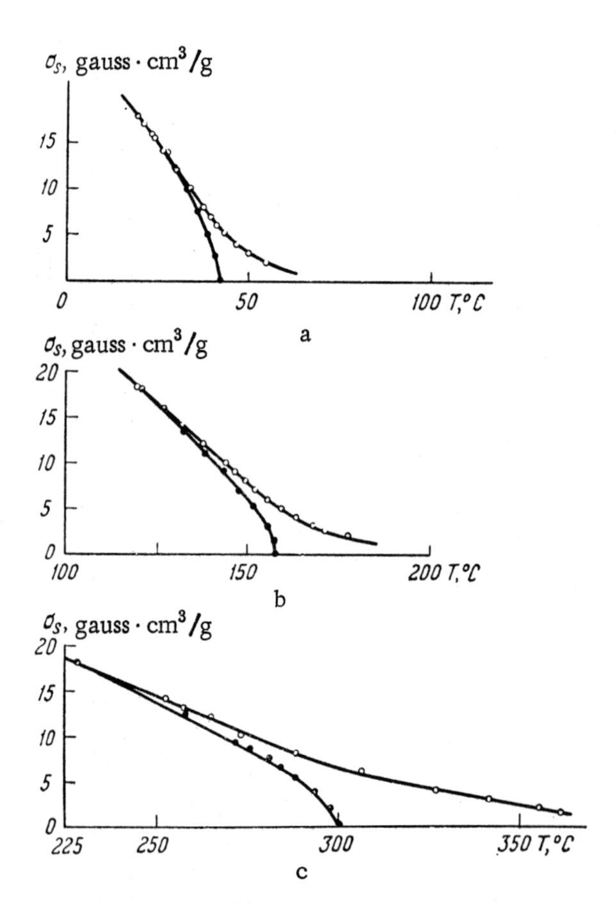


Fig. 34. "Tails" of the spontaneous magnetization in an alloy of 21 atomic percent Mn and 79 atomic percent of Ni, for various amounts of annealing. a) 1 hour at 380°C; b) 6 hours at 380°C; c) 84 hours at 380°C.

dependence of $(\sigma_s/\sigma_0)^2$ on $T/\theta$, that contrary to expectations even after an anneal lasting 84 hours, the curves do not acquire a linear shape, although, as follows from Fig. 33, the process of ordering would seem to have been completed in the alloys: the Curie temperature $\theta$, the saturation magnetization $\sigma_k$ (at room temperature) and $\sigma_0$ (at 0°K) have reached their limiting values. Furthermore it can be seen from Fig. 34 that the "tails" of the spontaneous magnetization have not only not become shorter with increase of the duration of the anneals, but on the contrary have become much longer.

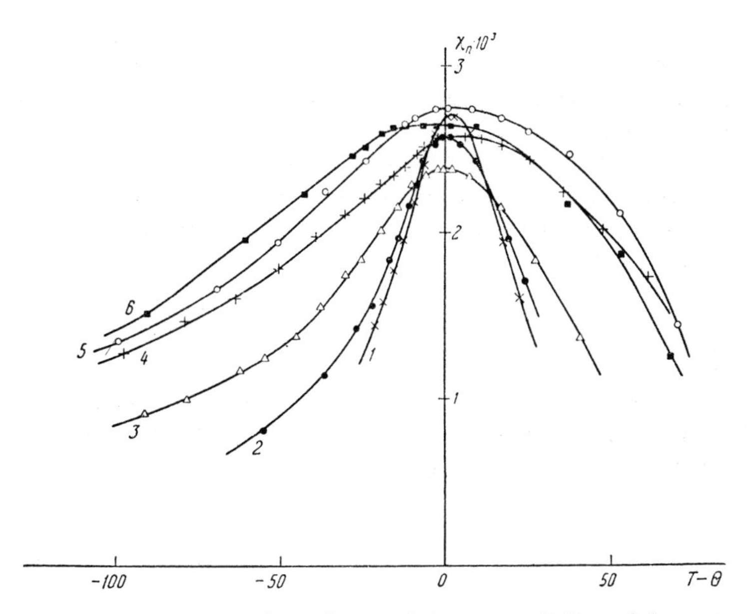


Fig. 35. Temperature dependence of the susceptibility of the para-process in an alloy of 21 atomic percent Mn and 79 atomic percent Ni, with various amounts of annealing. 1) 1 hour; 2) 2 hours; 3) 6 hours; 4) 16 hours; 5) 36 hours; 6) 84 hours, at temperature 380°C.

Finally let us point out one more very interesting experimental fact. It can be seen from Fig. 32 that with increase of the duration of the anneal the slopes of the curves relative to the temperature axis become very much smaller; this indicates that the ferromagnetic transition has become decidedly "smeared out"; this is also confirmed by curves of $\chi$ (T) (Fig. 35). With increase of the duration of the annealing the width of the curve is very much increased. The observed "smearing out" of the ferromagnetic transition is probably due to the fact that along with the main ordered phase the alloy contains "islands" of disordered phase, which cause fluctuations of the exchange interaction throughout the volume of the specimen, and consequently cause a "smearing out" of the transition.

An analogous phenomenon has been observed by Simpson and Tredgold [57] in the alloy $Pt_3Co$; they found that the curve of $\frac{\sigma_s}{\sigma_0}(T/\theta)$ for the disordered alloy lies higher than the curve for the ordered alloy.

Unlike the low-temperature region, where structural factors do not have any large effect on the shape of the curve of the spontaneous magnetization, in the region of the Curie temperature the shape of the curve of spontaneous magnetization is very mucn affected by the structural peculiarities of the material. Consequently curves of the spontaneous magnetization taken in the neighborhood of the Curie point can be used for more detailed study of the effect of structure on the ferromagnetic properties of a material.

## § 6. The "Discontinuity" of the Specific Heat at the Curie Point

The thermodynamic theory of the ferromagnetic transition provides a formula for the determination of the "discontinuity" $\Delta C_p$ of the specific heat at the Curie point (cf. Chapter I)

$$\Delta C_p = \theta \frac{(\alpha'_\theta)^2}{2\beta_\theta}. \qquad (64)$$

Taking the values of $\theta$, $\alpha'_\theta$, and $\beta_\theta$ from experiment, Goryaga [53] has determined the values of $\Delta C_p$ for a number of ferromagnetic materials (Table 6).

TABLE 6. Values of $\Delta C_p$, Calculated from the Formula (64) and Obtained Experimentally

| Material | $\theta$, °K | $\alpha'_\theta$ | $\beta_\theta$ | $\sigma_0$ | $\Delta C_p$, cal · g$^{-1}$ · deg$^{-1}$ | |
|---|---|---|---|---|---|---|
| | | | | | calculated | experimental |
| Ni | 624 | 104 | 1.8 | 56.8 | 0.042 | 0.032 (Lapp[66]) |
| Fe | 1032 | 27.5 | 0.063 | 222.0 | 0.148 | 0.16 (Klinghardt [67]) |
| 36% Ni, 64% Fe | 565 | 8.4 | 0.112 | 184.4 | 0.0042 | — |
| 15% Cu, 85% Ni | 478 | 39.0 | 4.9 | 42.0 | 0.0018 | — |

The quantity $\Delta C_p$ shows an extremely strong dependence on the impurities in an alloy and on the heat treatment of the specimen. Therefore it is difficult to compare the values of $\Delta C_p$ calculated from Eq. (64) with experimental values that can be found in the literature. It can be seen from Table 6, however, that the calculated values of $\Delta C_p$ are very close to those measured experimentally.

The size of the "discontinuity" of the specific heat must obviously depend on the degree of "smearing out" of the ferromagnetic transition in a given ferromagnetic material. Table 7 shows values of the "discontinuity" of the specific heat in an alloy of 20% Cu and 80% Ni for various amounts of annealing, as calculated on the basis of magnetic data by using Eq. (64).

TABLE 7. Influence of Annealing on the Value of $\Delta C_p$ for an Alloy of 20% Copper and 80% Nickel

| Annealing time, hours (at T = =1000°C) | $\beta_\theta$ | $\alpha'_\theta$ | $\theta$, °K | $\Delta C_p$, cal · $g^{-1}$ · $deg^{-1}$ |
|---|---|---|---|---|
| 10 | 34 | 22.5 | 440.5 | 0.000078 |
| 20 | 13.4 | 25.5 | 436 | 0.00025 |
| 30 | 7.7 | 30.0 | 432.5 | 0.0006 |
| 40 | 7.1 | 37.0 | 432 | 0.001 |

As the degree of annealing is increased the size of the "discontinuity" of the specific heat increases sharply. This is due to the fact that in the case of a well annealed specimen the ferromagnetic transition occurs in a narrower range of temperatures near the Curie point and the energy of the spontaneous magnetization is released in just this range of temperatures. Analogous results have also been obtained for other alloys. Figure 36 shows a curve of the dependence of the "discontinuity" of the specific heat on the duration of the anneal for an alloy of 21 atomic percent Mn and 79 atomic percent Ni, for an annealing temperature of 380°C. It can be seen that as time of annealing is increased the "discontinuity" of the specific heat decreases continuously.

This behavior of the "discontinuity" of the specific heat in the nickel-manganese alloy also confirms the idea presented above about the dependence of the "discontinuity" of the specific heat on the "smearing out" of the ferromagnetic transition.

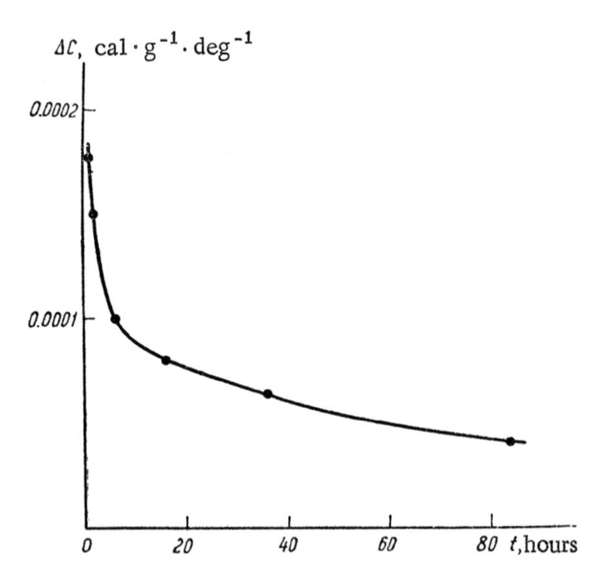


Fig. 36. Dependence of the "discontinuity" of the specific heat in an alloy of 21 atomic percent Mn and 79 atomic percent Ni on the duration of the anneal.

In conclusion we note that in experiments one measures not the "discontinuity" of the specific heat at the Curie point, as is required by the thermodynamic theory, but more or less smeared out maxima of the specific heat (therefore we have used the word "discontinuity" in quotation marks).

## § 7. The Effect of Allotropic Transitions on the Temperature Dependence of the Magnetization

A large class of ferromagnetic materials exists in which allotropic transitions occur on heating; in these cases the temperature of the transition to the other crystalline modification is lower than the Curie temperature of the original modification. Such transitions strongly distort the temperature dependence of the spontaneous magnetization and as a consequence of this they also change the temperature dependence of the various magnetic and "nonmagnetic" properties of the material. Classical examples of such ferromagnetic materials are cobalt and certain alloys of iron and cobalt.

The temperature dependence of the magnetization of cobalt has been studied by many authors. It has been found [68] that the curve of the temperature dependence of the magnetization shows a sharp change of the magnetization at a temperature 870°C, which corresponds to a transition from the hexagonal lattice to a face-centered cubic lattice. An analogous change has been found by Pal and Tarnotsi [69] in the curve of the differential susceptibility. Thus in the case of cobalt both crystalline modifications are ferromagnetic.

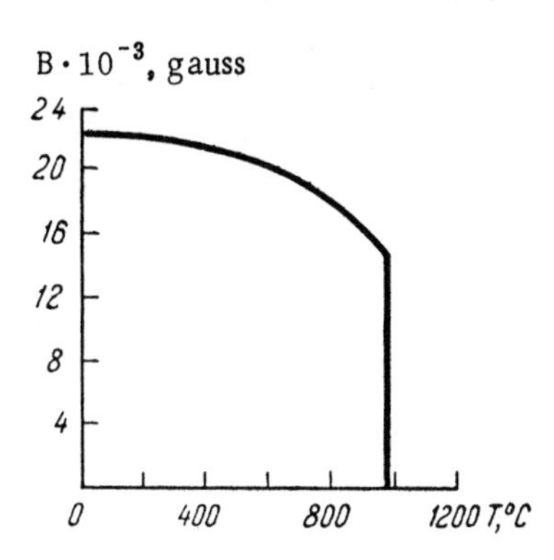


Fig. 37. Effect of the structural change in an alloy of 50% cobalt and 50% iron on the temperature dependence of the magnetic induction.

Figure 37 shows the shape of the temperature dependence of the magnetic induction in an alloy of 50% Co and 50% Fe.

The sharp drop of the curve to the temperatue axis is also due to the transition from the $\alpha$ modification to the $\gamma$ modification (at 980°C). Since in this case the $\gamma$ phase is nonferromagnetic, the alloy loses its ferromagnetic properties when heated to 980°C; this temperature is an "apparent" Curie point.

Similar phenomena have been discovered by Guillaud [70] in alloys Mn-As (Fig. 38) and Mn-Bi.

The transition $\alpha \rightleftarrows \gamma$ in nickel-iron alloys at nickel concentrations from 10 to 30% has a very marked effect on the magnetic behavior. Here one is frequently dealing not with a true Curie temperature but with transitions from the ferromagnetic body-centered $\alpha$ phase to the face-centered $\gamma$ phase, which may or may not possess ferromagnetic properties, depending on the composition. In alloys with nickel content up to 28% the $\gamma$ phase does not have ferromagnetic properties at room temperature (its Curie point lies below room temperature), but in alloys with nickel content larger than 28% the $\gamma$ phase is ferromagnetic, so that in such alloys there can exist simultaneously two ferromagnetic phases $\alpha$ and $\gamma$. The same situation also occurs in alloys Fe-Ni-Co, Fe-Ni-Cr, and Fe-Pt.

Figures 39 and 40 show the results of measurements of the spontaneous magnetization and of the magnetostriction (as measured by Panina [82]) for one iron-nickel-cobalt alloy, as functions of the temperature. The first break in the cure (Fig. 39) corresponds to a Curie point 120°C and the second to a Curie point 220°C. In the curves of $\lambda(T)$ (Fig. 40) both breaks correspond to maxima of the magnetostriction of the para-process, which is particularly large for the $\gamma$ lattice.

In the case of nickel-iron alloys the situation is further complicated by the fact that the $\alpha \rightleftarrows \gamma$ transition is accompanied by a large temperature hysteresis on account of the retardation of the process of diffusion of atoms in the alloy. A result of this is that there is often a considerable difference between the temperature at which the spontaneous magnetization disappears as the material is heated and the temperature at which it reappears as the alloy is cooled. Analogous effects of hysteresis of the

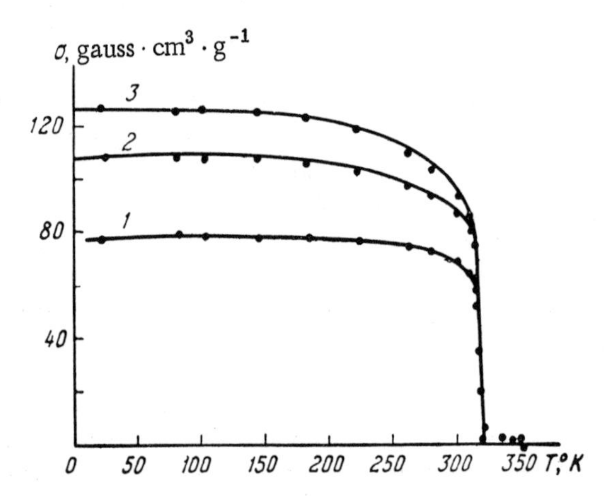


Fig. 38. Temperature dependence of the magnetization in an alloy Mn-As. 1) H = 1010 oe; 2) H = 2100 oe; 3) H = 3090 oe.

Curie point are observed in alloys Fe-Pt, in ternary alloys Fe-Ni-Co, Fe-Ni-Cr, and Fe-Co-Cr, and also in certain compounds, for example iron antimonides (see Chapter V). A very large temperature hysteresis is

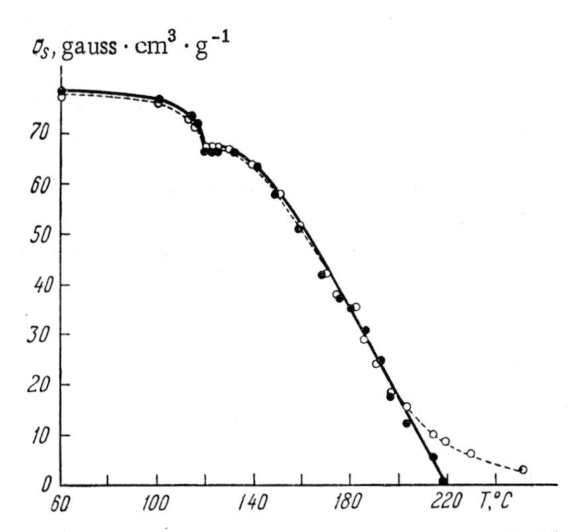


Fig. 39. Effect of the structural transition in alloy of 29% nickel, 5% cobalt, and 66% iron on the temperature dependence of the spontaneous magnetization. ●) calculated from curves of $H/\sigma = f(\sigma^2)$; ○) from curves of $\lambda = f(\sigma^2)$.

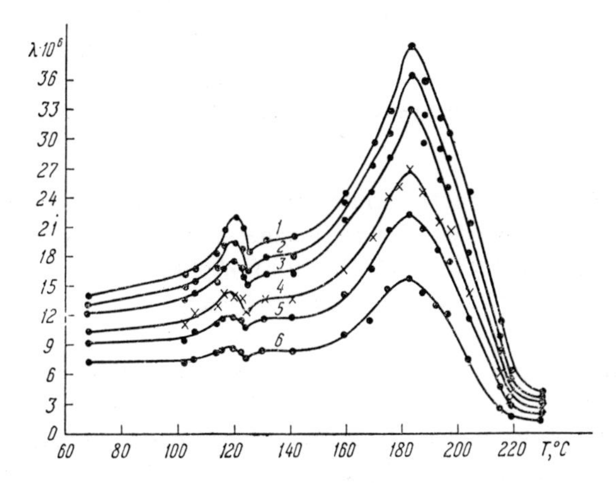


Fig. 40. Effect of structural transition in alloy of 29% nickel, 5% cobalt, and 66% iron on the temperature dependence of the magnetostriction at various field strengths. 1) H = 1900 oe; 2) H = 1700 oe; 3) H = 1500 oe; 4) H = 1200 oe; 5) H = 1000 oe; 6) H = 700 oe.

observed in the system Fe-N. Nitrogen forms the following phases with iron:

$\alpha$-phase - 0.3% N; $\gamma'$-phase - 5.9% N;
$\epsilon$-phase - 5.05% N; $\gamma$-phase - 2.4% N.

These phases are stable at room temperature but can disappear on heating. Evidence of this is seen in the curves of the temperature dependence of the magnetization shown in Fig. 41. The curves obtained when the alloy

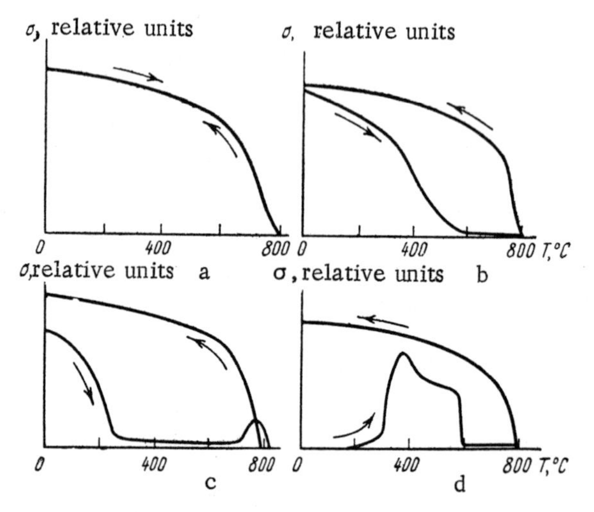


Fig. 41. Effect of structural transition on the temperature dependence of the magnetization in the system Fe-N. a) $\alpha$ phase (0.3% N); b) $\gamma'$ phase (5.9% N); c) $\epsilon$ phase (5% N); d) $\gamma$ phase (2.4% N).

is cooled are of the same shape for all three phases, since when the temperature is raised the specimens lose their nitrogen almost completely. The behavior of the $\gamma$ phase is the most complicated, because it is unstable at room temperature. Up to about 300°C there is no ferromagnetism. Between 300 and 400°C there is a transition to a stable state, in which there is formed from the $\gamma$ phase a mixture of the $\alpha$ and $\gamma'$ phases, both of which are ferromagnetic. The appearance of the $\gamma'$ phase is marked by a point of inflection (475°C). At 600°C the formation of the

$\gamma$ phase occurs, which is stable at this temperature; this process is manifested in a sharp drop of the curve. An unusual shape of the curve of the temperature dependence of the spontaneous magnetization is also often observed in alloys in which ordering occurs [71]. Here the change of shape of the curve is due to passage through intermediate states between the disordered and the completely ordered states.

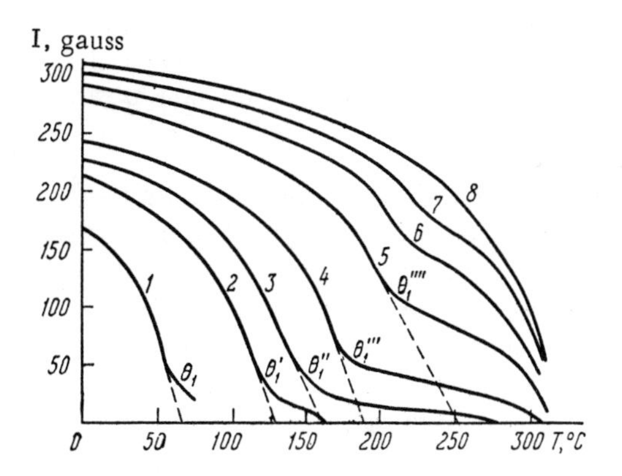


Fig. 42. Temperature dependence of the magnetization of an alloy of 84% nickel and 14% beryllium after annealing at 454°C for various lengths of time. 1) before annealing; 2) twenty minutes; 3) forty minutes; 4) eighty minutes; 5) 190 minutes; 6) 310 minutes; 7) 370 minutes; 8) 1210 minutes.

We remark in conclusion that there is also a large group of alloys in which precipitation hardening occurs, so that in the main solid solution there is segregation of chemical compounds which often also have ferromagnetic properties. In such a process the curve of the temperature dependence of the magnetization undergoes decided changes. If in the process of segregation ("hardening") both phases are ferromagnetic, then one can distinguish two Curie points on the curve of $\sigma(T)$ (Fig. 42). This type of alloy includes the binary alloys Ni-Au, Ni-Be, the ternary alloy Fe-Ni-Al, and others.

In the analysis of all the transitions one can make use of studies of the temperature dependence of the magnetization and of the temperature dependence of the related "nonmagnetic" properties (the magnetostriction, the galvanomagnetic effect, and so on). This means of studying transitions in alloys is in practice known by the name of thermomagnetic analysis.

## § 8. On the Causes of the Appearance of a "Tail" of the Spontaneous Magnetization

The following are possible causes for the appearance of a "tail" of the spontaneous magnetization: 1) fluctuations of the concentration of components (or impurities) throughout the volume of the specimen; 2) inhomogeneous mechanical deformations which lead to distortions of the lattice.

These causes have the consequence that the ferromagnetic transition occurs not at a single temperature but over a certain range of temperatures which form a Curie region, so that the transition is "smeared out." Experiment shows that the most important cause for the appearance of a "tail" of the spontaneous magnetization is found in inhomogeneities of the concentrations of the components in an alloy (fluctuations of the concentration throughout the volume of the specimen). Because of such inhomogeneities the specimen contains regions with somewhat different Curie temperatures. In those parts of the specimen where the Curie temperature is higher than in the main part of the volume of the specimen the spontaneous magnetization is still retained when a large part of the ferromagnetic material has already gone over into the paramagnetic state. These "remnants" of the spontaneous magnetization cause the appearance of a "tail" and a broadening of the transition. We shall give a calculation which shows that in a ferromagnetic material that is inhomogeneous in concentration the curve for the temperature dependence of the spontaneous magnetization near the Curie point is broadened [51]. This calculation is only of an illustrative character, but it gives an idea of the large effect that fluctuations can have on the nature of the ferromagnetic transition.* Let the alloy consist of regions that differ in concentration and consequently have somewhat different Curie points. It is natural to assume that the largest volume belongs to the parts of the specimen which have a composition corresponding to the average composition of the alloy. Let us denote the Curie temperature of this volume by $\theta_0$. The volumes of the parts of the specimens with Curie temperature $\theta$ different from $\theta_0$ will become smaller as we take

* A detailed analysis of this question is given in the papers of Paches [51].

larger values of the difference $\theta - \theta_0$. We can assume that the most probable distribution of the volume belonging to the parts of the specimen with different Curie temperatures will be to first approximate a Gaussian distribution. For convenience in the calculation we shall measure the Curie temperature from the temperature $\theta_0$. In our system of measurement we shall denote the Curie temperature of any part of the specimen by $\vartheta = \theta - \theta_0$.

In order to write the law of distribution for the volumes with various values of $\vartheta$, we express the relative volume dV/V (V is the volume of the entire specimen) of the part of the specimen with Curie temperature lying in the range from $\vartheta$ to $\vartheta + d\vartheta$ in the form

$$\frac{dV_\vartheta}{V} = \frac{\varphi_\vartheta}{V}\, d\vartheta,$$

where $\varphi_\vartheta / V$ plays the role of a probability density. We can choose the distribution law for the quantity $\varphi_\vartheta / V$ in the form

$$\frac{\varphi_\vartheta}{V} = \frac{1}{\varepsilon\sqrt{2\pi}}\, e^{-\frac{\vartheta^2}{2\varepsilon^2}}. \tag{65}$$

In this formula $\epsilon$ is the characteristic width of the "smearing out" of the ferromagnetic transition. The larger the value of $\epsilon$, the larger the temperature range in which the Curie points of the various regions in the specimen lie.

The expression (65) is normalized to unity:

$$\frac{1}{V}\int_{-\infty}^{+\infty} \varphi_\vartheta\, d\vartheta = 1, \tag{66}$$

i.e., the sum of the fractional volumes of all the regions with different Curie temperatures is equal to 1.

The presence of spontaneous magnetization in the specimen is due to the change (decrease) of the energy of the specimen by the amount of the energy of the spontaneous magnetization $E = KJ_s^2$, where $J_s$ is the spontaneous magnetization per unit volume. Let us denote by $E_\vartheta(\tau)$ the change of the energy per unit volume at temperature $\tau = T - \theta_0$ of the part of the specimen for which the Curie point lies in the range between $\vartheta$ and $\vartheta + d\vartheta$. Then the change of the energy per unit volume of the entire inhomogeneous ferromagnetic specimen will be given by

$$E(\tau)=\int_{-\infty}^{+\infty}\frac{\varphi_\vartheta}{V}E_\vartheta(\tau)\,d\vartheta. \tag{67}$$

The rapid convergence of the probability integral allows us to use infinite limits in this expression. Substituting in Eq. (67) the values

$$E(\tau)=KJ_s^2(\vartheta) \text{ and } E_\vartheta(\tau)=KJ_{s\vartheta}^2$$

and assuming for simplicity that the coefficient K is the same for all the regions, we get

$$J_s^2(\tau)=\int_{-\infty}^{+\infty}\frac{\varphi_\vartheta}{V}J_{s\vartheta}^2(\tau)\,d\vartheta, \tag{68}$$

where $J_{s\vartheta}(\tau)$ is the spontaneous magnetization of the portion that has the Curie temperature $\vartheta$.

Using the relation

$$J_{s\vartheta}^2(T)=\frac{a'_\theta}{b}(\theta-T)$$

and the notation $a'_\theta/b = c$, we can write this expression in our reference system for temperatures in the following way:

$$J_{s\vartheta}^2(\tau)=c(\vartheta-\tau), \qquad \tau\leqslant\vartheta.$$

Substituting this in Eq. (68) and using Eq. (65), we get

$$J_s^2(\tau)=\frac{c}{\varepsilon\sqrt{2\pi}}\int_\tau^\infty e^{-\frac{\vartheta^2}{2\varepsilon^2}}(\vartheta-\tau)\,d\vartheta.$$

This equation holds for the temperature dependence of the spontaneous magnetization of an inhomogeneous alloy with a Gaussian distribution of concentration. The solution of the equation is

$$J_s^2(\tau)=\frac{c\varepsilon}{\sqrt{2\pi}}e^{-\frac{\tau^2}{2\varepsilon^2}}-\frac{c\tau}{\sqrt{2\pi}}\int_\tau^\infty e^{-\frac{\vartheta^2}{2\varepsilon^2}}\,d\vartheta.$$

The second integral is the probability integral. Let us consider two cases, for $\tau < 0$ and $\tau > 0$:

$$J_s^2(\tau) = \frac{c\varepsilon}{\sqrt{2\pi}} e^{-\frac{\tau^2}{2\varepsilon^2}} - \frac{c\tau}{2}\left[1 + \frac{2}{\sqrt{2\pi}} \int_0^{\left|\frac{\tau}{\varepsilon}\right|} e^{-\frac{\vartheta^2}{2}} d\vartheta\right], \quad \tau < 0, \qquad (69)$$

$$J_s^2(\tau) = \frac{c\varepsilon}{\sqrt{2\pi}} e^{-\frac{\tau^2}{2\varepsilon^2}} - \frac{c\tau}{2}\left[1 - \frac{2}{\sqrt{2\pi}} \int_0^{\left|\frac{\tau}{\varepsilon}\right|} e^{-\frac{\vartheta^2}{2}} d\vartheta\right], \quad \tau > 0. \qquad (70)$$

Figure 43 shows the temperature dependence of the spontaneous magnetization calculated from the formulas (69) and (70). For $\epsilon = 0$ (the case of an ideal homogeneous ferromagnetic material) we get a parabola, i.e., the shape of $J_S(T)$ required by the thermodynamic theory. For $\epsilon \neq 0$, beginning at a certain temperature, the curve of the temperature dependence of $J_S$ lies above the curve that corresponds to the ideal homogeneous ferromagnetic substance and gradually approaches the temperature axis. With increase of $\epsilon$, i.e., with increase of the "smearing out" of the ferromagnetic transition, the difference between the two curves increases. Thus by means of the calculation we have given, which is only of an illustrative character, we can get a qualitative explanation of the appearance of a "tail" of the spontaneous magnetization in the neighborhood of the Curie point.

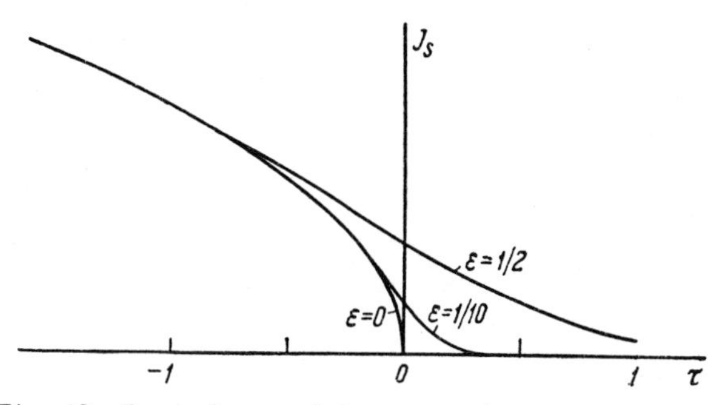


Fig. 43. Dependence of the curve of spontaneous magnetization against temperature on the degree of inhomogeneity of an alloy.

The "smearing out" of the transition which is caused by fluctuations of concentration manifests itself particularly clearly in alloys after they have been cast, and also in alloys in which one component is nonferromagnetic (eliquation phenomenon). Various impurities in an alloy (carbon, sulfur, oxygen, hydrogen, and so on) which are distributed nonuniformly in the lattice also lead to a "smearing out" of the transition. "Smearing out" can also be caused by processes of carbide formation in an alloy. The second cause can lead to the formation of "tails" of the spontaneous magnetization, which was indicated at the beginning of this section; its effect may be as follows.

It is well known that compression or stretching causes changes of the Curie temperature; the sign and magnitude of such a change depends on the magnitude and character of the applied forces. In a polycrystalline specimen in which the crystals are chaotically located, inhomogeneous internal stresses can have the effect that the different crystals will undergo the ferromagnetic transitions at different temperatures, and this brings out a "smearing out" of the transition.

It must be noted that the amount of change of the Curie temperature caused by elastic stresses in the majority of ferromagnetic materials is relatively small, and this cause cannot produce a large "smearing out" of the transition (as compared with the effect of fluctuations of concentration).

Finally, let us say a few words about the effect of fluctuation of the long-range magnetic order (or, what is equivalent, the short-range order). Owing to the thermal motion, when there is an exchange interaction in a ferromagnetic material it is possible that even above the Curie point there can occur groups of similarly directed spins (in Vonsovskii's expression "swarms" of spins) in particular small volumes, which, however, disappear at once and reappear in other parts of the specimen. The result is a peculiar "flickering" of the spontaneous magnetization through the volume of the specimen. It is clear that this cannot lead to the appearance of a "tail" of the spontaneous magnetization. In fact, measurements made by Smith [72] on a single crystal of synthetic magnetite, for which there is almost no "tail" caused by inhomogeneities of the concentration and by lattice defects (and consequently the part played by the short-range order can be most easily seen in such a crystal), have shown that in this case there is an extraordinarily sharp drop of the spontaneous magnetization. As can be seen from Fig. 44, there is almost no "tail" in this case. From this result we can conclude that if the fluctuations of the long-range magnetic order do have any effect on the temperature dependence of the spontaneous magnetization in the region of the Curie point, this effect is extremely small.

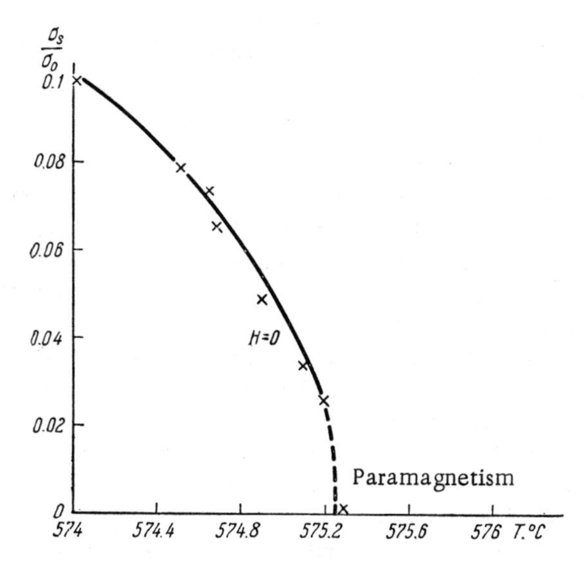


Fig. 44. Temperature dependence of the spontaneous magnetization in a crystal of synthetic magnetite in the direction of the [111] axis and near the Curie point.

## § 9. The Effects of Elastic Stresses on the Magnetization in the Region of the Para-process

At the present time it is reliably known that elastic deformations (both in all directions [73] and in a single direction [74]) have an effect on the magnetization in the region of the para-process (or, what is the same thing, on the magnitude of the saturation magnetization). These effects are especially large near the Curie point [74]. The microscopic nature of these effects is that changes of the inter-atomic distances in elastic deformations cause changes of the exchange interaction, which leads to changes in the magnetization in the region of the para-process (there is a change of the saturation magnetization). A description of the effect of elastic deformations on the magnetization near the Curie point can be given by using the thermodynamic theory of phase transitions of the second kind.

As Ginzburg [75] has shown, near the temperature of a phase transition of the second kind the thermodynamic potential can be expanded in a power series in the ordering parameter and the components of the elastic deformation tensor or the elastic stress tensor. This form for the thermodynamic potential has been used for the description of piezoelectric and electrostrictive phenomena in ferroelectric materials [76].

A similar form of the potential can be written down for ferromagnetic materials, but here we must take into account the following facts. In the thermodynamic potential of a ferromagnetic substance there are no terms that are linear in the magnetic field or in the magnetization, and consequently piezomagnetic phenomena are impossible (the appearance of a magnetization on elastic deformation in the absence of a field).* Besides this, unlike the case of ferroelectric materials, in which there is a strong change of the configuration of the lattice on passage through the Curie point [78], in ferromagnetic materials there is an extremely tiny change of the configuration of the lattice: the main effect near the Curie point is a change of the volume of the lattice (the effect of the magnetic anisotropy terms is very small). Consequently in the case of a ferromagnetic material we can confine ourselves in first approximation to the "isotropic" terms in the expansion of the thermodynamic potential, i.e., we can make the expansion in terms of the volume deformation, or, what is equivalent, in terms of the elastic stress P (in all directions or in a single direction) which produces the volume deformation [20]:

$$\Phi = \Phi_0 + aJ^2 + bJ^4 + cP + gP^2 + eJ^2P - JH. \qquad (71)$$

Here $eJ^2P$ is the "exchange-elastic" energy associated with a change of the exchange interaction in the lattice produced by stress P, $e$ is the magnetostriction constant,† $gP^2$ is the energy of the elastic deformation, and $g$ and $c$ are elastic constants.

---

* I. E. Dzyaloshinskii has recently shown [77] that in some uncompensated antiferromagnetic materials there can be a piezomagnetic effect (for details see Chapter IV).

† The effect in question is the volume magnetostriction of the paraprocess.

From the condition that the energy be a minimum, $(\partial\Phi/\partial J) = 0$, we get

$$(\alpha+\gamma P)(\sigma_s+\sigma_i)+\beta(\sigma_s+\sigma_i)^3=H, \tag{72}$$

where $\alpha = (2a/\sigma_0)$, $\beta = (4b/\sigma_0^3)$, and $\gamma = (2e/\sigma_0)$. This relation is the equation for the curve for the true magnetization (para-process) near the Curie temperature, with effects of elastic stresses included.

Let us write Eq. (72) in the form

$$(\alpha+\gamma P)+\beta\sigma^2=\frac{H}{\sigma},$$

where $\sigma = \sigma_s + \sigma_i$. If we represent the experimental data in the form of straight lines for $H/\sigma$ as a function of $\sigma^2$, it is easily seen that the effect of the elastic stress P is to displace these straight lines parallel to themselves, to the right or to the left depending on the type of elastic stress (compression or stretching) and on the sign of the magnetostriction constant. Figure 45 shows curves of this sort for an alloy of 32% nickel and 68% iron. It can be seen that the experimental data are in agreement with the results of the theory.

It is not hard to see that the changes introduced by the elastic stress P in the curve of $H/\sigma\,(\sigma^2)$ can be expressed by saying that P changes the value of the spontaneous magnetization $\sigma_s$, because the distance between the intercepts of the straight lines in Fig. 45 is simply the change of the value of $\sigma_s$ as affected by P. This same result also follows from Eq. (72). In fact, whereas in the absence of an elastic stress the value of the spontaneous magnetization is given by $\sigma_s^2 = -\alpha/\beta$, when there are elastic stresses it is given (for H = 0 and $\sigma_i = 0$) by

$$(\sigma_s^2)_{P\neq 0}=-\frac{\alpha+\gamma P}{\beta}. \tag{73}$$

Thus under the action of elastic stresses there is a change of the spontaneous magnetization ($\Delta\sigma_s$ effect [63]):

$$\Delta\sigma_s=(\sigma_s)_{P\neq 0}-(\sigma_s)_{P=0}=-\frac{\gamma P}{\beta\,[(\sigma_s)_{P\neq 0}+(\sigma_s)_{P=0}]}, \tag{74}$$

i.e., the $\Delta\sigma_s$ effect depends linearly on P. Since according to what has been said $\sigma_s \sim \sqrt{\theta - T}$, it follows from Eq. (74) that as we approach the Curie point the quantity $\Delta\sigma_s$ should reach a maximum value. The values of $\Delta\sigma_s$ at various temperatures can be determined from Fig. 45

from the intercepts on the axis of abscissas of the straight lines measured for P = 0 and P ≠ 0. Figure 46 a shows a curve found in this way. In agreement with what we have said, $\Delta \sigma_s$ has a maximum in the neighborhood of the Curie point.

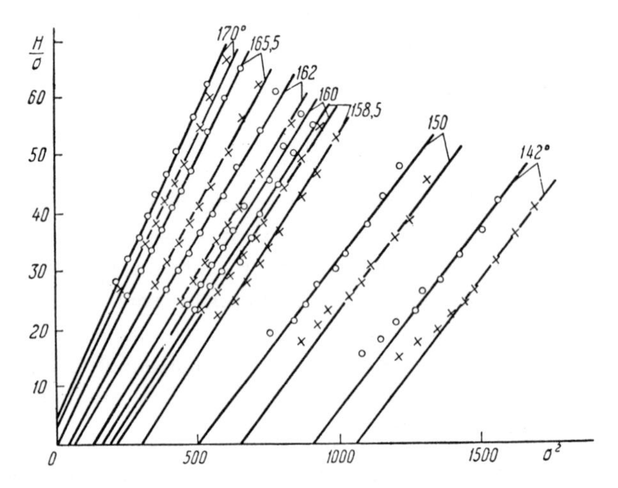


Fig. 45. Dependence of $H/\sigma$ on $\sigma^2$ at various temperatures for an alloy of 32% nickel and 68% iron near the Curie point. X) with elastic stretching; O) without stretching.

It follows from Eq. (74) that the $\Delta\sigma_s$ effect should have a linear dependence on the elastic stress. This conclusion from the theory is also in agreement with experiment. In invar alloys the effect of elastic stresses on the spontaneous magnetization is so large that it can be determined without difficulty with a ballistic apparatus. Figure 46 b shows for an alloy of 33% nickel and 67% iron curves of $\sigma_s(T)$ determined by the method of thermodynamic coefficients. It can be seen that the stretching increases the value of $\sigma_s$ and shifts the Curie point [80].

The change of the spontaneous magnetization of a ferromagnetic material when it is subject to elastic stress can in practice also be detected experimentally from the change of the total magnetization $\sigma$, which is equal to $\sigma_s + \sigma_i$. This effect has the name "magnetoelastic effect" in the region of the para-process [63].

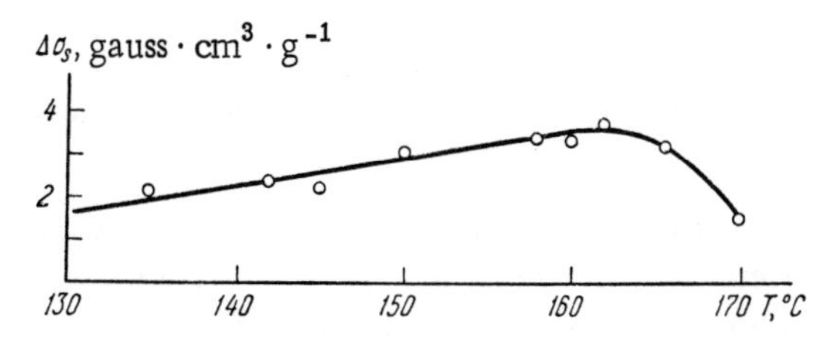


Fig. 46 a. Dependence of the $\Delta\sigma_s$ effect on the temperature for an alloy of 32% nickel and 68% iron.

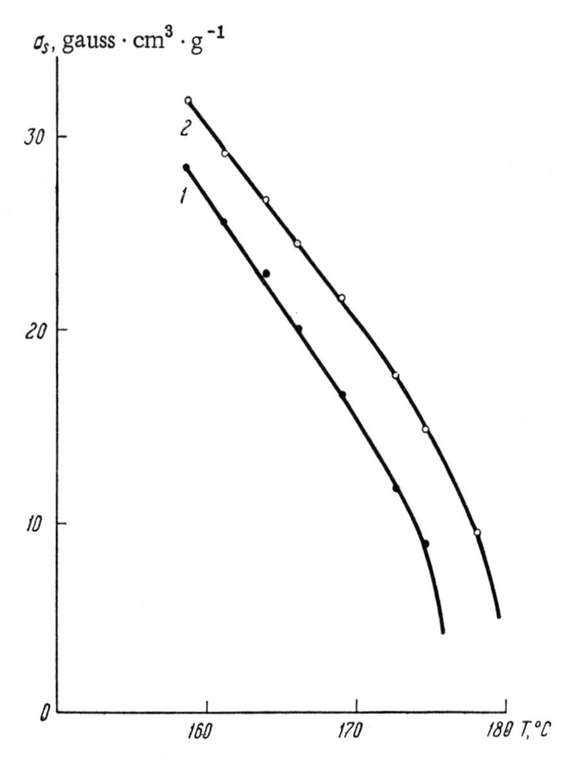


46 b. Temperature dependence of $\sigma_s$ in an alloy of 33% nickel and 67% iron. 1) Without stretching; 2) for unidirectional stretching, 21.8 kg/mm$^2$.

The magnetoelastic effect produced by a pressure in the region of the para-process at room temperature has been studied by Ebert and Kussmann [73]. An effect of similar origin, caused by stretching in one direction, has been studied by the present author [74]. It was found that this effect depends essentially on the quantities T, P, and H.

We now show that the dependence of the magnetoelastic effect on the magnetic field, the stretching, and the temperature can be determined from Eq. (72). Suppose we have two curves of the true magnetization taken at the same temperature near the Curie point. Suppose further that one of the curves is from measurements when there is no elastic stress on the specimen, i.e., this curve is described by the equation

$$\alpha\sigma_1 + \beta\sigma_1^3 = H,$$

and the second curve is from measurements when there is an elastic stretching, i.e., it is described by the equation

$$(\alpha + \gamma P)\,\sigma_2 + \beta\sigma_2^3 = H.$$

Equating the left members of these equations we get

$$\Delta\sigma = \sigma_2 - \sigma_1 = -\frac{\gamma\sigma_2 P}{\alpha + \beta\left(\sigma_1^2 + \sigma_1\sigma_2 + \sigma_2^2\right)}, \tag{75}$$

where $\Delta\sigma$ is the magnetoelastic effect caused by the stretching, as measured in the field H. From the relation (75) it follows first of all that the magnetoelastic effect in the region of the para-process has a linear dependence on the quantity P. Figure 47 shows the data from measurements of the dependence of $\Delta\sigma$ on a stretching P in one direction in the neighborhood of the Curie temperature for an alloy of 36% nickel and 64% iron. It can be seen that the experimental data are in agreement with the relation (75). From the slopes of the straight lines in Fig. 47 one can determine the magnetostriction constant $\gamma$ in the region of the Curie point. We note that the direct determination of $\gamma$ from measurements of the magnetostriction near the Curie point is a matter of very great experimental difficulty.

We can also use the relation (75) to explain the nature of the variation of $\Delta\sigma$ with the temperature if we make use of the facts that $\alpha = \alpha'_\theta\,(T-\theta)$ and $\sigma^2 \sim (T-\theta)$. As the temperature $\theta$ is approached the denominator decreases more rapidly than the numerator, so that the value of $\Delta\sigma$ increases. Figure 48 shows curves of $\Delta\sigma(T)$ measured in various fields for an alloy of 33% nickel and 67% iron. The effect increases as the temperature approaches the Curie point, and reaches a maximum at the Curie point itself. After the temperature passes through the Curie point the value falls off sharply.

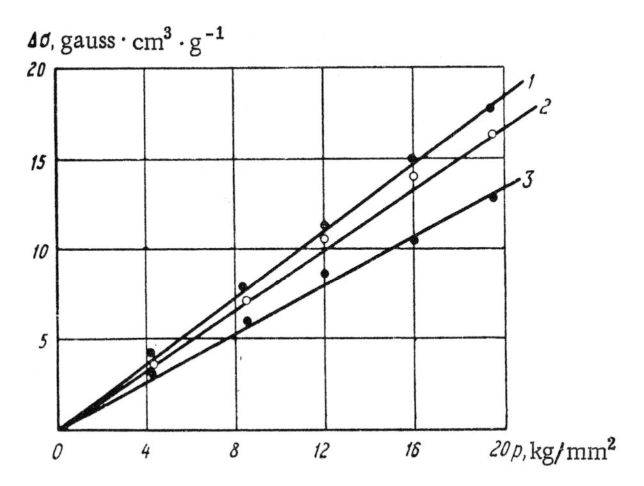


Fig. 47. Dependence of the magnetoelastic effect on the elastic stress (H = 1000 oe) in the region of the Curie point for an alloy of 36% nickel and 64% iron. 1) 262°C; 2) 280°C; 3) 200°C.

Let us now see how $\Delta\sigma$ depends on the magnetic field. This dependence is seen most distinctly right at the Curie point. Setting $\alpha = 0$, $\sigma_1 \approx \sigma_2 \approx \sigma$ in Eq. (75) and using the fact that $\sigma = H^{1/3}/\beta^{1/3}$ we have:

$$(\Delta\sigma)_{T=\theta} = \frac{\gamma_0 \beta_0^{1/3}}{3} \frac{P}{H^{1/3}}. \tag{76}$$

It follows from this relation that the quantity $\Delta\sigma$ decreases with increasing magnetic field, which is in agreement with Fig. 48. Figure 49 shows the dependence of $\Delta\sigma/P$ on $H^{1/3}$. It is seen that the results of the measurements are in qualitative agreement with the relation (76). Figure 50 shows the change of the magnetic flux with pressure in a specimen of 30% nickel and 70% iron as a function of $H^{-1/3}$ as calculated from the data of Ebert and Kussmann [73]. The Curie point of this alloy is close to room temperature, and therefore the relation (76) can also be applied to it. As can be seen from the diagram, these experimental data are also described qualitatively by the formula (76).

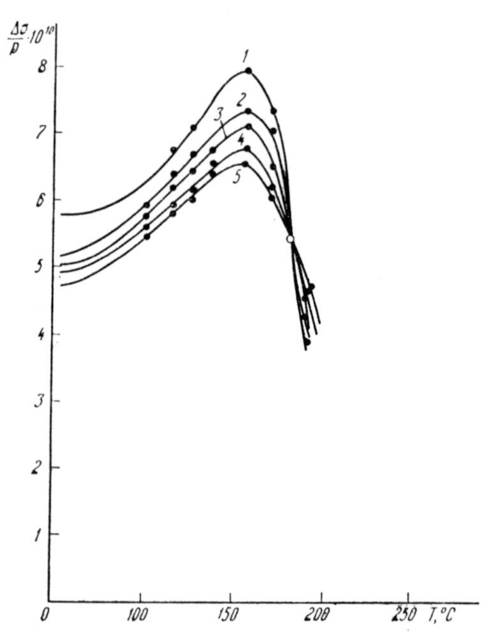


Fig. 48. Temperature dependence of the magnetoelastic effect P in an alloy of 33% nickel and 67% iron for various field strengths. 1) H = 300 oe; 2) H = 500 oe; 3) H = = 800 oe; 4) H = 1000 oe; 5) H = 1500 oe.

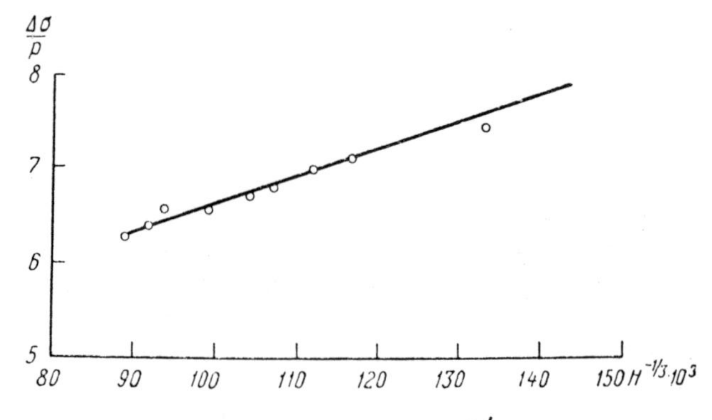


Fig. 49. Dependence of $\Delta\sigma/P$ on $H^{-1/3}$ near the Curie point for an alloy of 33% nickel and 67% iron.

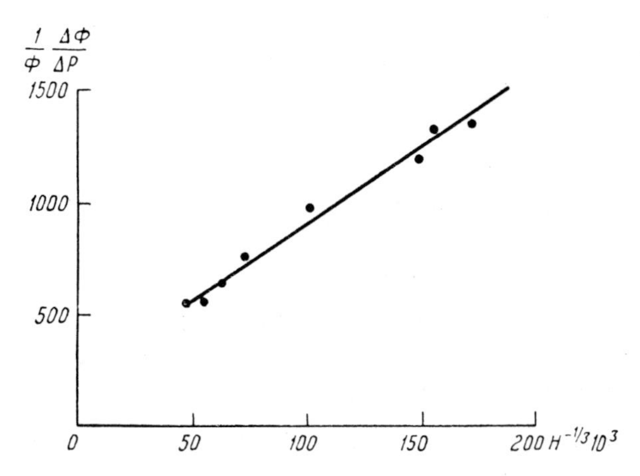


Fig. 50. The change of the magnetic flux in an alloy of 30% nickel and 70% iron caused by a hydrostatic compression, plotted as a function of $H^{-1/3}$.

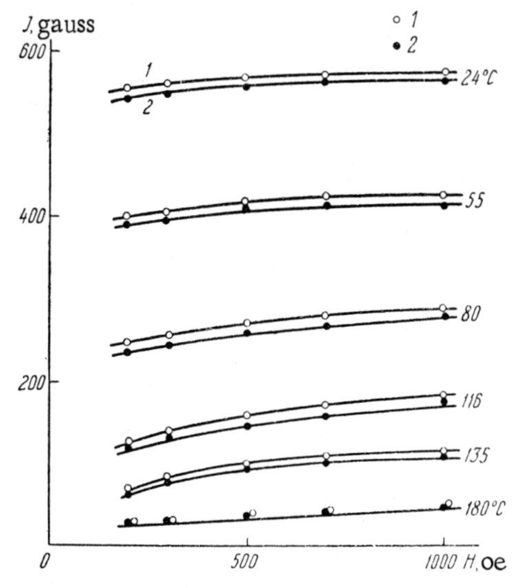


Fig. 51. Curves measured by the method of increments, in fields above the point of technical saturation, as constructed at different temperatures for an alloy of 32% nickel and 68% iron. 1) Under tension of 11.5 kg/mm²; 2) without stress.

It must be noted that above the Curie point, where $\alpha$ takes a rather large value, the term $\beta(\sigma_1^2 + \sigma_1\sigma_2 + \sigma_2^2)$ can be neglected (since $\sigma_1$ and $\sigma_2$ become very small). We then get from Eq. (75)

$$(\Delta\sigma)_{T>\theta} = -\frac{\gamma P \sigma}{\alpha}.$$

For temperatures $T \gg \theta$, we have $\sigma = H/\alpha$, from which we get

$$(\Delta\sigma)_{T>\theta} = -\frac{\gamma P}{\alpha^2} H,$$

i.e., above the Curie point $\Delta\sigma$ must increase with the field, showing a behavior opposite to that which is observed in the temperature range $T < \theta$. This conclusion is also confirmed by experiment.

It can be seen from Fig. 48 that for temperature $T > \theta$ (i.e., in the region of sharp drop of the curve after the passage through the maximum) the curves have a point at which they intersect; beyond this point the magnetoelastic effect increases with increasing field.

We note that the magnetoelastic effect of the para-process leads to a change of the magnetic saturation flux in ferromagnetic materials (Fig. 51), i.e., in other words, under the action of elastic stresses the susceptibility of the para-process remains practically unchanged. This has recently been confirmed by experiments of Parfenov and Voroshilov [81].

## § 10. Magnetostriction

Magnetostriction can be due to exchange and magnetic interactions in a material. Near the Curie point the magnetic interaction is very small, and therefore here the main effect is that of magnetostriction on account of exchange forces. Since the exchange energy depends only on the absolute value of the magnetization, a change of the exchange energy can come only from an increase of the true magnetization in the field, and the magnetostriction will be a volume effect (magnetostriction of the para-process).

The thermodynamic theory of phase transitions of the second kind makes it possible to establish general relations for the dependence of the magnetostriction of the para-process near the Curie point on the magnetization, the magnetic field, and the elastic stresses. Differentiating Eq. (71) with respect to P (a positive value of P corresponds to a stretching in all directions), we obtain the volume magnetostriction

$$\omega = \frac{\partial \Phi'}{\partial P} = C' + 2g'P + \frac{\gamma'}{2}(\sigma_s + \sigma_i)^2, \qquad (77)$$

where $\Phi' = \sigma_0 \rho \Phi$ ($\rho$ is the density), $g' = \sigma_0 \rho g$, $\gamma' = \rho \gamma$, $C' = \sigma_0 \rho C$, and C' is an additive constant which can be omitted in further discussion. For the linear magnetostriction of the para-process ($\lambda = {}^1/_3\ \omega$) with P = = 0 we get:

$$\lambda = \frac{\gamma'}{6}(\sigma_s + \sigma_i)^2 = \frac{\gamma'}{6}\sigma^2, \qquad (78)$$

where $\sigma = \sigma_s + \sigma_i$ is the experimentally measured magnetization.

A similar relation can be derived from the Weiss-Heisenberg theory if we consider the dependence of the molecular-field constant N on the volume [8]. We must, however, point out the "artificial" nature of such an argument. The dependence of N on the volume (or on the temperature) does not follow from the Weiss-Heisenberg theory itself, and the consideration of such a dependence is an artificial device, whereas Eq. (78) has been obtained on the basis of a rigorous thermodynamic theory.

The dependence of $\lambda$ on H and P can be found from the relations (77) and (51).

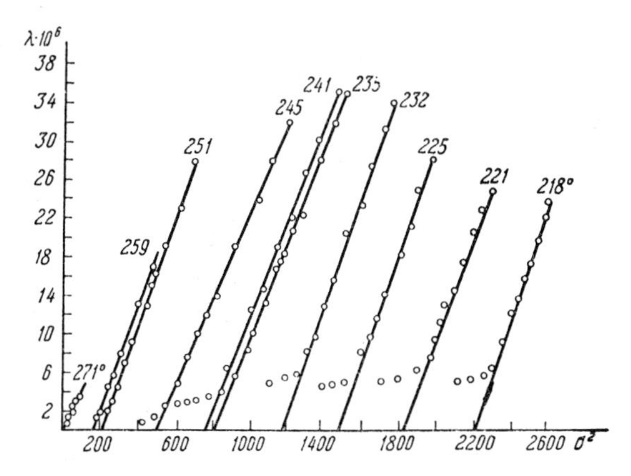


Fig. 52. Dependence of the magnetostriction that accompanies the true magnetization on the quantity $\sigma^2$ for an alloy of 31% Ni, 5% Co, and 64% Fe, at various temperatures.

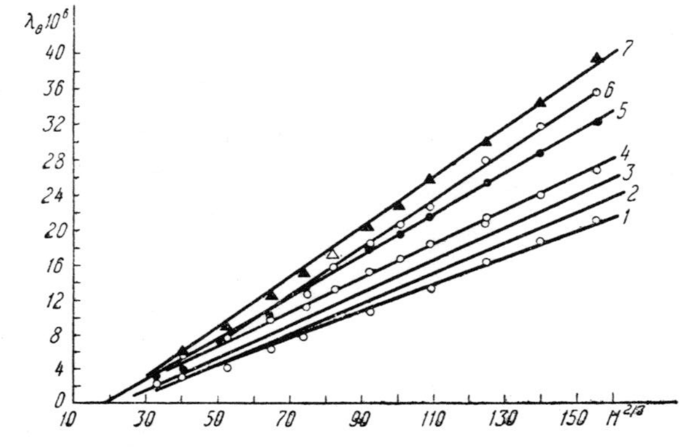


Fig. 53. The magnetostriction near the Curie point plotted against the quantity $H^{2/3}$. 1) 29% Ni, 71% Fe; 2) 36% Ni, 64% Fe; 3) 32% Ni, 68% Fe; 4) 31.3% Ni, 1% Co, 67.7% Fe; 5) 33% Ni, 67% Fe; 6) 31.5% Ni, 49% Co, 19.5% Fe; 7) 29.2% Ni; 5% Co, 65.8% Fe.

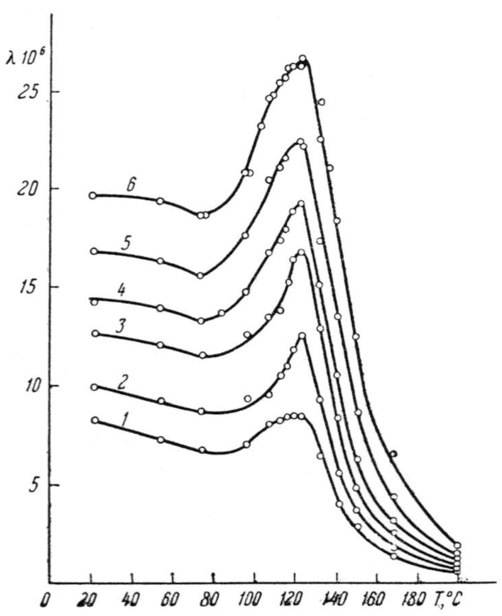


Fig. 54. The temperature dependence of the magnetostriction of an alloy of 31.3% Ni, 1% Co, and 67.7% Fe, at various field strengths. 1) H = 500 oe; 2) H = 700 oe; 3) H = 1000 oe; 4) H = 1200 oe; 5) H = = 1500 oe. 6) H = 1900 oe.

In the immediate neighborhood of the Curie point we have:

$$(\lambda)_{T=\theta}=\frac{2}{3}gP+\frac{\gamma'}{6\beta^{2/3}}H^{2/3}. \qquad (79)$$

For the case P = 0 we get:

$$(\lambda)_{T=\theta}=\frac{\gamma'}{6\beta^{2/3}}H^{2/3}. \qquad (79')$$

The relations (78) and (79') are well confirmed by experiment (Figs. 52 and 53). As we see from Eq. (79), in the presence of elastic stresses the straight line $\lambda_\theta(H^{2/3})$ must undergo a parallel displacement through a distance equal to $^2/_3$gP. This effect has not yet been observed experimentally.

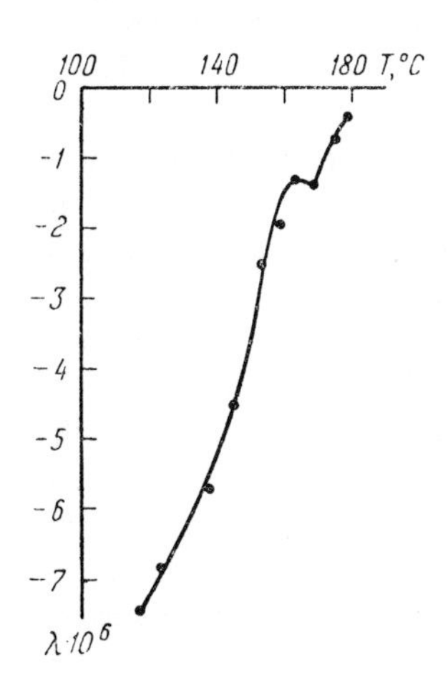


Fig. 55. Temperature dependence of the magnetostriction of an alloy of 97.6% nickel and 2.4% silicon (H = 600 oe).

We now present data on the temperature dependence of the magnetostriction. Figs. 54 and 55 show curves of the temperature dependence of the magnetostriction for alloys containing 31.3% Ni, 1% Co, 67.7% Fe, and 97.6% Ni, 2.4% Si [82]. The experimental curve of $\lambda(T)$ is complex; one can separate out from it a curve of $\lambda_m(T)$, the magnetostriction caused by orientation of the magnetic moments of the regions of spontaneous magnetization (this part of the magnetostriction falls off monotonically with approach to the Curie temperature [83]), and a curve $\lambda_n(T)$, the magnetostriction of the para-process (which increases with approach to the Curie point). Owing to the superposition of the two curves, the total curve of $\lambda(T)$ has a complex character. In the case of the invar alloy of 31.3% Ni, 1% Co, and 67.7% Fe, in which $\lambda_n(T)$ is large, the distortions introduced into the curve of $\lambda(T)$ are very large, whereas in the alloy of 97.6% Ni and 2.4% Si they are small (the bend of the curve in Fig. 55), and the entire course of the curve of $\lambda(T)$ is almost completely determined by the curve of $\lambda_m(T)$.

## § 11. Determination of the Spontaneous Deformation of the Lattice in the Ferromagnetic Transition

When a ferromagnetic material is cooled below the Curie point, there appears along with the spontaneous magnetization a simultaneous spontaneous deformation of the lattice. In the general case this deformation occurs both on account of exchange interactions [84] and also on account of the magnetic interaction [8, 14]. In cubic crystals the exchange energy is isotropic and therefore the corresponding spontaneous deformation is a change of the volume of the lattice. The magnetic energy, on the other hand, is of an anisotropic nature, and in the general case it can produce a change of the configuration of the lattice.

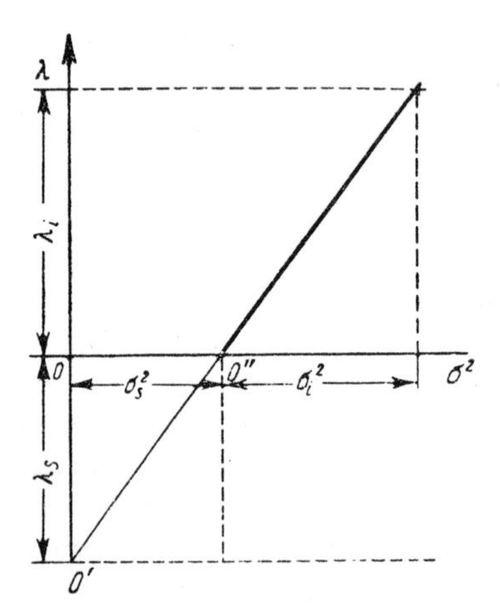


Fig. 56. For use in explaining the method of determining the spontaneous deformation of the lattice in the ferromagnetic transition.

As we have already remarked, in ferromagnetic materials in the immediate neighborhood of the Curie point the magnetically anisotropic energy plays a small role, and therefore the spontaneous deformation of the lattice is mainly a volume deformation. The study of the spontaneous volume deformation of the lattice is of interest, since this effect gives a direct manifestation of the dependence of the exchange energy on the interatomic distances. This deformation can be determined from measurements of the magnetostriction of the paraprocess by the following method [50]. Let us take a graphical representation of the relation (78) (Fig. 56). In the absence of spontaneous magnetization (and for H = 0) there is also no spontaneous deformation. Let this state correspond to the point 0' in Fig. 56. When a spontaneous magnetization appears (for example, when the material is cooled below the Curie temperature) a deformation of the lattice occurs, which according to Eq. (78) is given by

$$\lambda_s = \frac{1}{6}\gamma\sigma_s^2. \tag{80}$$

To this state there corresponds the point 0 (with coordinates $\sigma_s^2$ and $\lambda_s$). If, however, one applies a magnetic field, then there is a true magnetization $\sigma_i$, and accompanying this magnetization there is a magnetostriction $\lambda_i$, which is added to the spontaneous lattice deformation $\lambda_s$ and increases as $\sigma_i$ increases.

In practice we cannot measure $\lambda_s$ directly; this magnetostriction exists in the ferromagnetic material in a latent form. When a field is applied we observe only the magnetostriction $\lambda_i$. This corresponds to the fact that the origin of coordinates in Fig. 56 is transferred to the point 0. It follows from Fig. 56 that if we measure the magnetostriction $\lambda_i$ as a function of the square of the magnetization, then by means of an extrapolation of the straight line $\lambda_i(\sigma_i^2)$ we can determine not only the spontaneous magnetization but also the spontaneous lattice deformation $\lambda_s$ in the ferromagnetic material which is caused by the exchange forces.

For example, if we extrapolate the straight line shown in Fig. 52 to the axis of abscissas we get the values of the magnetization $\sigma_s$ for the alloy of 31% Ni, 5% Co, 64% Fe. This method for determining $\sigma_s$ is analogous to the well known method for determining $\sigma_s$ from curves of the magnetocaloric effect. If we continue the straight lines of Fig. 52 to the axis of ordinates, then we obtain intercepts on this axis which are equal to the values of $\lambda_s$. Thus from curves of the type shown in Fig. 52 one easily determines for each given temperature the values of $\sigma_s$ and the accompanying deformation $\lambda_s$.

The form of the temperature dependence of $\lambda_s$ near the Curie point can also be determined from thermodynamic considerations. Substituting in Eq. (80) the relations (62) and (53), we have

$$\lambda_s = \frac{1}{6} \frac{\alpha'_\theta \gamma'}{\beta} (T - \theta), \tag{81}$$

i.e., near the Curie temperature $\lambda_s$ must have a linear dependence on T just as $\sigma_s^2$ does. In alloys this linear dependence is not always found, and this is due to the effect of inhomogeneities of the concentration of the alloy. These lead to a "smearing out" of the ferromagnetic transition, with the result that the lines of $\sigma_s^2(T)$ and $\lambda_s(T)$ become curved (Fig. 57). This curvature, however, is of the same nature for both curves. It means that the formula (80), which establishes the linear dependence of $\lambda_s$ on $\sigma_s^2$, must hold even for inhomogeneous ferromagnetic materials. Figure 58 gives good confirmation of this conclusion for many alloys. In order to eliminate the "tails" on the curves of Fig. 57, it is necessary to determine the quantity $\lambda_s$ by the method of thermodynamic coefficients, i.e., one must substitute into the relation (81) the values of the coefficients $\beta$, $\alpha'_\theta$, and $\gamma'$. In this case we cut off the "tails" and there is better agreement with the relation (81) (dashed curves in Fig. 57).

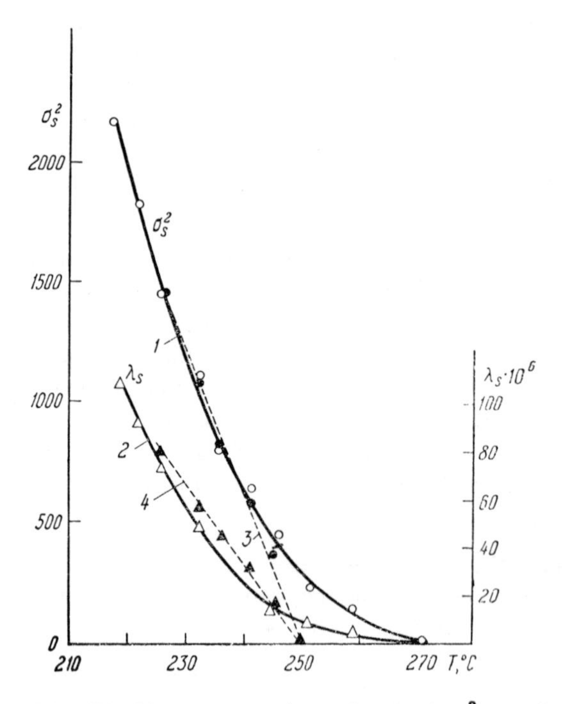


Fig. 57. Temperature dependence of $\sigma_s^2$ and $\lambda_s$ for an alloy of 31% nickel, 5% cobalt, and 64% iron. 1 and 2 are curves determined graphically from the relation $\lambda(\sigma^2)$; 3 and 4 are curves determined by the method of thermodynamic coefficients.

A knowledge of the size of the spontaneous deformation of the lattice enables us to determine the ferromagnetic anomaly of the thermal expansion. For any ferromagnetic substance the experimentally observed thermal expansion coefficient $\alpha$ consists of two parts:

$$\alpha = \alpha_{\sigma_s=0} \pm \frac{d\lambda_s}{dT}. \tag{82}$$

Here $\alpha_{\sigma_s} = 0$ is the thermal expansion coefficient in the absence of spontaneous magnetization, and $d\lambda_s/dT$ is the value of the ferromagnetic anomaly of the expansion coefficient determined by the temperature dependence of the spontaneous deformation of the lattice. The sign of the second term is fixed by the sign of $d\lambda_s/dT$ during heating. For nickel $d\lambda_s/dT$ is positive (which leads to a positive anomaly of $\alpha$), and for invar alloys $\alpha$ is negative.

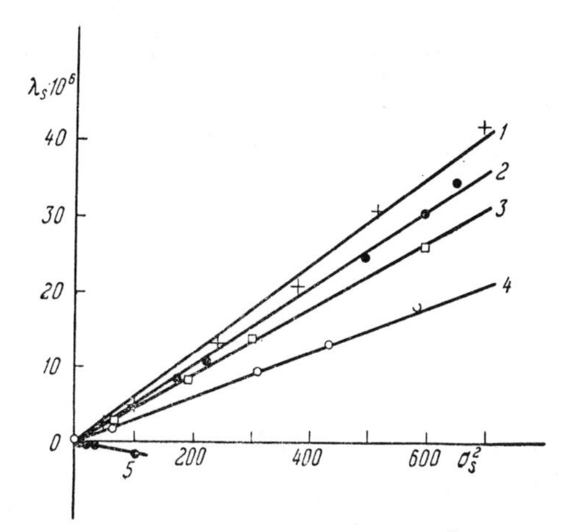


Fig. 58. Dependence of $\lambda_s$ on $\sigma_s^2$ for various alloys. 1) 32% Ni, 68% Fe; 2) 31% Ni, 5% Co, 64% Fe; 3) 33% Ni, 67% Fe, 4) 36% Ni, 64% Fe; 5) 97.6% Ni, 2.4% Si.

Figure 59 shows the temperature dependence of $\alpha$ for superinvar (31% Ni, 5% Co, 64% Fe), as obtained with a Chevenart dilatometer. By adding to these values of $\alpha$ (at each temperature) the experimental values of $d\lambda_s/dT$ we get the temperature dependence of $\alpha_{\sigma_s=0}$, which agrees to first approximation with the shape of the dependence of $\alpha$ on T for nonferromagnetic metals.

This construction thus shows that the anomaly of the thermal expansion in ferromagnetic materials is caused by the spontaneous deformation

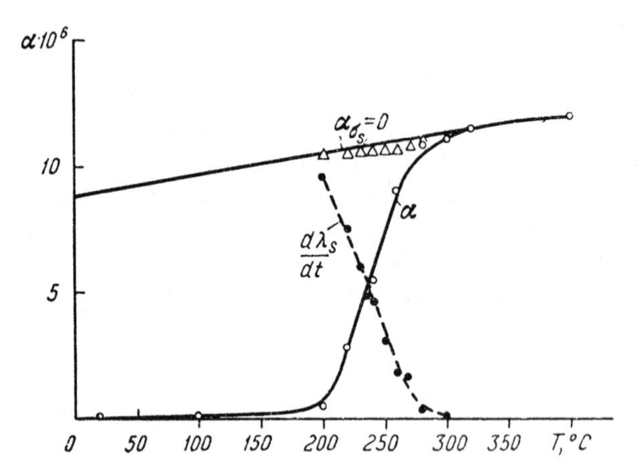


Fig. 59. Illustrating the explanation of the anomaly of the thermal expansion of superinvar.

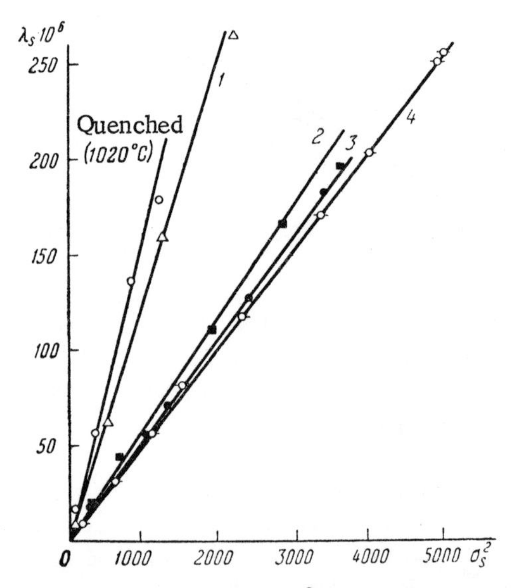


Fig. 59a. Dependence of $\lambda_s$ on $\sigma_s^2$ for an alloy of 58% by weight of platinum with 42% by weight of iron, annealed at 600°C for periods of 1) 20 minutes; 2) 1 hour 20 minutes; 3) 4 hours 20 minutes; 4) 12 hours.

of the lattice which arises in the ferromagnetic transition. The anomaly of the thermal expansion is especially large in invar alloys of iron and platinum, but the character of these anomalies is very decidedly changed by heat treatment. Figure 59a shows the dependence of the spontaneous deformation of the lattice near the Curie point on the quantity $\sigma_s^2$ for various heat treatments, according to data found in measurements by the author and Sirota [82]. It can be seen that the coefficient $\gamma$ is very large in the quenched alloy and decreases sharply with annealing. This is due to the fact that annealing of the alloy leads to atomic ordering. This fact makes this alloy a very interesting object of study, because it enables us to investigate the effects of the location of atoms in the alloy not only on the anomalies of the thermal expansion, the spontaneous deformation of the lattice, and other properties, but also provides a possibility for judging the influence of these locations on the character of the exchange interaction. Since with increase of ordering in an alloy the magnitude of the spontaneous deformation decreases, we must conclude that a regular ordering of the positions of the atoms leads to a less sharp dependence of the exchange integral on the interatomic distance, whereas in a quenched (unordered) alloy the curve of the dependence of the exchange integral on the interatomic distance must have a very steep slope.

We must point out that there is a certain lack of agreement as to which deformation of the lattice in ferromagnetic materials is to be called the spontaneous deformation. In a number of cases (cf., e.g., [8]) this term is taken to mean the deformation of the lattice caused by magnetic forces; it is usually determined by extrapolating the curve of $\lambda(H)$ to $H = 0$. In order to elucidate the meaning of the spontaneous deformation of the lattice that occurs on account of magnetic forces ($\lambda_m$) and on account of exchange forces ($\lambda_s$), let us consider the following model.

We assume that we have a crystalline ferromagnetic material in the shape of a sphere, which we imagine to be cut out in such a way that its entire volume consists of a single region of spontaneous magnetization. If the sphere is heated above the Curie temperature $\theta$, then it has the dimensions corresponding to the paramagnetic state. When it is cooled below $\theta$, owing to the occurrence of spontaneous magnetization, the paramagnetic sphere changes its radius, i.e., a spontaneous deformation $\lambda_s$ appears, which is caused by exchange forces. At the same time magnetic forces come into play at temperatures below $\theta$, and the sphere receives an additional magnetostrictive deformation; on account of the anisotropy of the magnetic forces in the lattice, this latter deformation will also be anisotropic, and therefore the sphere changes its shape and becomes an ellipsoid. In the immediate neighborhood of the Curie point the magnetic forces are still small, and the deformation of the sphere is practically only $\lambda_s$, but as we go further from $\theta$ toward lower temperatures the sphere changes progressively into an ellipsoid. The sphere undergoes all of these deformations with $H = 0$. From this it can be expected that crystals in which the directions of easy magnetization coincide with the axes of the cube (the case of Fe) will become weakly tetragonal below the Curie point, and crystals in which the axes of easy magnetization are oriented along the space diagonals of the cube (case of Ni) will become rhombohedral. Thus we can distinguish two types of spontaneous deformation of the lattice: deformation on account of exchange forces $\lambda_s$, and deformation on account of magnetic forces $\lambda_m$. The deformation $\lambda_m$ was calculated earlier from the purely classical magnetic interaction of dipoles [8, 14]. A quantum-mechanical calculation of $\lambda_m$ has been given by Vonsovskii [85] and Gusev [86].

## § 12. Displacement of the Curie Point under the Influence of Elastic Stresses

It is now known that elastic deformations, both those in all directions and those in a single direction, cause displacements of the Curie point in ferromagnetic materials. Experiments on the effect of hydrostatic pressure on the Curie point in metals and alloys have been made in recent times by Patrick [87]. As for the effect of elastic stress in a single direction on the Curie point, fewer data have been obtained on this, although in some materials this effect is quite appreciable. Figure 60 shows the temperature dependence of the thermodynamic coefficient $\alpha$ measured under various degrees of elastic stretching applied to an alloy of 33% nickel and 67% iron [80]. It can be seen that the curve undergoes parallel displacement to the right as the stretch is increased, that is, the condition for the Curie point ($\alpha = 0$) is satisfied at higher and higher temperatures as the stretching is increased; this means that the Curie point is displaced to higher temperatures. It has been established that the shift of the Curie point by elastic stresses in a single direction is caused by the change of volume which accompanies such a deformation. Because of this the effect cannot be observed in shearing deformations [80]. The experiments show that the amount of displacement $\Delta\theta$ is to first approximation a linear function of the stretching (Fig. 61).

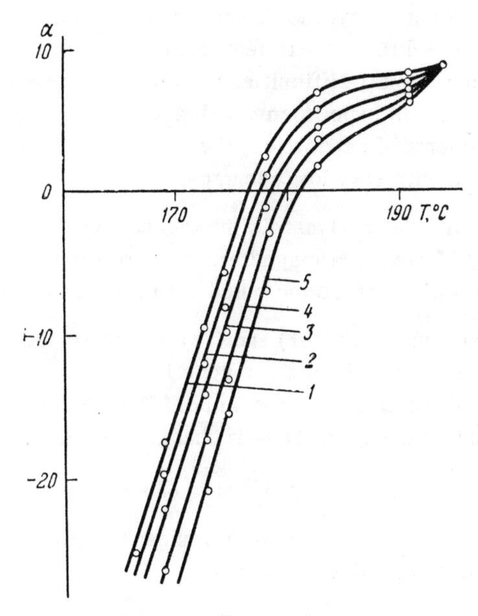


Fig. 60. Temperature dependence of α for an alloy of 33% nickel and 67% iron under various stretching loads. 1) P = 0; 2) P = 6 kg/mm²; 3) P = 10.5 kg/mm²; 4) P = 16 kg/mm²; 5) P = 21.8 kg/mm².

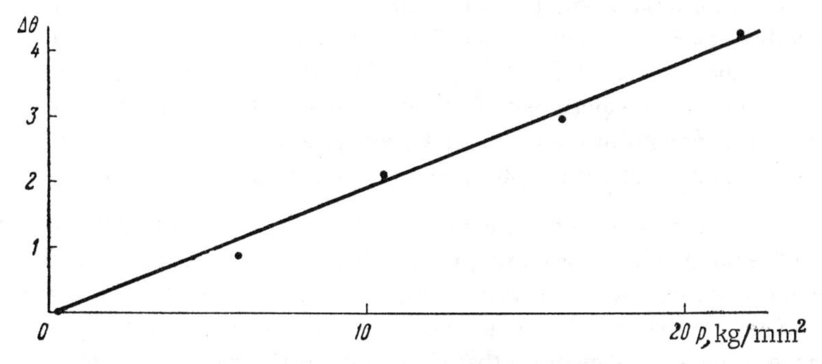


Fig. 61. Dependence of the amount of displacement of the Curie point on the stretching in an alloy of 33% nickel and 67% iron.

It must be noted that the determination of the amount of shift of the Curie point from direct experiment is not very accurate. This is due to the great experimental difficulties that must be overcome in such experiments (especially in experiments with hydrostatic pressure). For example, in the experiments of Patrick [87] the values of $\Delta\theta/\Delta P$ for Fe and Co were measured with very low accuracy.

By using the thermodynamic theory one can, however, calculate the quantity $\Delta\theta/\Delta P$ from the magnetostriction of the para-process (near the Curie point), which can be measured with less difficulty.

A comparison of Eqs. (51) and (72) shows that the effect of elastic stresses on the magnitude of the magnetization can be reduced to a change of the value of the coefficient $\alpha$ in Eq. (51); when the stress is increased by an amount $\Delta P$ the quantity $\alpha$ is changed to a new value $\alpha_p$:

$$\alpha_p = \alpha + \gamma\,\Delta P = \alpha'_\theta (T - \theta) + \gamma\,\Delta P.$$

The condition for the Curie point $\theta_p$ under the stress $\Delta P$ is $\alpha_p = 0$; consequently, for small values of $\theta_p - \theta$,

$$\alpha'_\theta (\theta_p - \theta) + \gamma\,\Delta P = 0.$$

Writing $\theta_p - \theta = \Delta\theta$, we get

$$\frac{\Delta\theta}{\Delta P} = -\frac{\gamma}{\alpha'_\theta}. \tag{83}$$

Thus by determining the magnetostriction constant (for example, from the curves of Fig. 52) and $\alpha'_\theta$ (from the curves of Fig. 12) we can calculate the value of $\Delta\theta/\Delta P$. The results of these calculations are shown in Table 8. It can be seen that the values of $\Delta\theta/\Delta P$ calculated from Eq. (83) and determined in the experiment of Patrick, and also the values calculated from measurements of the effect of a stretching in one direction on the spontaneous magnetization [63], agree with each other fairly well.

The data on the magnitude and sign of $\Delta\theta/\Delta P$ are usually studied from the point of view of getting information about the dependence of the exchange interaction in various materials on the interatomic distance. Here one uses the so-called Bethe curve for the dependence of the exchange integral on a quantity that characterizes the ratio of the lattice parameter to the diameter of the unfilled shell in the atom [63, 68]. This sort of interpretation, however, requires not only information about the magnitude and sign of $\Delta\theta/\Delta P$, but also detailed data on the lattice para-

TABLE 8. Displacement of the Curie Temperature in Ferromagnetic and Ferrimagnetic Materials Caused by Hydrostatic Compression

| Material | $\frac{\Delta\theta}{\Delta P}$ 10 deg/atm | | | θ, °C |
|---|---|---|---|---|
| | Patrick [87] (compression) | Belov [63] (stretching) | calculated from Eq. (83) | |
| Ni | + 0.35 | — 0.4 | — | 360 |
| Fe | 0 ± 0.1 | — | — | 770 |
| 29% Ni, 71% Fe | — 5.8 | — | — 5.6 | 58 |
| 32% Ni, 68% Fe | — | + 4.5 | — 5.5 | 124 |
| 36% Ni, 64% Fe | — 3.6 | + 3.8 | — 4.0 | 235 |
| 31% Ni, 64% Fe, 5% Co | — | + 5.0 | — 5.4 | 250 |
| 28% Cu, 72% Ni | + 0.07 | — | + 0.3 | 66 |
| Gd | — 1.2 | — | — | 16 |
| $0.5Mn \cdot 0.5Zn \cdot Fe_2O_4$ | + 0.9 | — | — | 90 |
| $0.75La \cdot 0.25Sr \cdot MnO_3$ | + 0.6 | — | — | 80 |

meters and atomic constants, which of course also undergo changes in elastic deformation of a ferromagnetic material. The results shown in Table 8 do not give any more information than data about the magnitude and sign of the magnetostriction of the para-process or of the thermal expansion at the Curie point, which are also used for the same purpose. It must also be noted that the Bothe curve is of a crudely qualitative character, and is not the result of a rigorous theory. According to Vonsovskii and Vlasov [43], the value of the Curie temperature is determined not only by the d-d exchange interactions, as is usually assumed in dealing with the Bethe curve, but also by the s-d exchange interaction:

$$\theta_{sdd} = \frac{\theta_{dd}}{1 - \frac{A_{sd}}{A_{dd}}},$$

where $\theta_{dd}$ is the Curie point that corresponds to the d-d interaction alone, $\theta_{sdd}$ is the Curie point when there are both d-d and s-d interactions, $A_{sd}$ is the energy of the s-d interaction, and $A_{dd}$ is the energy of the d-d interaction.

Elastic stresses have different effects on the d-d and s-d interactions. At present the distinction between these effects cannot be made experimentally. There is need for further theoretical development of this problem and for the accumulation of experimental information.

## § 13. Magnetothermal and Galvanomagnetic Effects

At the present time it is common practice to consider the various changes of "nonmagnetic" properties of ferromagnetic materials as functions of the magnetization. This approach is the most correct one, but the experimental study of magnetothermal and galvanomagnetic phenomena (including the Hall effect) as functions of the magnetization at high temperatures is a difficult problem. Since, however, for the region of the Curie point we have an exact thermodynamic law of the variation of the magnetization as a function of the field, Eq. (51), this difficulty can be avoided, and we can study the phenomena in question as functions of the field.

By using Eq. (58) and setting $\Delta T = K\sigma^2$, we can write for the magnetocaloric effect near the Curie point the following relation:

$$\frac{\alpha + \gamma P}{K^{1/2}} + \frac{\beta}{K^{1/2}} \Delta T = \frac{H}{\Delta T^{1/2}}. \qquad (84)$$

Figure 62 shows the dependence of $H/\Delta T^{\frac{1}{2}}$ on $\Delta T$ as obtained from the data of Weiss and Forrer [3]. The experimental points fit straight lines very well. It follows from Eq. (84) that under the action of an elastic

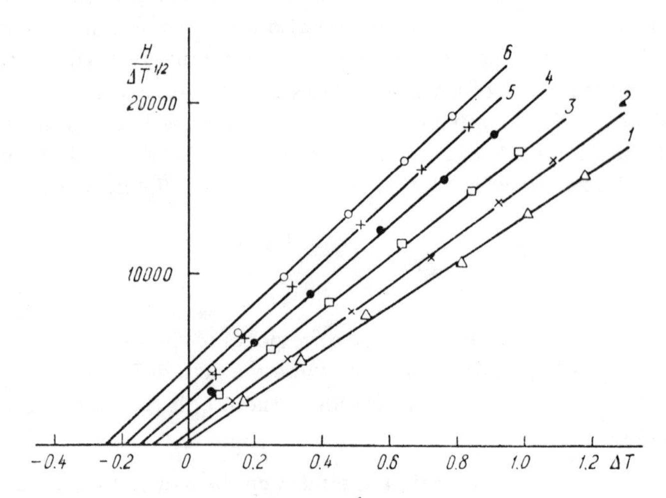


Fig. 62. Dependence of $H/\Delta T^{\frac{1}{2}}$ on $\Delta T$ for nickel at various temperatures near the Curie point. 1) 354.4°C; 2) 352.53°C; 3) 350.66°C; 4) 348.78°C; 5) 346.09°C; 6) 345.02°C.

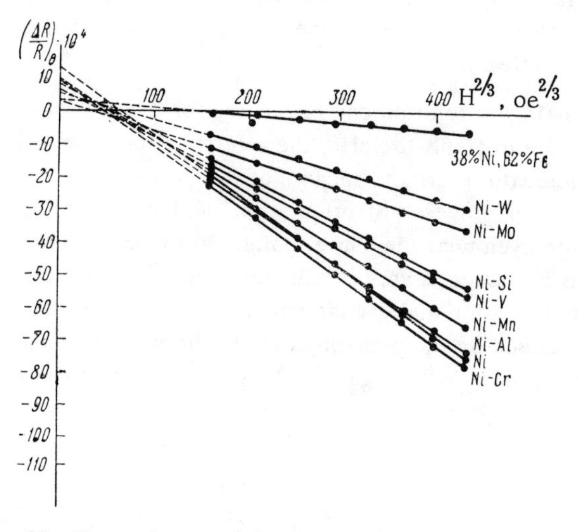


Fig. 63. Dependence of the longitudinal galvanomagnetic effect $(\Delta R/R)_\theta$ on $H^{2/3}$ near the Curie point, for nickel containing small amounts (1 to 1.5 atomic percent) of nonferromagnetic elements, and also for pure nickel and for an alloy of 38% nickel and 62% iron.

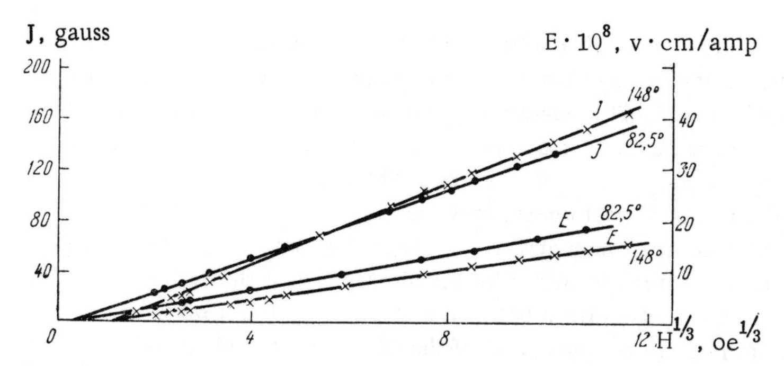


Fig. 64. Dependence of the Hall emf and the magnetization on $H^{1/3}$. ×) alloy of 56% Co, 10% Cr, $34_1$ Fe; ●) alloy of 35.5% Ni, 5.7% Cr, 58.8% Fe; curves taken at temperatures 82.5° and 148°C (the Curie points).

stress these straight lines must undergo parallel displacement (there have as yet been no experiments on the effect of elastic stresses on the magnetocaloric effect).

An analogous relation can be written for the galvanomagnetic effect, but it is more difficult to verify the relation experimentally than it is for the magnetocaloric effect, because of the influence on the galvanomagnetic effect of processes of orientation of domains, which are often appreciable even near the Curie point. In the case of the magnetocaloric effect this influence is very small; the magnetocaloric effect produced by processes of rotation and displacement is two orders of magnitude smaller than that caused by the para-process. In the immediate neighborhood of the point where $\alpha = 0$ we get for the galvanomagnetic effect (for $P = 0$):

$$\left(\frac{\Delta R}{R}\right)_\theta = \frac{C_\theta^{\frac{3}{2}}}{\beta_\theta} H^{\frac{2}{3}}, \tag{85}$$

where $C_\theta$ is the proportionality coefficient in the relation $\Delta R/R = C_\theta \sigma^2$. For the Hall effect one gets a somewhat different relation, since the Hall emf E is proportional to the first power of $\sigma$:

$$E_0 = \frac{R_\theta}{\sqrt[3]{\beta_\theta}} H^{\frac{1}{3}}, \tag{86}$$

where $R_\theta$ is the Hall constant at the Curie point. As can be seen from Figs. 63 and 64, the formulas (85) and (86) are well confirmed by experiment [88, 89]. The quantities $C_\theta$ and $R_\theta$, which are electrical constants of the ferromagnetic materials, can be determined from the slopes of the straight lines. The displacement of the straight lines of Fig. 63 relative to the origin of coordinates must be explained by the effect of "remnants" of the technical magnetization. Using the thermodynamic theory, Paches [51] has obtained formulas for the description of the isotherms of the galvanomagnetic effect below the Curie point [Eq. (85) is valid only in the immediate neighborhood of the Curie point] and has made a detailed comparison of these formulas with experiment. In the case of the galvanomagnetic effect below the Curie point it is necessary to take into account the influence of the technical magnetization, and this has been done by Paches.

## § 14. Effects of the Crystallographic Magnetic Anisotropy and the Domain Structure in the Neighborhood of the Curie Point

Near the Curie point the magnetically anisotropic interaction is small in magnitude as compared with the isotropic exchange interaction, but in some cases the anisotropy must be taken into account.

The effects of the crystalline magnetic anisotropy near the Curie point can be taken into account by a thermodynamic treatment. In fact, by using the cubic symmetry of the crystal, we can write the expansion of the thermodynamic potential in the following form

$$\Phi = \Phi_0 + aJ^2 + b_1 J^4 + b_2 \left(J_x^2 J_y^2 + J_y^2 J_z^2 + J_x^2 J_z^2\right) + b_3 J_x^2 J_y^2 J_z^2. \quad (87)$$

Here $\Phi_0$ is the potential in the absence of spontaneous magnetization (i.e., for $T > \theta$); $J_x, J_y, J_z$ are the components of the relative magnetization along the principal axes of the crystal; and $a$, $b_1$, $b_2$, $b_3$ are thermodynamic coefficients which depend on the temperature and the elastic stresses. Thus in addition to the isotropic exchange terms the thermodynamic potential contains anisotropic terms which must be ascribed to the influence of magnetic forces. The description used for these anisotropic terms is the same as the generally accepted expressions for the energy of crystallographic magnetic anisotropy, with $b_2$ and $b_3$ playing the part of the anisotropy constants $K_1$ and $K_2$.

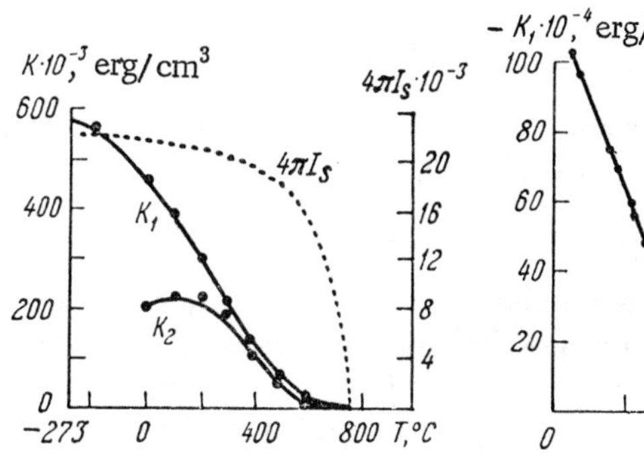


Fig. 65. Temperature dependence of the anisotropy constants $K_1$ and $K_2$ for iron.

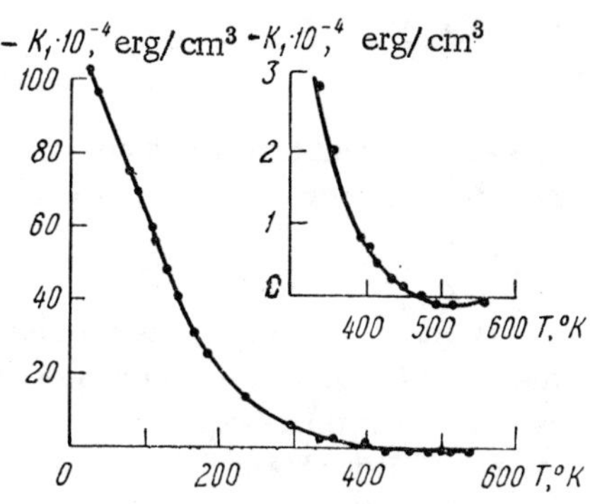


Fig. 66. Temperature dependence of the anisotropy constant $K_1$ for nickel.

There have been a number of studies of the temperature dependence of the anisotropy constants $K_1$ and $K_2$. For example, in [90, 91, 92] it has been shown that there is a strong decrease of $K_1$ with increase of the temperature. Fig. 65 shows the dependence of the anisotropy constants on the temperature for a crystal of iron, according to the data of [93] and [94]. At 600°C, where the saturation magnetization ($4\pi I_s$) is still very close to its value at room temperature, the anisotropy constants become vanishingly small in size. For nickel the situation is complicated by the fact that as the temperature is raised the sign of $K_1$ changes from negative to positive [95]. Figure 66 shows the temperature dependence of $K_1$ for nickel, according to the data of [96]. In the neighborhood of the Curie point the anisotropy constant is positive and very small in magnitude.* In the immediate neighborhood of the Curie point it was not possible to study the exact temperature dependence of the constant $K_1$ because of its smallness. There are very few data on the temperature dependence of the constant $K_2$ at the present time, since this constant has been determined with still lower accuracy [92].

From thermodynamic considerations it must be supposed that the dependence of $K_1$ on T near the Curie point must be linear [13]. In fact, we can expand the energy of the anisotropy near the Curie point in a series of even powers of the spontaneous magnetization. Confining ourselves to the first terms of the series, we can write

$$E_k = a_0 + a\sigma_s^2 + \ldots$$

Using Eq. (9), we have

$$E_k = a_0 + C(\theta - T),$$

where C is a constant which does not depend on the temperature. Dropping the additive constant $a_0$, we can now write

$$(K_1)_{T \to \theta} = C'(\theta - T). \tag{88}$$

A test of this relation is not possible at the present time because of the lack of sufficient experimental material. It must be noted that a similar linear relationship should also hold for the magnetostriction constant $\lambda_m$; it is obtained by expanding the expression for the energy of the magnetoelastic anisotropy in powers of $\sigma_s^2$ (the resulting relation is

* An indirect indication of the change of sign of $K_1$, in nickel is the anomalous temperature dependence of the permeability in this metal [92].

[$\lambda_m \sim (\theta - T)$]. In this case, however, a linear dependence of $\lambda_m$ on T is not always found. In any given case the value of $\lambda_m$ can be found only by extrapolating curves of $\lambda(H)$ to zero field (in order to exclude the influence of the para-process). Near the Curie point such an extrapolation is extremely difficult, because in this strong field region (the region of the para-process) the dependence of $\lambda$ on H is decidedly nonlinear. Besides this, near the Curie point inhomogeneities of the concentration of components in an alloy have a strong effect on the shape of the curve of $\lambda(H)$ [61]. As a result of these effects one as a rule finds near the Curie point a nonlinear dependence of $\lambda_m$ on T.

A question directly connected with our present problem is that of the domain structure of ferromagnetic materials near the Curie point. Suitable experiments have been made recently by the use of the newest methods for studying domain structure (x-ray methods [97], electron-optical and optical methods [98], and also the method of the ferromagnetic probe [99]). The observations have shown that as the temperature increases the destruction of the domain structure does not proceed as rapidly as the decrease of the anisotropy constant. For example, Katszer [99] has shown in the case of magnetite that as the temperature changes from 20 to 100°C there is practically no change of the domain structure. Kirenskii and Degtyarev [98] have used the Kerr effect to observe the domain structure in 3% silicon iron as it was heated from 20 to 700°C, and found that in the (110) plane the domain structure has high temperature stability, in spite of the fact that in this range of temperatures the magnetic anisotropy constant and the character of the magnetization processes undergo extremely strong changes. Neutron-diffraction experiments [97] have shown that complete destruction of the domain structure occurs only in the immediate neighborhood of the Curie point itself. This problem, however, has not yet been studied in much detail.

## § 15. Relaxation Phenomena in Ferromagnetic Materials in the Neighborhood of the Curie Point

Owing to the intense development of fluctuations near phase transition points of the second kind, relaxation processes should occur, accompanied by relaxation energy losses, and in particular there should be an anomaly in the absorption of sound. A phenomenological theory of such phenomena has been given by Landau and Khalatnikov [25]. In the case of a ferroelectric material an anomalous absorption of sound at the Curie point has recently been observed experimentally by Yakovlev, Velichkina, and Baranskii [100].

Let us consider this problem in connection with the ferromagnetic transition.* We assume that near the Curie point a magnetic spin system is taken out of its position of thermodynamic equilibrium. We must determine how the process of restoration of thermodynamic equilibrium in this system proceeds in the course of time (we shall here neglect the domain structure). Let the spin system be described by its magnetization $\sigma$ (ordering parameter). At a given temperature the rate of approach of the magnetization $\sigma$ to its equilibrium values $\sigma_s$ is determined, according to [25], from the kinetic equation

$$\frac{d\sigma}{dt} = -\gamma_0 \frac{\partial \Phi}{\partial \sigma}, \tag{89}$$

where $\Phi$ is the thermodynamic potential of the spin system and $\gamma_0(T)$ is the kinetic coefficient. Expanding $\partial\Phi/\partial\sigma$ in a series of powers of the difference $\sigma - \sigma_s$, we get

$$\frac{\partial \Phi}{\partial \sigma} = \left(\frac{\partial \Phi}{\partial \sigma}\right)_{\sigma_s} + \left(\frac{\partial^2 \Phi}{\partial \sigma^2}\right)_{\sigma_s} (\sigma - \sigma_s). \tag{90}$$

Using the fact that at equilibrium $(\partial\Phi/\partial\sigma)_{\sigma_s}$ and that

$$\frac{\partial^2 \Phi}{\partial \sigma^2} = \alpha + 3\beta\sigma_s^2 = 2\beta\sigma_s^2 \qquad (\text{for } H = 0),$$

we have from Eqs. (89) and (90):

$$\frac{d\sigma}{dt} = -2\beta\gamma_0\sigma_s^2(\sigma - \sigma_s).$$

Solving this equation we get

$$\sigma - \sigma_s = Ae^{-2\beta\gamma_0\sigma_s^2 t} = Ae^{-\frac{t}{\tau}}, \tag{91}$$

where $\tau = 1/2\beta\gamma_0\sigma_s^2$ is the relaxation time; substituting from Eqs. (62) and (53), we have finally:

$$\tau = \frac{1}{2\gamma_0\alpha_0'(\theta - T)}. \tag{92}$$

It follows from this that as the Curie point is approached the relaxation time $\tau$ that characterizes the establishment of equilibrium of the spin system must increase rapidly (if we assume that $\gamma_0$ does not have any singularity in its variation with temperature at $T = \theta$). As a result of this

---

* The calculations given here were made by the author together with R. Z. Levitin.

there must be a relaxation absorption of energy, for example an anomalous absorption of sound and of elastic vibrations near the Curie point. Owing to the slowness of establishment of the equilibrium magnetization near the Curie point there should be found here a magnetic "viscosity" on account of the para-process, and the tangent of the loss angle for the para-process should go through a maximum value. It must be noted that all of these relaxation phenomena should occur only in the region $T < \theta$, since by their nature they depend on the existence of a spontaneous magnetization. In the region $T > \theta$ the relaxation effects vanish.

In the derivation of the formula (92) it was assumed that the external field is small and does not have much effect on the relaxation time. It follows from simple physical considerations, however, that the relaxation time $\tau$ must decrease as the field is increased, because the field suppresses "magnetic" fluctuations. There have not yet been any complete experimental tests of the formula (92) for ferromagnetic materials. To make such a test it is necessary to eliminate the ordinary magnetic viscosity caused by processes of displacement and rotation [79] by the application of a sufficiently strong field; this, however, means a decrease of the relaxation time $\tau$. (See note added in proof.) This is the main source of difficulty in such experiments.

## § 16. The Temperature Dependence of Ferromagnetic Resonance

Recently there has been intense study of magnetic resonance phenomena in ferromagnetic materials in microwave fields, because this gives additional information about the nature of the interaction between spin and lattice. The theory of this phenomenon has been developed by Landau and Lifshits [101], Kittel [102] and Van Vleck [103]. Experimental resonance curves in nickel and certain alloys were first observed by Arkad'ev [104], Griffiths [105], and Zavoiskii [106].

The explanation of the physical nature of the resonance phenomena in ferromagnetic materials is found in the precessional character of the motion of the magnetic moment of the electron, which is due to the fact that it has angular momentum. These phenomena are usually observed by applying to the ferromagnetic material a rather strong constant magnetizing field so that there is no domain structure in the specimen, and studying the magnetization produced by a microwave field (in the centimeter range of wavelengths), which is usually of small amplitude, and which is applied perpendicular to the constant field. A resonance absorption of energy can be observed at a definite frequency. Kittel has emphasized that the precessing spin magnetic moments of the electrons in the ferromagnetic material are subject to the action of strong internal fields— the field of magnetic anisotropy, the demagnetizing field, and so on—and therefore the conditions for resonance and the width of the resonance absorption line will have a marked dependence on the sizes of these fields. The resonance frequency $\omega_0$ will be determined by a certain total effective field

$$\omega_0 = \gamma H_{\mathrm{eff}}$$

where $\gamma = ge/2mc$ is the gyromagnetic ratio. If we take into account the effects of the demagnetizing field which corresponds to the shape of the ferromagnetic specimen, and of the field of magnetic anisotropy, then for the case of an ellipsoidal specimen of a cubic crystal, we have, according to Kittel

$$\omega_0 = \gamma \sqrt{[H_z + (N_x - N_z) I_z + \varphi_1][H_z + (N_y - N_z) I_z + \varphi_2]},$$

where $N_x$, $N_y$, $N_z$ are the values of the demagnetization factors along the X, Y, Z axes, $I_z$ is the magnetization along the Z axis, and $\varphi_1$ and $\varphi_2$ are notations for expressions that give the effect of the magnetic anisotropy.

If the XZ plane coincides with the crystal plane (001), then

$$\varphi_1 = \frac{2K_1}{I_s} \cos 4\theta; \quad \varphi_2 = \frac{K_1}{2I_s}(3 + \cos 4\theta),$$

where $K_1$ is the anisotropy constant, $I_s$ is the saturation magnetization, and $\theta$ is the angle between the Z axis and the [100] direction. Thus in the case of a single crystal there must be an anisotropy of the resonance frequency, and this provides a possibility for determining $K_1$. At present this way of determining $K_1$ is widely used. From experiments on ferromagnetic resonance one can also determine the gyromagnetic ratio $\gamma$ (or the g factor) for ferromagnetic materials. This is important because from the values of $\gamma$ or of the g factor one can draw conclusions about the nature of the elementary magnetic moments, and in particular about the part played by orbital magnetic moments in the phenomena of ferromagnetism.

In this connection it must be noted that this sort of determination from experiments on ferromagnetic resonance is much simpler than the determination from magnetomechanical experiments. The value of $\gamma$ is calculated from the identity

$$\frac{h}{2\pi}\omega_0 \equiv \gamma\mu_B H_{\text{eff}}$$

(at resonance the maximum absorption of energy occurs when the quantum energy of the microwave field is equal to the energy of the spin in the effective field). An extremely interesting question is that of the temperature dependence of the g factor and of the width of the resonance absorption line (the distance between the branches of the resonance peak at half height). To clear up this question Bloembergen [107] has studied the temperature dependence of ferromagnetic resonance for nickel and supermalloy (Figs. 67 and 68). As the temperature is raised the width of the

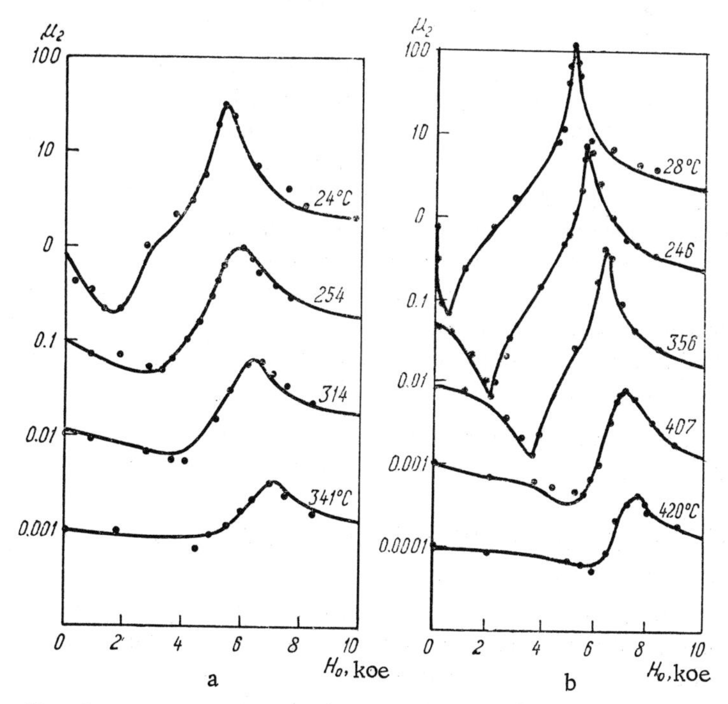


Fig. 67. Temperature dependence of ferromagnetic resonance. a) for nickel, b) for supermalloy; $u_\Gamma$ is the effective magnetic permeability and $H_0$ is the constant magnetic field.

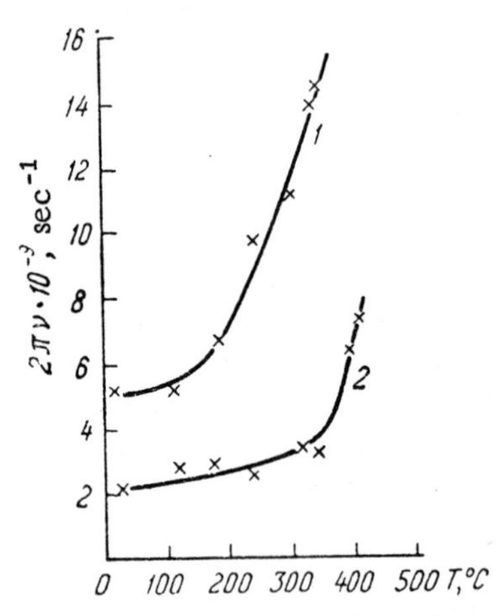


Fig. 68. Temperature dependence of the width of the resonance line. 1) for nickel; 2) for supermalloy.

line increases monotonically. As the Curie point is approached the increase of the line width becomes more rapid, but there is no discontinuity of the curve as the temperature passes through $\theta$, and there is no rapid decrease of the absorption with increase of temperature after passing the value $\theta$. At the present time we do not have any very clear ideas about the cause of the increase of the width of the absorption line as the temperature approaches the Curie point. It is possible that the cause of this broadening is to be found in the thermal fluctuations of the spontaneous magnetization and in structural inhomogeneities. As the Curie temperature is approached these inhomogeneities cause an inhomogeneous magnetization in the ferromagnetic material. This can cause an increase of the line width. If the intensity of the spin waves in the specimen is small (at low temperatures), then the magnetization is homogeneous and the main factor that affects the width of the absorption line in this case is to be found in the process of spin relaxation and in the structural inhomogeneities. Experiments have shown that the $g$ factor is practically independent of the temperature.

We shall return to the problem of the temperature dependence of the width of the absorption line near the Curie point in Chapter IV.

## § 17. Ferromagnetic Materials in the Region Above the Curie Point

It was noted long ago that a ferromagnetic material does not go over at once into the paramagnetic state but makes the transition gradually, remaining in an intermediate state between ferromagnetism and paramagnetism in a certain range of temperatures above the Curie point (the so-called transition region). In pure ferromagnetic materials this range of temperatures is relatively narrow, whereas in alloys it is as a rule considerably wider.

To define the boundaries of the transition region, in addition to the ferromagnetic Curie point $\theta_f$ there has been introduced the so-called paramagnetic Curie point $\theta_p$, which fixes the "upper" boundary of the transition region.

There has not yet been much study of the properties of ferromagnetic materials in the transition region. Nevertheless a knowledge of these properties would be of great interest both for the theory of magnetism and also for the theory of phase transitions of the second kind. The present section presents the experimental results of studies of the magnetic phenomena in the transition region, which are unfortunately not very numerous. We shall just now give a short summary of the results of studies of ferromagnetic materials in the region $T > \theta_p$ (the paramagnetic region).

Magnetization Curves in the Transition Region. Before going on to examine the peculiarities of the magnetization of ferromagnetic substances in the transition region we shall indicate the characteristic features of the magnetization of paramagnetic and ferromagnetic substances.

1. The magnetization of paramagnetic materials is characterized by small numerical values of the magnetic susceptibility. At room temperatures the susceptibility does not reach a value of the order of $10^{-3}$ for any paramagnetic element; ordinarily the magnitude of the paramagnetic susceptibility is of the order of $10^{-4}$–$10^{-6}$. On the other hand, ferromagnetic materials have unusually large magnetic susceptibility (from $10^{-3}$ to $10^{4}$).

2. The magnetization of paramagnetic materials has a linear dependence on the field strength over a comparatively wide range of field strengths, and there is a departure from linearity only in extremely strong fields; that is, the paramagnetic susceptibility is practically independent of the field strength. In ferromagnetic materials, on the other hand, the susceptibility is an extremely complicated function of the field strength. Besides this, ferromagnetic materials are characterized by the presence of phenomena of magnetic hysteresis.

3. The majority of paramagnetic materials satisfy the Curie-Weiss law (a linear dependence of the reciprocal of the paramagnetic susceptibility on the temperature). Ferromagnetic materials differ from paramagnetic materials in having a complicated temperature dependence of the susceptibility.

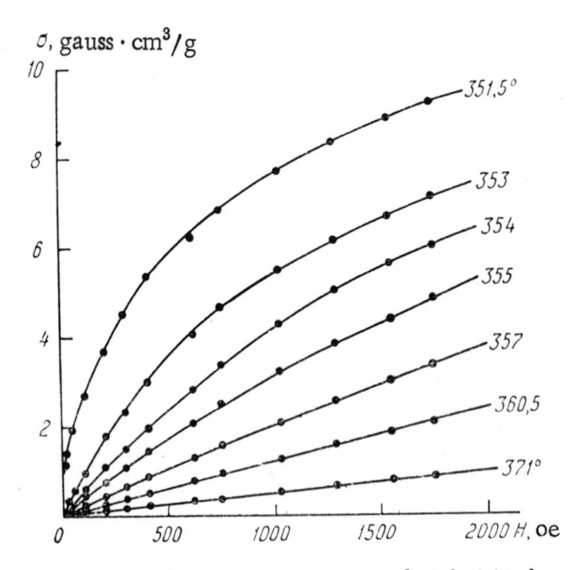


Fig. 69. Magnetization curves of nickel in the region $\theta_f < T < \theta_p$.

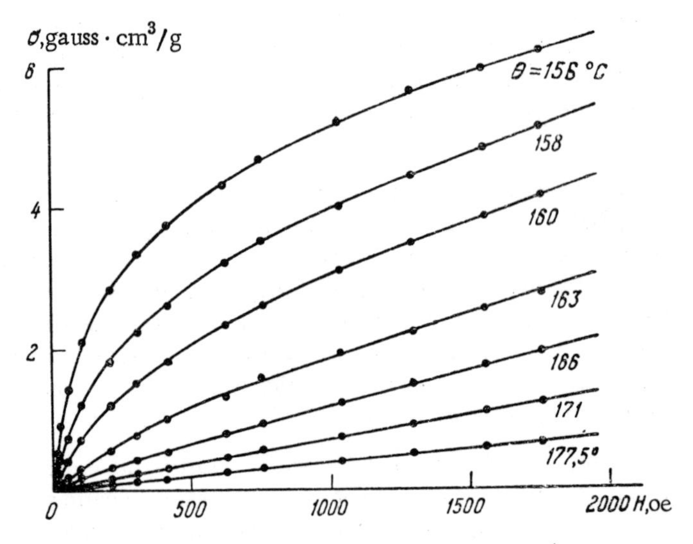


Fig. 70. Magnetization curves of an alloy of 20% copper and and 80% nickel in the region $\theta_f < T < \theta_p$.

Let us now turn to the magnetization curves of ferromagnetic materials in the transition region. Figures 69 and 70 show a series of magnetization curves taken for pure nickel and an alloy of 20% copper and 80% nickel in the region $\theta_f < T < \theta_p$ (as was specified previously, we take as the point $\theta_f$ the temperature at which the thermodynamic coefficient $\alpha$ becomes zero). In other words, we are considering the magnetization in the range of temperatures where there exist "tails" of the spontaneous magnetization.

As can be seen from the diagrams, in the immediate neighborhood of the Curie point on the high temperature side, the magnetization has a nonlinear dependence on the field at all values of the field strength. When the temperature is increased, the nonlinearity remains in the weak-field region, but in strong fields there is a linear section of the magnetization curve. With further increase of the temperature the linear section of the curve extends further toward weaker fields, and finally the magnetization curve goes over entirely into a straight-line shape.

Let us examine whether we can use the thermodynamic equation (51) for the description of the magnetization curves shown in Figs. 69 and 70.

It follows formally from Eq. (51) for the region $T > \theta_f$ (for $\sigma_s = 0$):

$$\alpha\sigma_i + \beta\sigma_i^3 = H. \tag{93}$$

The application of this equation to the description of the magnetization of ferromagnetic materials in the transition region is not at all justified from the point of view of the thermodynamic theory of the ferromagnetic transition. The point is that according to this theory long-range order should disappear completely at the Curie point, and above this point there is complete disorder in the positions of the spins, i.e., the ferromagnetic substance should instantly turn into a paramagnetic substance. Thus Eq. (93) can be applied only in the paramagnetic region above the point $\theta_p$.

Since in the region $T > \theta_p$ the magnetization $\sigma_i$ is very small, the cubic terms in (93) can be neglected, so that we have

$$\sigma_i = \frac{1}{\alpha} H, \tag{94}$$

that is, the magnetization curve is a straight line, which is in agreement with experiment. Only in extremely strong fields ("ultrahigh" fields) does the cubic term in Eq. (93) have any effect, and then there is a deviation from the straight line (94). Thus, Eq. (93) is valid for the temperature region $T > \theta_p$; however, use of (93) to describe true magnetization in the region $\theta_f < T < \theta_p$ is unjustified. The nonlinearity of the magnetization curve in the transition region is caused by the combined effects of technical magnetization, which can still exist in the region $\theta_f < T < \theta_p$ because of the fact that there are "remnants" of the spontaneous magnetization, and of the para-process.

The fact that processes of technical magnetization can exist in the region $\theta_f < T < \theta_p$ is indicated by the following experimental facts.

1. Careful measurements by Forrer [54] have shown that for cold forged nickel a coercive force exists in the region above $\theta_f$ right up to the point $\theta_p$. Kühlewein [108] and Zaimovskii [109] have obtained similar results. For an alloy of 50% nickel and 50% iron Zaimovskii found that the coercive force even increases somewhat above the Curie temperature. This can evidently be due to the fact that above the Curie temperature, where the larger part of the material is already in the paramagnetic state, the ferromagnetic state is highly dispersed. Under these circumstances there must occur a peculiar single-domain structure, since only small and widely separated portions of the specimen are in the ferromagnetic state, and the result is that the coercive force $H_c$ must become larger. There also exists a residual magnetization in the region above the Curie point, but it is of such small size that Forrer, for example, was not able to observe it.

2. Unlike other "nonmagnetic" phenomena, the longitudinal galvanomagnetic effect caused by the true magnetization always has a negative sign (the resistance decreases with increase of the magnetization), whereas the effect caused by the technical magnetization has a positive sign in the majority of metals and alloys. This fact makes it possible to establish the presence of technical magnetization by graphing $(\Delta R/R)(H)$ in the region $\theta_f < T < \theta_p$.

Experiments of Paches [51] on the longitudinal galvanomagnetic effect in nickel and nickel alloys in the region $T > \theta_f$ have shown that in nickel and in an alloy of nickel with silicon there is still a positive galvanomagnetic effect in the transition region in weak fields, which effect, however, is masked by stronger negative galvanomagnetic effects caused by the para-process. In this case the positive effect is detected only from the anomalous curvature of the graph of $(\Delta R/R)(H)$.

A probable outline of the process of magnetization of a ferromagnetic material in the transition region is as follows. When the field is applied there first occurs orientation of the "remnants" of the spontaneous magnetization (technical magnetization), which leads to the appearance of a nonlinearity of the magnetization curves. In stronger fields, in which this orientation has already been completed, there occurs a rotation of individual spins and "swarms" of spins which arise as the result of fluctuations. Owing to the turning of "swarms" of spins there is a considerable increase of the magnetization, which causes a large slope of the straight line sections in strong fields (and, consequently, a large value of the magnetic susceptibility). As we go further from the point $\theta_f$ toward higher temperatures, the "remnants" of the spontaneous magnetization become smaller and smaller, and the probability of the formation of "swarms" of spins decreases; therefore the nonlinearity of the curve in weak fields and the slope of the straight line portion in strong fields both become smaller. The magnetization curves in the transition region can be characterized to first approximation by an equation $\sigma_i = \sigma_s(H) + \kappa H$, where the first term gives the nonlinearity of the curve which is caused by "remnants" of the technical magnetization, and the second term corresponds to the process of turning of "swarms" of spins and of turning of individual spins ($\kappa$ is a susceptibility which does not depend on the field strength).

This picture of the magnetization process in the transition region is confirmed qualitatively by the curves shown in Figs. 69 and 70.

Just as in an ordinary gas there occurs, in particular portions of the volume, condensation of the molecules into droplets of liquid (fluctuations of the gas density), in the magnetic gas of spins there are formed "swarms" of spins pointing in a single direction. This "heterogeneous" system of gases — spins and "swarms" of spins — is extremely mobile because of the effects of the thermal motions. At any given temperature the "swarms" of spins are disappearing in some places and occurring in other places. Evidence of this is found in the experiments of Fraunberger [110], who showed that above the Curie point the lifetime of the "swarms" (or "microdomains") is extremely small. It is obviously impossible to observe the structure of the distribution of "swarms" of spins in the transition region.

Effects of Fluctuations of the Long-Range Magnetic Order on the "Nonmagnetic" Properties of Ferromagnetic Materials in the Transition Region. It is hard to determine the role of fluctuations of the long-range magnetic order in the transition region by means of purely magnetic measurements alone. The task is easier if we bring in measurements of the "nonmagnetic" properties of ferromagnetic materials (specific heat, electric resistance, etc.).

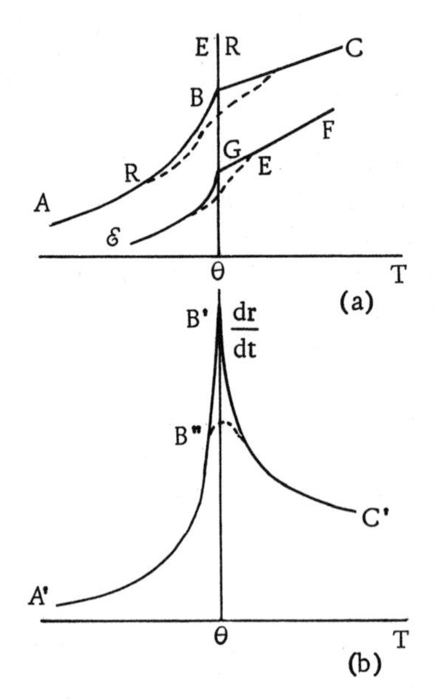


Fig. 71. For the explanation of the "tails" of nonmagnetic properties in the region $\theta_f < T < \theta_p$.

Let us consider the problem for the case of the temperature dependence of the electric resistance. Let the ferromagnetic material be homogeneous, that is, we assume that there are no fluctuations of the exchange integral which would lead to "remnants" of the spontaneous magnetization above the point $\theta_f$.

Since the magnitude of the anomaly of the electric resistance at the Curie point is proportional to the energy of the spontaneous magnetization, we can use a knowledge of the temperature variation of the energy to construct a curve of the quantity dR/dT against the temperature. In fact, by carrying out a graphical differentiation of a curve such as ABC or ℰGF (Fig. 71, a), we get a curve such as A'B'C' with a very sharp maximum (Fig. 71, b). Experimentally, as is well known, the curve of the quantity dR/dT against the temperature has a somewhat flattened maximum.

In order to get at least qualitative agreement with experiment it is necessary to take into account the energy of fluctuations of the magnetic order. When we carry out a graphical differentiation of the energy curve (with the fluctuations of the long-range order taken into account as in the dashed part of the curve as at E or R) we get a curve A'B"C' (Fig. 71, b), which represents the temperature dependence of dR/dT (T) in ferromagnetic materials in the regions both below and above the Curie temperature. The "tail" of the curve of dR/dT above the Curie point is caused by the effects of fluctuations of the long-range magnetic order. It must be noted that in an inhomogeneous material the peak in the curve of the temperature coefficient of the resistance must be still more strongly "smeared out." When there is very great inhomogeneity of the material (for example, in invar alloys, copper-nickel alloys with large content of copper) the peak may be altogether absent [63].

Thus by studying the temperature dependence of "nonmagnetic" properties of homogeneous ferromagnetic materials (for example, crystals) above the Curie point one can bring out the part played by fluctuations of the long-range magnetic order in the transition region. Up to this time, however, there have been no careful measurements of "nonmagnetic" properties in ferromagnetic materials in the transition region.

Width of the Transition Region in Alloys. The width of the transition region, i.e., the difference $\theta_p - \theta_f$, was first measured by Forrer for various metals and alloys [54]. He took as the point $\theta_f$ the temperature at which the residual magnetization vanishes and as $\theta_p$ the point on the temperature axis that is obtained by extrapolation of the straight line in the plot of the reciprocal of the paramagnetic susceptibility against the temperature. Table 9 shows the data from Forrer's measurements for alloys of Ni-Cu and Ni-Fe.

TABLE 9. Width of the Transition Region $\theta_p - \theta_f$ for Alloys of Ni-Cu and Ni-Fe.

| Ni–Cu | | | Ni–Fe | | |
|---|---|---|---|---|---|
| Ni content, percent by wt. | $\theta_p-\theta_f$ | $\theta_f$, °K | Ni content, percent by wt. | $\theta_p-\theta_f$ | $\theta_f$, °C |
| 50.84 | 76 | 140 | 29.7 | 42 | 120 |
| 55.67 | 66 | 194 | 31.8 | 37 | 160 |
| 59.98 | 67 | 240 | 35.3 | 38 | 261 |
| 64.52 | 44 | 333 | 37.0 | 37 | 285 |
| 70.3 | 53 | 393 | 40.8 | 59 | 321 |
| 74.38 | 41 | 399 | 42.0 | 36 | 346 |
| 79.54 | 19 | 456 | 43.5 | 30 | 403 |
| 85.87 | 24 | 502 | 49.6 | 16 | 506 |
| 90.92 | 10 | 545 | 57.7 | 10 | 590 |
| 94.71 | 11 | 591 | 67.0 | 10 | 612 |
| 100.0 | 14 | 631 | 80.2 | 25 | 576 |
| | | | 87.7 | 28 | 511 |
| | | | 100.0 | 22 | 360 |

For nickel Forrer found values of $\theta_p - \theta_f$ from 14 to 22°, and for cobalt values of the order of 20°.

It can be seen from Table 9 that in alloys the width of the transition region is as a general rule always larger than in ferromagnetic metals.

Volkov and Chechernikov [111] have measured the quantity $\theta_p - \theta_f$ for alloys of nickel with the elements Mo, Si, Al, and Cu (the results are shown in Fig. 72). In these experiments the temperature $\theta$ was measured by a more exact method, namely the method of thermodynamic coefficients. It can be seen from Fig. 72 that for a given concentration of the nonferromagnetic component in the alloy the width of the transition region is largest in alloys of Ni-Si and Ni-Mo.

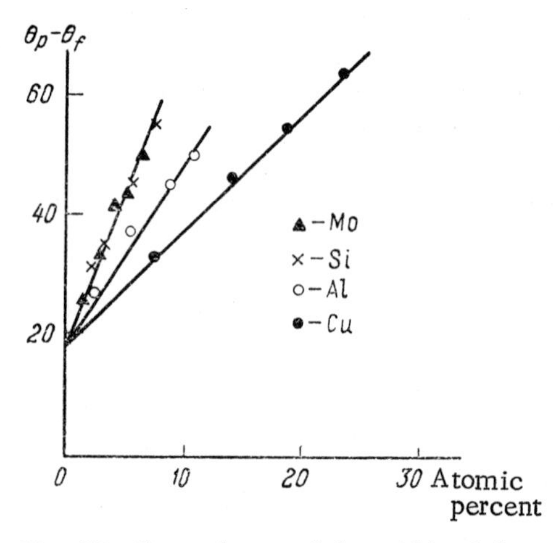


Fig. 72. Dependence of the width of the transition region $\theta_p - \theta_f$ on the concentration of the nonferromagnetic elements (Mo, Si, Al, Cu) in nickel alloys.

<u>Investigation of the Magnetization of Ferromagnetic Materials above the Paramagnetic Curie Point.</u> In the region $T > \theta_p$ ferromagnetic materials should obey the Curie-Weiss law. This law can be obtained from the thermodynamic theory of the ferromagnetic transition. In fact, differentiating Eq. (94) with respect to H and substituting the relation

$$\alpha = \alpha'_\theta (T - \theta) = \frac{2a'_\theta}{\sigma_0}(T - \theta),$$

we get

$$\chi = \frac{\sigma_0}{2a'_\theta (T - \theta)}, \qquad (95)$$

where

$$\chi = \frac{d\sigma_i}{dH}.$$

According to our earlier statement the equation (94) can be applied only to the region in which there is complete disorder in the positions of the spins, and therefore in Eq. (95) we must set $\theta = \theta_p$. Thus we have

$$\chi = \frac{C}{T - \theta_p}, \tag{96}$$

where $C = \sigma_0 / 2a'_\theta$ is the Curie-Weiss constant. Thus we get the Curie-Weiss law in its usual form.

The most complete data on the temperature dependence of the magnetic susceptibility above the point $\theta_p$ available at the present time are those for nickel. For iron and cobalt departures from the Curie-Weiss law are observed, which are due to structural changes that occur in these materials on heating. Fallot has made detailed studies not only for pure nickel, iron, and cobalt but also for alloys of these metals with non-ferromagnetic components [112]. It has been found that for alloys the Curie-Weiss law must be written in the following form [113]:

$$\chi = \chi_k + \frac{C}{T - \theta_p}, \tag{97}$$

where $\chi_k$ does not depend on the temperature.

The most complete and systematic experimental data on the magnetic properties of alloys in the region $T < \theta_p$ have been obtained by Volkov and Chechernikov [111]. They have shown that even for nickel it is the law (97) that holds, and not Eq. (96). Figure 73 shows a curve of the dependence of $\chi$ on $1/(T - \theta_p)$ for nickel, according to the data of

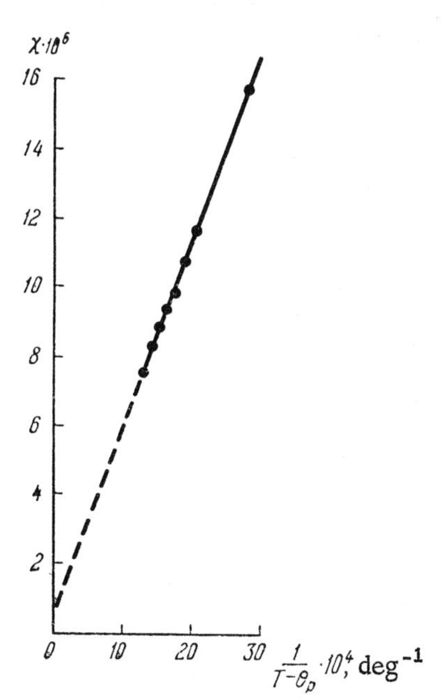


Fig. 73. Dependence of the magnetic susceptibility of nickel on the quantity $1/(T - \theta_p)$.

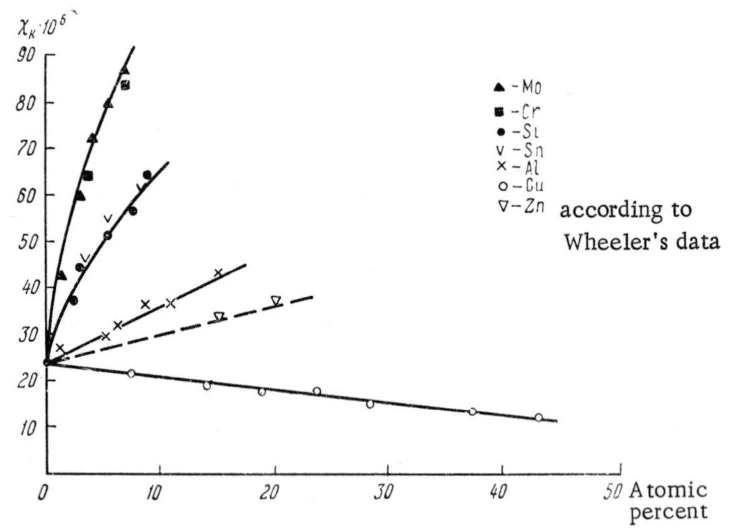


Fig. 74. Dependence of the quantity $\chi_k$ on the concentration of the nonferromagnetic element in nickel alloys.

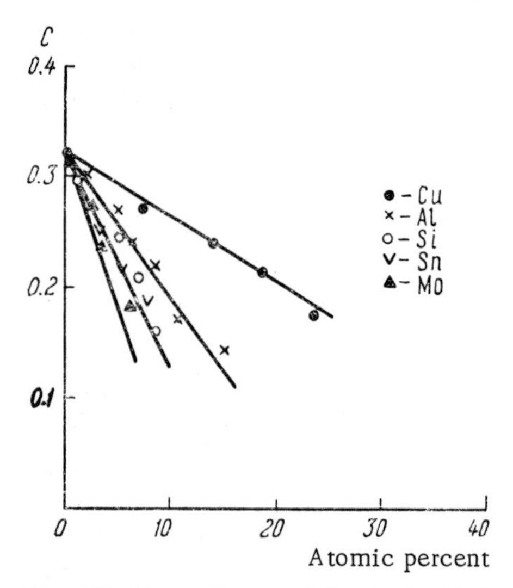


Fig. 75. Dependence of the Curie-Weiss constant on the concentration of the nonferromagnetic element in nickel alloys.

[111]. There is a definite intercept $\chi_k$ on the axis of ordinates, although it is rather small. Analogous results have been obtained for a large group of nickel alloys.

Figure 74 shows the dependence of the quantity $\chi_k$ on the atomic concentration of the nonferromagnetic component in nickel alloys. For alloys Ni-Cu, $\chi_k$ decreases with increasing copper content. For the other alloys $\chi_k$ increases with the concentration of the nonferromagnetic component. Figure 74 also shows values of $\chi_k$ for alloys Ni-Zn, calculated from the data of Wheeler [114].

Thus $\chi_k$ has an extremely strong dependence on the atomic environment and on the type of atoms. It can be seen from Figs. 73 and 74 that the quantity $\chi_k$ is close to the value of the paramagnetic susceptibility of conductivity electrons in alkali metals that was calculated by Pauli [115].

Figure 75 shows the dependence of the constant C on the concentration. It can be seen that C and $\chi_k$ (cf. Fig. 74) have a mutual dependence; decrease of one of these quantities leads to increase of the other (except for alloys Ni-Cu). This means that in the relation (97) the quantity $\chi_k$ cannot be regarded as a simple additive constant.

Vlasov and Vonsovskii [44] have expressed the constants C, $\chi_k$, and $\theta_p$ in the law (97) in terms of atomic constants.

Using the model of s-d exchange, they showed that $\chi_k$, C, and $\theta_p$ satisfy the following relations:

$$\chi_k = \left[1 + \frac{n_d}{n_s}\left(1 - \frac{\theta_{dd}}{\theta}\right)\right] \frac{\theta}{\theta_{dd}} \frac{3n_s}{20\beta} N\mu_B^2;$$

$$C = \left(1 + \varkappa \frac{n_s}{n_d}\right)\left(1 + \varkappa \frac{n_s}{n_d} \frac{\theta}{\theta_{dd}}\right) \frac{\theta}{\theta_{dd}} \frac{n_d N \mu_B^2}{k};$$

$$\theta_p = \frac{\theta_{dd}}{1 + \dfrac{3\gamma^2}{10\beta b} \dfrac{N_s}{N_d}}.$$

Here b is a quantity of the order of the exchange integral, N is the number of magnetically active atoms per cubic centimeter, $n_s = N_s/N$ and $n_d = N_d/N$ are the numbers of elementary magnetic moments provided by s and d electrons respectively, $\theta_{dd} = b/2k$, $\varkappa = 3\gamma/20\beta$, $\gamma = \alpha' - 10\lambda\beta'/3 = A_0/2 - 2A$, are coefficients.

Chapter IV

# THE ANTIFERROMAGNETIC TRANSITION

Néel [116] was the first to point out the fact that matter can exist in an antiferromagnetic state. Somewhat later, Landau [117] used thermodynamic considerations to treat the transition of a substance from the paramagnetic state into the antiferromagnetic state as a magnetic phase transition. The present belief is that this transition, like the transition in ferromagnetic materials, is of the nature of a phase change of the second kind. Since in antiferromagnetic materials the resulting magnetization is equal to zero, observations of the change of the macroscopic magnetic properties on passage through the antiferromagnetic Curie point (which is sometimes called the Néel point in Western literature) is detected in observations of the anomalous variation with temperature of the magnetic susceptibility and of various "nonmagnetic" properties. Antiferromagnetic transitions have been observed experimentally by Trapeznikova and Shubnikov [118], Shalty [119], and Bizette and his co-workers [120]. In recent years studies have been made of a large number of chemical compounds of the transition elements (oxides, sulfides, chlorides, etc.), which have antiferromagnetic properties. The number of antiferromagnetic substances is very large, and new antiferromagnetic materials are constantly being found, especially at low temperatures. It has been found that the elements Mn and Cr [121] and a number of alloys based on Mn and Cr (for example, MnAu, MnCu, CrSb) are antiferromagnetic [122]. Antiferromagnetism is a more widespread phenomenon than it was earlier believed to be. There is a greater variety of antiferromagnetic properties and of the ways in which they are manifested than is the case with ferromagnetism.

The most complete summary of known antiferromagnetic materials and their properties is given in the monograph by Dorfman [15] (cf. also [123]).

## § 1. On the Thermodynamic Theory of the Antiferromagnetic Transition

As in the case of ferromagnetic materials, a strong exchange interaction is the main factor that establishes the antiferromagnetic ordering of spins. The actual magnetic interaction leads to the crystallographic anisotropy of the magnetic properties. Therefore in the general case the thermodynamic potential of an antiferromagnetic material must contain both exchange and magnetic terms. The exchange terms contain combinations of the magnetic moments that depend only on their relative orientations and not on their general orientation in relation to the crystal lattice. The magnetic terms depend on the direction of the magnetic moments in relation to various directions in the crystal.

The first theory of the antiferromagnetic transition was given by Landau [117] on the basis of the thermodynamic theory of phase transitions. He obtained explanations of the increase of the magnetic susceptibility of an antiferromagnetic material as the antiferromagnetic transition point (Curie point) is approached, and of the strong anisotropy of this susceptibility. Using the dichlorides of transition metals as an example, Landau examined the complex structure of the positions of the magnetic spins in crystals of these substances. In these substances there are atomic planes in which the spins are directed to the right under the action of the exchange forces, while in adjacent planes they are directed to the left. Negative exchange forces act between adjacent layers, and as the result the crystal as a whole does not have any resultant spontaneous magnetization in the absence of a field (compensated antiferromagnetism). We shall give an abbreviated form of Landau's derivation.

If $J_1$ is the relative magnetization of the layers with spins pointing to the right and $J_2$ is the corresponding quantity for those pointing to the left, then near the Curie point we can represent the exchange free energy of these layers as series expansions in even powers of $J_1$ and $J_2$:

$$F_1 = aJ_1^2 + bJ_1^4 + \ldots, \tag{98}$$

$$F_2 = aJ_2^2 + bJ_2^4 + \ldots \tag{99}$$

In first approximation we can regard the exchange free energy of adjacent layers (with spins pointing to the right and to the left) as proportional to the scalar product of the magnetizations of these layers:

$$F_3 = AJ_1J_2. \tag{100}$$

By symmetry we can take the energy of the magnetic anisotropy of the layers to be proportional to the square of the components of magnetization parallel to the symmetry axes of the crystal:

$$F_4 = \frac{K}{2}\left(J_{1x}^2 + J_{1y}^2\right), \tag{101}$$

$$F_5 = \frac{K}{2}\left(J_{2x}^2 + J_{2y}^2\right), \tag{102}$$

where K is the magnetic anisotropy constant. Finally, the energy that depends on the external field is given by

$$F_6 = -J_1 H, \tag{103}$$

$$F_7 = -J_2 H. \tag{104}$$

The total free energy of the antiferromagnetic material is

$$F = \sum_{i=1}^{i=7} F_i. \tag{105}$$

As a result of the action of the external magnetic field H the anitferromagnetic material has a resultant magnetization $J_1 - J_2$. Differentiating F with respect to this difference and equating the result to zero, we find the condition for the energy to be a minimum, and after some transformations we get from this expression for the magnetic susceptibility in the neighborhood of the Curie point:

$$\chi_z = \frac{\frac{1}{2\beta}}{T - \left(\theta - \frac{2A}{\beta}\right)}; \quad \chi_x = \chi_y = \frac{\frac{1}{2\beta}}{T - \left(\theta - \frac{K+2A}{\beta}\right)} \quad (T > \theta); \tag{106}$$

$$\chi_z = \frac{\frac{1}{\beta}}{(\theta - T) + \frac{2A}{\beta}}; \quad \chi_x = \chi_y = \frac{\frac{1}{\beta}}{K + \frac{2A}{\beta}} \quad (T < \theta). \tag{107}$$

Here $\theta$, A, and $\beta$ are numerical coefficients. Thus in antiferromagnetic substances we must consider two susceptibilities: one along the direction of easy magnetization $\chi_z = \chi_{\parallel}$, or along H, and the other in the perpendicular direction, $\chi_x = \chi_y = \chi_{\perp}$.

The usual Curie-Weiss law holds in the region $T > \theta$, where $K \approx 0$. At $T = \theta$ we have $\chi_z = \chi_x = \chi_y = 1/2A$, i.e., precisely at the Curie point the susceptibility is finite and there is no anisotropy. As the temperature is lowered further, we find in agreement with experiment that the susceptibility becomes smaller than its value at the Curie point. Furthermore the quantities $\chi_{\parallel}$ and $\chi_{\perp}$ must have different temperature dependences. The susceptibility in the perpendicular direction is practically independent of the temperature, while that in the parallel direction depends on the temperature [cf. Eq. (107)], i.e., below the Curie point there must be a strong anisotropy of the susceptibility. These results of the thermodynamic theory are in agreement with experiment.

The subsequent treatments of antiferromagnetism have been based on ideas about models.

## § 2. Theoretical Models of Antiferromagnetism

Van Vleck [124] has given a theory of the temperature dependence of the magnetic susceptibility of antiferromagnetic materials, based on the ideas of Néel [116] and Bitter [45] about magnetic sublattices and on the Weiss molecular-field model. Van Vleck divides the crystal lattice of an antiferromagnetic substance into two or more magnetic sublattices "inserted" into each other; in each of these sublattices all the magnetic spins are oriented parallel to each other under the action of exchange forces, but the spins that belong to different sublattices are oriented in antiparallel directions owing to a negative exchange interaction. In the case of the simple cubic lattice and the body-centered cubic lattice the division is into two sublattices with antiparallel magnetizations; the face-centered lattice is divided into four sublattices, and so on. It must be noted that in a certain sense the hypothesis of magnetic sublattices, which Néel [116] introduced for the treatment of antiferromagnetism, is equivalent to the hypothesis of a magnetic layer structure which was used by Landau. In fact, an analysis of the most common antiferromagnetic materials (MnO, FeO, MnS, $MnF_2$, $FeF_2$, etc.) shows that they have a laminar magnetic structure; the layers of magnetic ions of the metal, located in the octahedral spaces of the close-packed nonmetallic ions, are arranged successively so that the magnetic moments of the ions in adjacent layers are antiparallel, while the magnetic moments of the ions in each particular layer are parallel to each other.

The essential point of the method of the molecular field is that we regard each magnetic ion as being in a certain effective field, which is the result of the action of exchange forces from all the surrounding magnetic ions. According to Néel and Van Vleck the ordering of the magnetic spins in the sublattices falls off with the temperature according to the Langevin-Weiss function or according to the somewhat more complicated modification known as the Brillouin function. Using the expansion of these functions in a power series in the magnetization (near the antiferromagnetic Curie point) and taking into account the direction of the magnetizations in the sublattices relative to the external magnetic field, Van Vleck found expressions for $\chi_{\parallel}$ and $\chi_{\perp}$; it is thus found that $\chi_{\parallel}$ depends on T and $\chi_{\perp}$ does not depend on T, which is the same result as in the Landau theory, but with the difference that in the Van Vleck formulas the quantity that characterizes the magnetic anisotropy is absent. At the same time it is well-known that in antiferromagnetic materials the magnetic anisotropy can play an important role and that it must be taken into account even near the Curie point. The molecular-field method is an extremely crude one, and one must be careful about accepting the quantitative conclusions obtained from this method, especially in the neighborhood of the Curie point. Nevertheless the application of this method has had great significance as an explorative method which has provided a qualitative understanding of the fundamental phenomena in the field of antiferromagnetism.

Attempts to make the molecular-field method more precise have so far not led to the desired result. The molecular-field method does not take into account the inverse action of the field on the surrounding ions. Inclusion of this action leads to complicated mathematical expressions, and a rigorous solution of this problem is possible only for a one-dimensional chain of interacting ions. It turns out, however, that a one-dimensional chain does not lead to antiferromagnetism. For the plane two-dimensional lattice and for the three-dimensional lattice only an approximate calculation is possible. Just as in the case of ferromagnetism, a rigorous and consistent theory of antiferromagnetism can be obtained only on a quantum-mechanical basis. In such a treatment one must take into account not only the isotropic exchange interaction but also the anisotropic magnetic interaction.

At the present time the most rigorous quantum-mechanical calculation of antiferromagnetism can be made in the low-temperature region [125, 126]. Since in most known antiferromagnetic compounds the magnetic ions ($Fe^{++}$, $Co^{++}$, $Cr^{++}$, $Mn^{++}$, etc.) in the lattice are separated by nonmagnetic ions ($O^{--}$, $Ce^{-}$, $F^{-}$, etc), in making the quantum calculation one introduces into the treatment the so-called superexchange or indirect exchange interaction, in which the nonmagnetic ions are transmitters of the exchange interaction between the magnetic ions.

In the temperature region near the antiferromagnetic Curie point one can make only an approximate quantum calculation. By using the method of energy centers of gravity and taking into account the magnetic dipole interaction, Vlasov [127] found the following expressions for $\chi_{\parallel}$ and $\chi_{\perp}$ near the Curie point:

$$\chi_{\parallel} = \frac{N\mu_B^2 (1 - J^2)}{k[T + \theta' (1 - J^2)]}; \quad \chi_{\perp} = \frac{N\mu_B^2}{k(\theta + \theta')}. \tag{108}$$

Here J is the relative magnetization of one sublattice, N is the number of spins per mole, $\mu_B$ is the Bohr magneton, $\underline{k}$ is the Boltzmann constant, and $\theta$ and $\theta'$ are quantities given by

$$\theta = \frac{(P - Q) + (P' - Q') \cos^2 (\psi - \beta)}{k},$$

$$\theta' = \frac{(P + Q) + (P' + Q') \cos^2 (\psi - \beta)}{k},$$

where P and Q are sums of integrals which respectively characterize the size of the electrostatic and the magnetic interactions in the lattice; P' and Q' are sums of integrals that characterize only the magnetic interaction, and P and P' refer to one sublattice and Q and Q' to the other; $\beta$ is the angle between the direction of the magnetic field intensity and the direction of the antiferromagnetism for $H = 0$; $\psi$ is the angle between the direction of the magnetic field and the direction of the antiferromagnetism for $H \neq 0$.

Just as in the thermodynamic theory, in the Vlasov theory $\chi_{\parallel}$ depends on the temperature and $\chi_{\perp}$ does not have such a dependence, and as has already been remarked, this is in agreement with experiment. An interesting consequence of the Vlasov theory is that the antiferromagnetic Curie point turns out to depend on the orientation of the magnetization relative to the crystallographic axes (anisotropy of the Curie point). Vlasov also points out a difference in the effects of external fields on the Curie point in ferromagnetic and antiferromagnetic materials. In the case of a ferromagnetic material near the Curie point an external field causes a strong para-process, as a result of which there is ordering of the spins (ferromagnetic ordering) even above the Curie point. The magnetic field "hinders" the phase transition from ferromagnetism to paramagnetism. Therefore in this case we can speak of a Curie point only in the absence of a magnetic field. In the case of an antiferromagnetic material, on the other hand, the external field destroys the ordering of the spins (antiferromagnetic ordering), i.e., the field "assists" the phase transition from antiferromagnetism to paramagnetism. Therefore in this case we can speak of a Curie point even in the presence of a field.

## § 3. The Temperature Dependence of the Magnetic Susceptibility of Antiferromagnetic Materials

At the present time there is a large amount of experimental data on the temperature dependence of the magnetic susceptibility of antiferromagnetic materials near the Curie point. As the temperature approaches the antiferromagnetic Curie point the susceptibility reaches an extreme value, and therefore this sort of temperature dependence is usually used to determine whether a substance belongs to the class of antiferromagnetic materials.

Figure 76 shows the temperature dependence of the susceptibility for three anhydrous sulfates: $NiSO_4$, $FeSO_4$, and $CoSO_4$ [128]. All three of these substances, which have the respective antiferromagnetic Curie points 37, 21, and 15.5°K, are characterized by maxima of the susceptibility at the Curie point.

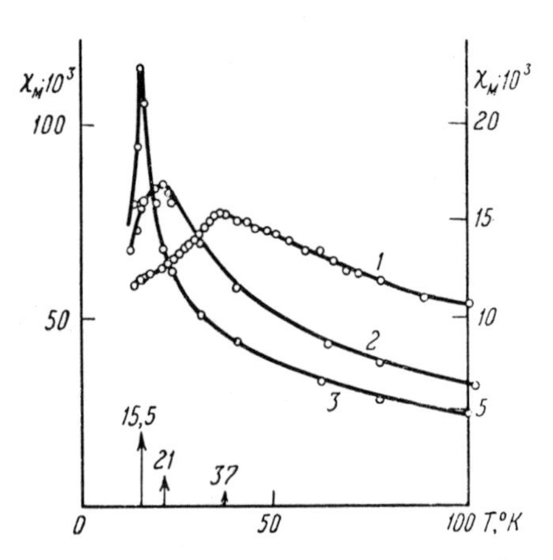


Fig. 76. Temperature dependence of the molar susceptibility for anhydrous sulfates: curve 1) right-hand scale; curves 2,3) left-hand scale). 1) $NiSO_4$; 2) $FeSO_4$; 3) $CoSO_4$ (the arrows show the values of the Curie points).

Paramagnetism appears at temperatures above the Curie point. In this range of temperatures the reciprocal of the susceptibility varies linearly with the temperature (i.e., the Curie-Weiss law holds). Below the Curie point the susceptibility varies with the temperature according to a more complicated law, and also there is a strong anisotropy. Another characteristic feature is the dependence of the susceptibility below the maximum (i.e., in the region $T < \theta$) on the magnetic field. Figure 77 shows the results of measurements of the susceptibility of anhydrous copper sulfate

($CuSO_4$), which has a sharp antiferromagnetic transition at 35° K [129]. Near the Curie point the susceptibility depends on the field intensity. With increase of the field strength the susceptibility decreases, and its maximum is displaced toward lower temperatures. As the field is varied from 3400 to 13,000 oe the quantity $\chi_M$ changes by 10%. In other antiferromagnetic materials (for example, in $CuCl_2 \cdot 2H_2O$) a dependence of the susceptibility on the field is observed not only near the Curie point but also below it, over the whole range of temperatures. It must be noted, however, that there are also antiferromagnetic materials in which the dependence of $\chi$ on H is not such a sharp one, and moreover one often

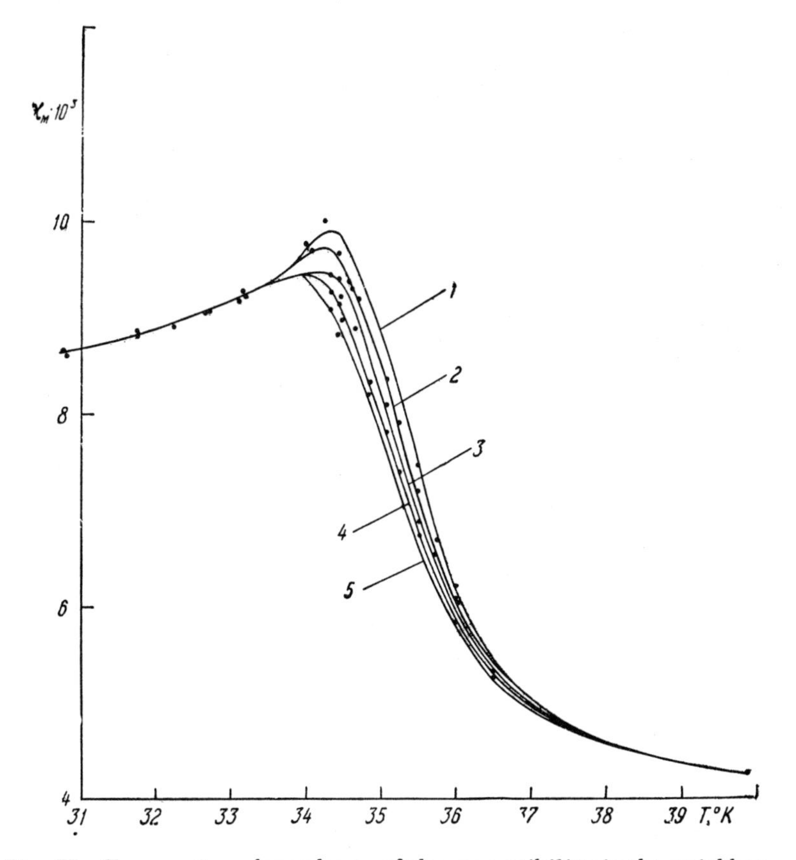


Fig. 77. Temperature dependence of the susceptibility in the neighborhood of the Curie point for $CuSO_4$. 1) H = 3370 oe; 2) H = 6660 oe; 3) H = 9700 oe; 4) H = 11780 oe; 5) H = 12900 oe.

observes not a decrease of $\chi$ with increase of the field, but on the contrary an increase, and also a hysteresis of the variations of $\chi$ with the field. These facts are not yet completely explained.

In the region below the Curie point Gorter [130] has observed a strong magnetic anisotropy in crystals of $CuCl_2 \cdot 2H_2O$ (dehydrated copper fluoride). This substance crystallizes in the rhombohedral system and has one natural direction of antiferromagnetism (along the a axis). For such crystals there is a certain critical field at which $\chi_{\parallel}$ increases sharply. This can be explained by the fact that in a single crystal of $CuCl_2 \cdot 2H_2O$ the spins that have antiparallel orientation are located along the natural direction of antiferromagnetism-in analogy with the direction of easy magnetization in ferromangetic materials. It turns out that the critical field, which can serve as a measure of the magnetic anisotropy, increases with the temperature [131]. The increase of the critical field with the temperature finds its explanation in the theory of Vlasov [127].

## § 4. "Nonmagnetic" Phenomena in the Neighborhood of the Antiferromagnetic Transition Point

Since, just as in the case of ferromagnetism, the transition from the paramagnetic to the antiferromagnetic state is a transition from disorder of the spins to an ordered position of the spins, i.e., a phase transition of the second kind, we can expect that also in the case of antiferromagnetism

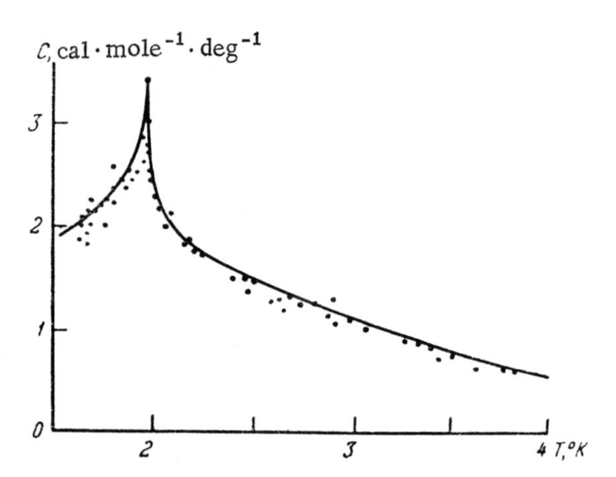


Fig. 78. Temperature dependence of the specific heat for anhydrous $MnCl_2$.

there will be phenomena at the transition point that depend on even powers of the ordering parameter (the square of the magnetization). At the antiferromagnetic Curie point one should observe anomalies of the specific heat and thermal expansion, a spontaneous deformation of the lattice, etc.

The most extensive studies of the temperature dependence of the specific heat of a number of antiferromagnetic quantities have been those carried out by Shalyt [119], who found discontinuities of the specific heat in the neighborhood of the Curie point.

The maximum on the curve of the susceptibility plotted against temperature occurs at practically the same temperature as the maximum of the specific heat (in the literature this temperature is commonly taken as the antiferromagnetic Curie point).

TABLE 10. Values of the "Discontinuity" of the Specific Heat at the Antiferromagnetic Curie Point.

| Substance | $\theta$, °K | $\Delta C_p$, cal · deg$^{-1}$ · mole$^{-1}$ |
|---|---|---|
| $CoF_2$ | 37.7 | 5 |
| $NiF_2$ | 73.2 | 4.2 |
| MnO | 116.0 | ~6.6 |
| CoO | 290.0 | ~6.0 |

Figure 78 shows results of measurements of the specific heat of anhydrous $MnCl_2$ from the data of [132]. In the range 1.6-1.95°K this substance undergoes an antiferromagnetic transition which is indicated by the maximum of the specific heat. It is to be expected that the "discontinuity" of the specific heat at the Curie point in an antiferromagnetic substance will be much larger (Table 10) than it is in typical ferromagnetic substances (in nickel, for example, $\Delta C_p \approx 2$ cal·deg$^{-1}$·mole$^{-1}$).

On the high-temperature side (that is, in the region $T > \theta$) the curve of the specific heat has a "tail." The origin of this "tail" is still not clear; the question as to whether it is due to a gradual disappearance of remnants of the short-range order of the spins or is caused by effects of structural factors calls for careful study. In mixed antiferromagnetic crystals the maximum of the specific heat at the antiferromagnetic Curie point is strongly "smeared out" (Fig. 79) [133].

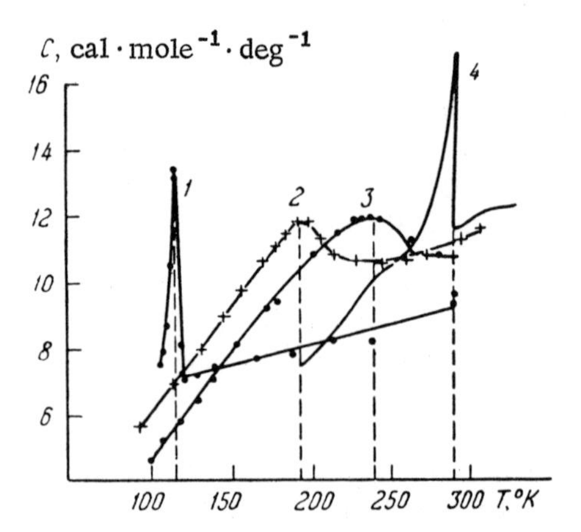


Fig. 79. Temperature dependence of the specific heat in mixed crystals MnO-CoO. 1) MnO; 2) 0.5 MnO, 0.5 CoO; 3) 0.25 MnO, 0.75 CoO; 4) CoO.

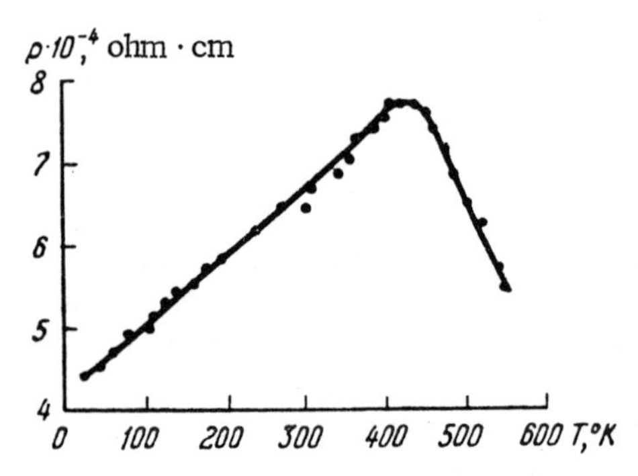


Fig. 80. Temperature dependence of the specific resistance of the antiferromagnetic compound CrSb.

In the literature there is evidence of extremely sharp anomalies of the electrical properties at the antiferromagnetic Curie point. For example, it has been found that in the antiferromagnetic compound CrSb [134] the temperature dependence of the electric resistance is like the temperature dependence of the magnetic susceptibility, i.e., there is a maximum of the curve $\rho$ (T) in the neighborhood of the Curie point (Fig. 80). Similar anomalies of the electrical properties have been observed also in other antiferromagnetic materials ($MnF_2$, MnSe). It seems probable that the magnetic phase transition in an antiferromagnetic material causes a great change in the interaction of the electrons, so that even the character of the conductivity is changed. It can be seen from Fig. 80 that whereas above the antiferromagnetic Curie point the temperature coefficient of the resistance has the negative sign that is characteristic of a semiconductor, below the Curie point it has the positive sign that is characteristic of metallic conductivity. There has not yet been much study of the electrical properties of antiferromagnetic substances.

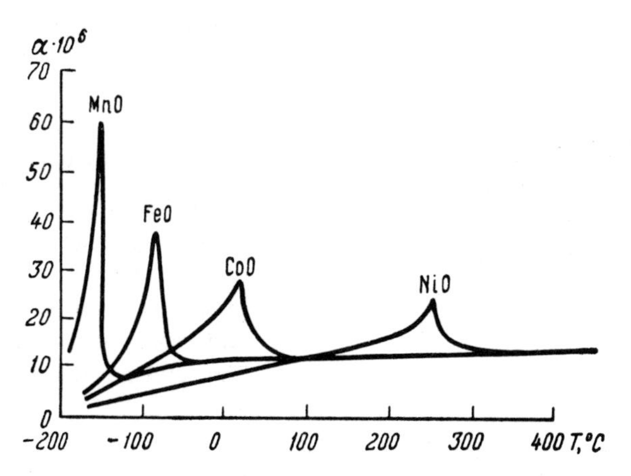


Fig. 81. Temperature dependence of the coefficient of thermal expansion of antiferromagnetic materials.

Very interesting data have also been obtained in the study of the temperature dependence of the thermal expansion of antiferromagnetic materials. Figure 81 shows the results of measurements on the temperature dependence of the thermal expansion coefficient for several antiferromagnetic materials [135]. It can be seen that near the Curie point there is a very large anomaly of the thermal expansion, much larger than the corresponding anomalies for ferromagnetic materials. Whereas in pure nickel the anomaly is $\Delta\alpha \approx + 2 \cdot 10^{-6}$ deg $^{-1}$ and in an invar alloy (36% Ni and 64% Fe) $\Delta\alpha \approx -10\text{-}12 \cdot 10^{-6}$ deg $^{-1}$ (the maximum anomaly for ferromagnetic materials), it is seen from Fig. 81 that in MnO $\Delta\alpha \approx + 50 \cdot 10^{-6}$ deg$^{-1}$ and in CoO $\Delta\alpha \approx + 20 \cdot 10^{-6}$ deg$^{-1}$.

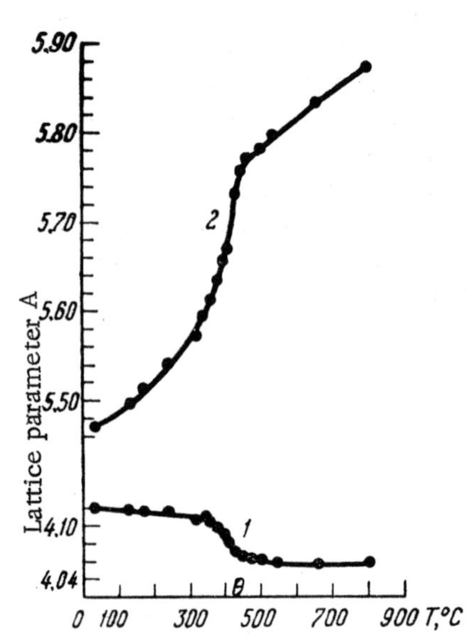

Fig. 82. Temperature dependence of the lattice parameters for CrSb. 1) a axis; 2) c axis.

It has been found through accurate x-ray studies [136] that when a material is cooled below the antiferromagnetic Curie point there is a change not only of the volume but also of the symmetry of the lattice. Whereas above the Curie point the crystals MnO, FeO, and NiO have cubic symmetry, when they are cooled below the Curie point the symmetry becomes rhombohedral. In the case of CoO the cubic symmetry changes below the Curie point into tetragonal symmetry.

By using an x-ray method Snow has studied the temperature dependence of the thermal expansion in the antiferromagnetic compound CrSb [137]. The results of the measurements are shown in Fig. 82. The breaks in the curves come at the Curie point. It can be seen that below the Curie point the crystal contracts along one axis and expands along the other, i.e., there is a strong anisotropy of the anomaly of the thermal expansion. No changes in the symmetry of the crystal lattice are found, however. At the point of the antiferromagnetic transition (below 675°C) in hematite ($\alpha$-$Fe_2O_3$) there is also a sharp change of the parameters of the lattice without a change of the symmetry.

In the majority of antiferromagnetic materials the fractional deformation of the lattice in the transition from the paramagnetic state to the antiferromagnetic state takes very large values, greatly exceeding the value of the spontaneous magnetostriction in ferromagnetic materials near the Curie point.

The cause of the structural changes which accompany the antiferromagnetic transition in the crystals MnO, FeO, NiO, and CoO probably lies in the fact that the magnetic structure of an antiferromagnetic material is closely connected with its atomic structure. For example, the magnetic structure of MnO for $T < \theta$ consists of a succession of octahedral planes (111) with parallel and antiparallel orientations of the spins in these planes. The transition through the antiferromagnetic Curie point is inevitably accompanied by a change of the interaction of these planes, which in turn leads to a considerable change in the dimensions of the lattice and even of its structure. Li Yün-Yüan [138] explains the change of the symmetry of the lattice in the antiferromagnetic transition in MnO, FeO, and other crystals in terms of the spontaneous magnetostriction, which has an anisotropic character in these substances. It is pointed out in this paper that the source of this high anisotropy must be sought in the indirect exchange interaction Mn-O-Mn. Consequently the situation is different from that with ferromagnetic materials, and in many antiferromagnetic substances near the Curie point the anisotropic forces can play an important part.

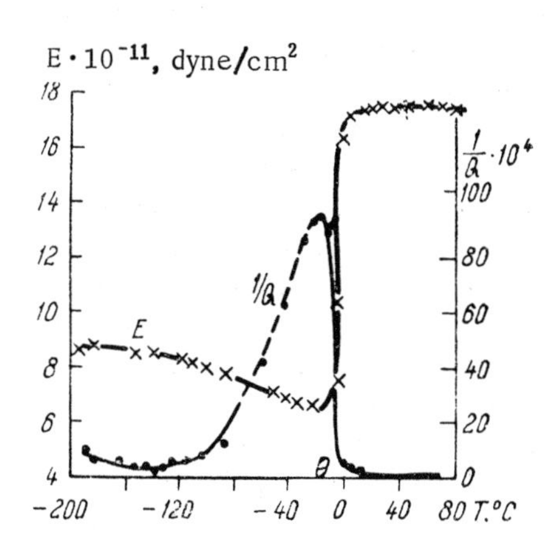


Fig. 83. Temperature dependences of the elastic modulus E and the internal friction coefficient 1/Q for CoO.

In concluding this section we must point out that in some antiferromagnetic materials extremely sharp anomalies of the elastic properties are observed at the Curie point. Figure 83 shows curves of the temperature dependence of Young's modulus and of the internal friction coefficient for CoO, from the data of [139]. It can be seen that as the point of the antiferromagnetic transition is approached these quantities change by more than 100%.

More detailed data on the properties of antiferromagnetic materials are contained in the papers [140-143].

## § 5. Resonance Absorption

If an antiferromagnetic substance is placed in a constant magnetic field and at the same time acted on by a weak high-frequency field directed perpendicular to the constant magnetic field, the magnetization vectors of the sublattices will precess around the direction of H. When the frequency of the alternating field coincides with the precession frequency there can be a resonance absorption of energy.

It must be noted that the magnetic moments of the sublattices in an antiferromagnetic substance have a strong (exchange) coupling, and therefore one cannot treat their precessions in an external field separately (at least in a field that is smaller than the "field" of the exchange forces).

The problem of investigating antiferromagnetic resonance thus reduces to that of establishing the conditions for the resonance of the magnetic moments of the sublattices, which are not only in the external field but also in the field of the exchange forces and of the magnetic anisotropy. The successful performance of experiments to observe antiferromagnetic resonance in the temperature range of the transition from paramagnetism to antiferromagnetism would give additional evidence about the nature of the antiferromagnetic state.

A study of resonance absorption in antiferromagnetic materials at the transition from the paramagnetic state into the antiferromagnetic state has been carried out in [144]. This study was made with powders by means of microwave apparatus. Figure 84 shows the temperature dependence of the height of the resonance absorption maximum for a number of antiferromagnetic substances. It can be seen that the absorption falls off to a small residual value at temperatures below the Curie point. The drop in the absorption near the Curie point is especially sharp in the antiferromagnetic materials $Cr_2O_3$ and $MnF_2$ and is less sharp in the antiferromagnetic materials MnS, MnTe, and MnO. The authors of the paper [144] believe that this is explained by the effect of short-range order. It is not possible as yet to explain the nature of the small residual absorption below the Curie point; it may possibly be due to the presence of traces of ferromagnetic impurities. No absorption has been detected in the antiferromagnetic region in the compounds CoO, NiO, CuO, and $VO_2$.

Thus the experiments show that whereas there is resonance absorption in the paramagnetic region, in the antiferromagnetic region there is either no observable absorption or else there is a small residual absorption.

A theoretical explanation of the vanishing of the resonance absorption in antiferromagnetic substances has been given by Kittel [145]. He has shown that the vanishing of the absorption is due to the effects of magnetic anisotropy and exchange energy. Owing to the increase of the anisotropy and the exchange energy on cooling below the Curie point the true

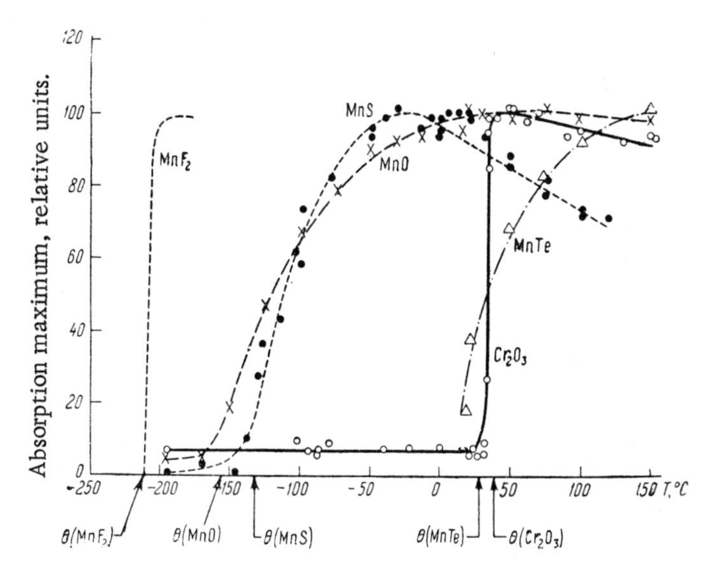


Fig. 84. Temperature dependence of the resonance absorption maximum in antiferromagnetic materials (the arrows show the location of the Curie points).

resonance frequency must be different from that in the paramagnetic region; it increases to values that are in the millimeter-wave range. Kittel has derived an equation for the motion of the magnetization of the sublattices by treating the exchange forces as an effective molecular field, and introducing in the same way as is done for ferromagnetic materials a term that takes account of the anisotropy of the orientation of the spins of the two sublattices relative to the axes of the cubic crystal lattice. It follows from the equation obtained by Kittel that

$$\frac{\omega_0}{\gamma} = H_0 \pm [H_a(H_a + 2H_e)]^{1/2}, \tag{109}$$

where $H_0$ is the constant external field, $H_a$ is the effective field of the anisotropy, $H_e$ is the effective field of the exchange forces, and $\gamma$ is the gyromagnetic ratio. If we substitute the values of these quantities into this expression, we find for the resonance frequency $\omega_0$ a value that is beyond the range of frequencies that can be obtained with present microwave apparatus. If, however, one makes experiments with antiferromagnetic materials that have small values of $H_e$ (that is, with materials that have low Curie points), then it is possible to observe antiferromagnetic resonance. Gorter and his co-workers [146] have observed antiferromagnetic resonance in the antiferromagnetic compound $CuCl_2 \cdot 2H_2O$ (Curie point near 0°K).

There are very few papers on the resonance absorption in antiferromagnetic substances. Nonetheless, the determination of the widths of absorption lines, the relaxation times, and other resonance characteristics is of considerable interest, because it would give valuable information about the antiferromagnetic state and about the mechanism of the antiferromagnetic transition.

We shall mention one further interesting possibility for using resonance methods to study antiferromagnetic materials. Poulis, Hardemann, and Bölger [131], in studying the nuclear resonance of the water of crystallization in the compound $CuCl_2 \cdot 2H_2O$, observed that the two sublattices magnetized in antiparallel directions have different effects on the resonance of the protons contained in the lattice of the antiferromagnetic substance. Thus proton resonance can serve as a method for studying the effective fields in the sublattices of antiferromagnetic substances.

We remark that at a temperature below the antiferromagnetic Curie point the dependence of the proton resonance on the frequency of the alternating field, for a constant external field directed along the axis a of the $CuCl_2 \cdot 2H_2O$ crystal, has two maxima. Above the transition point, on the other hand, there is only one maximum. This must be explained by the fact that to each proton that experiences, in addition to the action of the external constant field $H_0$, the action of a nearest-neighbor copper ion $Cu^{++}$, there corresponds another proton that is subject to the action of another $Cu^{++}$ ion whose magnetic moment has the opposite direction, i.e., which belongs to the other magnetic sublattice of the antiferromangetic material [147].

## § 6. Neutron-Diffraction Studies

The neutron-diffraction method has large possibilities for the study of the antiferromagnetic transition. This method makes it possible to study not only the magnetic structure of antiferromagnetic materials but also, which is especially important, to evaluate the temperature dependence of the spontaneous magnetization in the sublattices (which cannot be done from magnetic measurements). The method is based on the diffraction of neutrons by the magnetic ions of the antiferromagnetic substance. In the region above the Curie point there is a diffused paramagnetic scattering of the neutrons and the only maxima in the pattern are those that correspond to nuclear scattering. When the substance is cooled below the point of the antiferromagnetic transition additional maxima appear in the pattern, which correspond to scattering by the ordered structure of the magnetic moments of the ions. Figure 85 shows neutron-diffraction patterns for MnO taken at 80° and 293°K, from the data of [148] (the Curie point for MnO is 120°K).

The appearance of the additional maxima cannot be explained on the basis of the usual chemical elementary cell, because the position of the maxima corresponds to a lattice spacing which is about twice the crystallographic lattice constant. Such a spacing is characteristic of the positions of the magnetic ions in the lattice that have the same direction of their magnetic moments (between these ions there are ions with the opposite direction of their magnetic moments).

Shull and his co-workers [149] have determined the intensities of the magnetic diffraction maxima in MnO over the temperature range from 50 to 130°K; the sizes of the maxima are proportional to the spontaneous magnetization of the sublattices (Fig. 86). The curve in Fig. 86 reproduces the usual shape of curves of $\sigma_s(T)$; as can be seen from the Figure, the data from these measurements agree approximately with the data of the neutron-diffraction method.

Erickson and Shull [150] have determined by the neutron-diffraction method the temperature dependence of the spontaneous magnetization of the sublattices in the antiferromagnetic substances $MnF_2$, $FeF_2$, $CoF_2$, and $NiF_2$ (Fig. 87). In these researches [149] and [150], a residual magnetic coherent scattering was observed in the region above the Curie point. The authors explained this by the effect of short-range antiferromagnetic order in the position of the magnetic moments, which can exist in antiferromagnetic materials. The presence of a residual coherent scattering

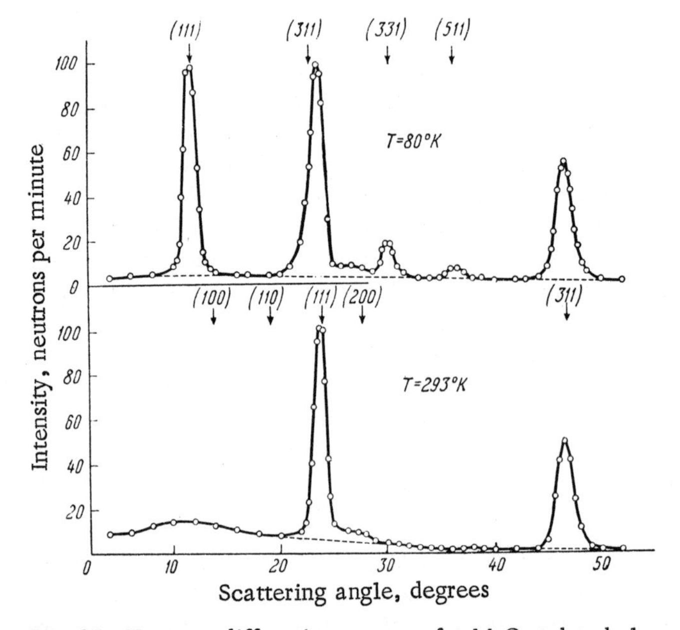


Fig. 85. Neutron-diffraction patterns for MnO, taken below and above the point of the antiferromagnetic transition.

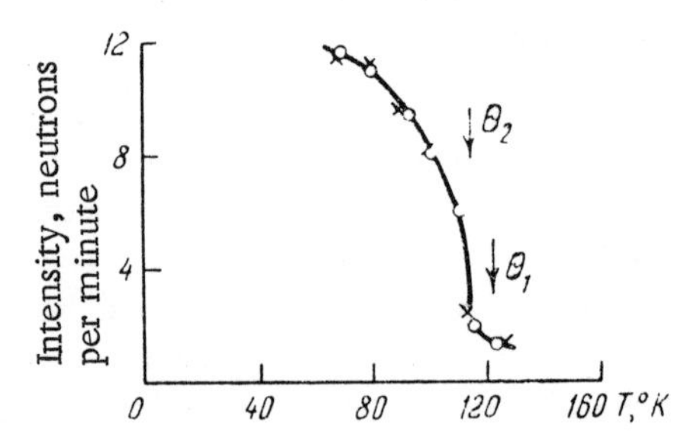


Fig. 86. Temperature dependence of the intensity of the magnetic diffraction maxima in the pattern for MnO; the arrows show the values of the Curie point from data on the magnetic susceptibility ($\theta_1$) and on the specific heat ($\theta_2$).

can, however, be due to a "smearing out" of the antiferromagnetic transition caused by fluctuations of the chemical composition in the antiferromagnetic specimen, as occurs in ferromagnetic materials.

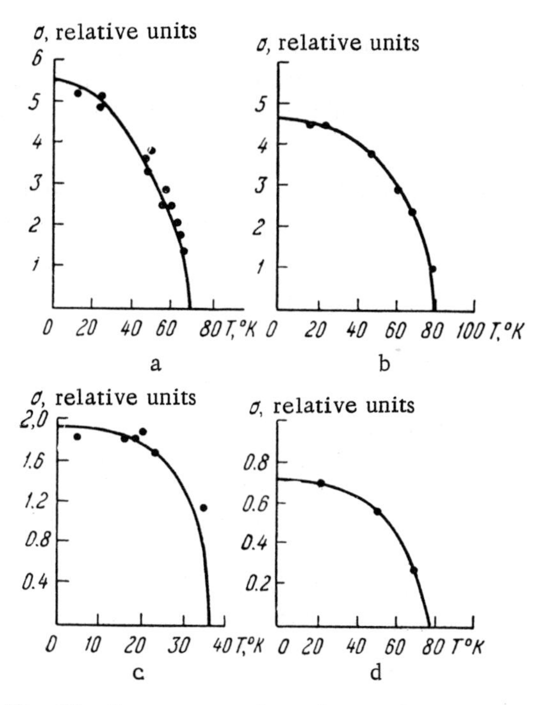


Fig. 87. Temperature dependence of the spontaneous magnetization in the sublatttices of antiferromagnetic materials. a) $MnF_2$; b) $FeF_2$; c) $CoF_2$; d) $NiF_2$.

## § 7. On the Thermodynamic Theory of Elastic and Volume Anomalies in Antiferromagnetic Materials

By using the thermodynamic theory of phase transitions of the second kind we can give a general description of the phenomena in antiferromagnetic materials that occur near the antiferromagnetic Curie point. For this case we can write the expansion of the thermodynamic potential, including effects of elastic stresses, in the following form*

$$\Phi = \Phi_0 + \frac{\alpha_1}{2}(\sigma_A^2 + \sigma_B^2) + \alpha_2\sigma_A\sigma_B + \frac{\beta}{4}(\sigma_A^4 + \sigma_B^4) + \\ + \frac{\gamma_1}{2}P(\sigma_A^2 + \sigma_B^2) + \gamma_2 P\sigma_A\sigma_B - \frac{\mu P^2}{2\rho} - H(\sigma_A + \sigma_B). \quad (110)$$

Here $\sigma_A$ and $\sigma_B$ are the specific magnetizations of the sublattices, P is the pressure, $\alpha_1$ and $\alpha_2$ are coefficients that depend on T and P, $\gamma_1$ and $\gamma_2$ are magnetostriction coefficients, $\mu$ is the elastic modulus, and $\rho$ is the density.

The expansion (110) does not include anisotropic terms, and therefore we shall be considering only the magnetostriction caused by the paraprocess.

From the conditions for equilibrium

$$\frac{\partial\Phi}{\partial\sigma_A} = 0, \quad \frac{\partial\Phi}{\partial\sigma_B} = 0, \quad \frac{\partial^2\Phi}{\partial\sigma_A^2} > 0, \quad \frac{\partial^2\Phi}{\partial\sigma_B^2} > 0$$

we get the system of equations:

$$\left.\begin{aligned} (\alpha_1 + \gamma_1 P)\sigma_A + (\alpha_2 + \gamma_2 P)\sigma_B + \beta\sigma_A^3 - H = 0, \\ (\alpha_1 + \gamma_1 P)\sigma_B + (\alpha_2 + \gamma_2 P)\sigma_A + \beta\sigma_B^3 - H = 0. \end{aligned}\right\} \quad (111)$$

Determination of the Spontaneous Magnetization, the Curie Point, and the Specific Heat. Since in antiferromagnetic materials $(\sigma_A)_s = (-\sigma_B)_s = \sigma_s$, we get from Eq. (111) for H = 0 a relation for the determination of the spontaneous magnetization of the sublattices:

$$\sigma_s^2 = -\frac{\alpha_1 - \alpha_2 + (\gamma_1 - \gamma_2)P}{\beta}. \quad (112)$$

It follows from Eq. (112) that

$$\alpha_1 - \alpha_2 + (\gamma_1 - \gamma_2)P < 0,$$

when $\sigma_s > 0$ $(T < \theta)$. For $T > \theta$

$$\alpha_1 - \alpha_2 + (\gamma_1 - \gamma_2)P > 0.$$

* The calculations presented here were made by the author together with R. Z. Levitin.

The antiferromagnetic Curie point ($\sigma_s = 0$) is determined from the condition

$$\alpha_1 - \alpha_2 + (\gamma_1 - \gamma_2) P = 0. \qquad (113)$$

If P = 0, Eq. (113) takes the form

$$\alpha_1 - \alpha_2 = 0. \qquad (114)$$

Near the Curie point we can expand $\alpha_1$-$\alpha_2$ in a power series in T- $\theta$. Confining ourselves to the first powers we can write:

$$\alpha_1 - \alpha_2 = \alpha_\theta' (T - \theta), \qquad (115)$$

where $\theta$ is the Curie point in the absence of the elastic stress P.

Substituting Eq. (115) in Eq. (113) and setting T = $\theta_p$, we have:

$$\alpha_\theta' (\theta_p - \theta) + (\gamma_1 - \gamma_2) P = 0. \qquad (116)$$

The difference $\theta_p$- $\theta$ is the amount of displacement of the Curie point of the antiferromagnetic substance under the influence of the stress P (or $\Delta$P):

$$\Delta\theta = \frac{\gamma_1 - \gamma_2}{\alpha_\theta'} \Delta P. \qquad (117)$$

For the calculation of $\Delta\theta$ we must have data on the magnetostriction of antiferromagnetic materials; these data are not available at the present time.

From Eq. (110) we can also calculate the discontinuity of the specific heat at the antiferromagnetic Curie point. For H = 0 and P = 0 the thermodynamic potential can be written in the following form by using the relations (112) and (115):

$$\Phi = \Phi_0 - \frac{(\alpha_1 - \alpha_2)^2}{2\beta} = \Phi_0 - \frac{\alpha_0'^2}{2\beta} (T - \theta)^2, \qquad (118)$$

where $\Phi_0 = \Phi_{T > \theta}$.

Differentiating $\Phi$ and $\Phi_0$ twice with respect to T, we have for the specific heat

$$C_{T<\theta} = -T \frac{\partial^2 \Phi_0}{\partial T^2} + T \frac{\alpha_\theta'^2}{\beta}, \qquad (119)$$

$$C_{T>\theta} = -T \frac{\partial^2 \Phi_0}{\partial T^2}. \qquad (120)$$

Subtracting the second equation from the first, we get for the discontinuity of the specific heat at the antiferromagnetic Curie point the result

$$\Delta C = \theta \frac{\alpha_0'^2}{\beta}. \qquad (121)$$

The Spontaneous Lattice Deformation and the Discontinuity of the Thermal Expansion. Differentiating Eq. (110) with respect to P, we get a relation for the volume deformation of the lattice ($\omega = \Delta v / v$)

$$\omega = -\rho \frac{\partial \Phi}{\partial P} = -\rho (\gamma_1 - \gamma_2) \sigma_s^2 + \mu P, \qquad (122)$$

where

$$-\rho (\gamma_1 - \gamma_2) \sigma_s^2 = \omega \qquad (123)$$

is the spontaneous volume deformation of the lattice of an antiferromagnetic substance caused by the vanishing of the spontaneous magnetization of the sublattices with approach to the Curie point, and $\mu P = \omega_0$ is the ordinary elastic (isotropic) deformation.

Differentiating with respect to T we find the expression for the linear thermal expansion coefficient:

$$\alpha_0 = -\frac{1}{3} \rho (\gamma_1 - \gamma_2) \frac{\partial \sigma_s^2}{\partial T} + \frac{1}{3} \frac{\partial \omega_0}{\partial T}.$$

Taking Eq. (112) into account, we have:

$$\alpha_{T<\theta} = \frac{1}{3} \rho (\gamma_1 - \gamma_2) \frac{\alpha_0'}{\beta} + \frac{1}{3} \frac{\partial \omega_0}{\partial T},$$

$$\alpha_{T>\theta} = \frac{1}{3} \frac{\partial \omega_0}{\partial T}.$$

Consequently we have for the discontinuity of the thermal expansion coefficient at the antiferromagnetic Curie point

$$\Delta \alpha = \frac{1}{3} \rho (\gamma_1 - \gamma_2) \frac{\alpha_0'}{\beta}. \qquad (124)$$

It can be seen from Eq. (124) that the sign of $\Delta\alpha$ is determined by the sign of the difference of the magnetostriction constants, $\gamma_1 - \gamma_2$.

It follows from Fig. 81 that for the antiferromagnetic substances CoO, MnO, NiO, and FeO the sign of the discontinuity of $\alpha$ at the Curie point is positive. This means that these substances have the negative sign for the volume magnetostriction [in Eq. (124) the quantity $\alpha'_\theta$ always has the negative sign and the quantity $\beta$ the positive sign].

The Discontinuity of the Compressibility. Differentiating Eq. (122) with respect to P, we find the expression for the compressibility

$$\varkappa = -\frac{\partial\omega}{\partial P} = +\rho(\gamma_1 - \gamma_2)\frac{\partial\sigma_s^2}{\partial P} - \mu.$$

Using Eq. (112), we have:

$$\varkappa_{T<\theta} = \rho(\gamma_1 - \gamma_2)^2\frac{1}{\beta} - \mu,$$

$$\varkappa_{T>\theta} = -\mu,$$

from which we get for the discontinuity of the compressibility at the Curie point the value

$$\Delta\varkappa = \rho\,\frac{(\gamma_1 - \gamma_2)^2}{\beta}. \tag{125}$$

It can be seen from Eq. (125) that the discontinuity of the compressibility should have the positive sign for all antiferromagnetic substances (independently of the sign of $\gamma_1 - \gamma_2$).

A Relation between the Discontinuities of the Specific Heat, the Compressibility, and the Thermal Expansion. From Eqs. (124) and (125) we get

$$\frac{(\Delta\alpha)^2}{\Delta\varkappa} = \frac{1}{9}\,\frac{\alpha'^2_\theta\rho}{\beta} \tag{126}$$

or, substituting Eqs. (117) and (124), we have

$$\Delta\varkappa = 3\,\frac{d\theta}{dP}\,\Delta\alpha, \tag{127}$$

where $d\theta/dP$ is the rate of displacement of the antiferromagnetic Curie point by pressure. Next, substituting Eqs. (121) and (126), we get the following relation:

$$\Delta C = \frac{9\theta (\Delta \alpha)^2}{\Delta \varkappa \rho} . \tag{128}$$

The formulas (126)-(128) establish a thermodynamic connection between the discontinuities $\Delta\alpha$, $\Delta\varkappa$, and $\Delta C$.

An experimental test of these relations cannot be obtained at the present time because of the absence of data on the quantities $\Delta\alpha$, $\Delta\varkappa$, $\Delta C$, and $d\theta/dP$ taken for the same specimen of an antiferromagnetic material. We can, however, give a quantitative estimate if we use the data that are available in the literature from measurements on CoO, for example. According to the data of [135], the discontinuity of the thermal expansion coefficient for CoO is $\Delta\alpha = 18 \cdot 10^{-6}$ deg$^{-1}$. Young's modulus changes from $E_{T<\theta} = 3.7 \cdot 10^{11}$ dyne . cm$^{-2}$ to $E_{T>\theta} = 10 \cdot 10^{11}$ dyne · cm$^{-2}$ and the shear modulus G changes from $1.35 \cdot 10^{11}$ dyne · cm$^{-2}$ to $3.8 \cdot 10^{11}$ dyne · cm$^{-2}$. To calculate the discontinuity $\Delta\varkappa$ we use the relation

$$\varkappa = \frac{9}{E} - \frac{3}{G} ,$$

from which we have $\Delta\varkappa = 0.07 \cdot 10^{-11}$ cm$^2$ · dyne$^{-1}$. Substituting these values of $\Delta\alpha$ and $\Delta\varkappa$ in Eq. (128), we get the value $\Delta C = 0.01$ cal · g$^{-1}$ · · deg$^{-1}$. The experimental value [133], however, is somewhat larger: $\Delta C \approx 0.07$ cal · g$^{-1}$ · deg$^{-1}$. From Eq. (127) we can determine the rate of displacement of the Curie point by pressure for CoO:

$$d\theta/dP = 0.02 \text{ deg} \cdot \text{cm}^2 \cdot \text{kg}^{-1}$$

The quantity is much larger than the value observed for ferromagnetic materials, $\sim 10^{-3}$ deg · cm$^2$ · kg$^{-1}$ (see Table 8). It is interesting to note that Grazhdankina [143] has recently obtained from experiments on the effective pressure on the Curie point of MnTe the value $2 \cdot 10^{-3}$ deg · cm$^2$· · kg$^{-1}$, which is of the same order of magnitude as the value for invar alloys. The anomalies $\Delta\alpha$ and $\Delta\varkappa$ at the Curie point are, however, of a different order of magnitude for MnTe from the values for CoO.

## § 8. On the Weak "Ferromagnetism" of Certain Antiferromagnetic Materials

Certain antiferromagnetic materials (hematite, $\alpha$-$Fe_2O_3$; the carbonates of cobalt and manganese, $CoCO_3$ and $MnCO_3$) show a weak uncompensated antiferromagnetism, i.e., there is a weak resultant spontaneous magnetization. Dzyaloshinskii [77] has analyzed the magnetic transitions in such substances from the thermodynamic point of view and has shown that their magnetic properties are a consequence of the magnetic symmetry which results from the position of the spins of the magnetic ions in such antiferromagnetic materials.

Let us take hematite as an example of this sort of magnetic transition. Hematite has been studied by many investigators, who have invariably detected a weak spontaneous magnetization in this substance. According to Néel [151] hematite is an antiferromagnetic substance; in his opinion the weak "ferromagnetism" owes its origin to the effects of lattice defects and impurities. The antiferromagnetic nature of hematite is confirmed by neutron-diffraction studies [149]; the diffraction patterns show, however, that at certain temperatures there is some change of the magnetic structure of hematite. Dzyaloshinskii has based his treatment on Landau's thermodynamic theory of phase transitions of the second kind and in writing down the expansion of the thermodynamic potential has taken into account not only the usual crystallographic symmetry but also the magnetic symmetry of the spins in the lattice which arises in the magnetic transition [77].

Magnetic symmetry is a special kind of symmetry; in determining it one uses not only the usual rotations, reflections, and translations, as in the case of crystallographic symmetry, but also combinations of these symmetry elements with a transformation that consists in changing the sign of the "time" or, what is the same thing, in changing the signs of all spins: $\boldsymbol{\mu} \to -\boldsymbol{\mu}$. Whereas the crystallographic symmetry is of the scalar type, i.e., it operates with a scalar function [for example, $\rho(x, y, z)$, the charge density in the lattice], the magnetic symmetry is a vector symmetry because it operates with the vector function $\boldsymbol{\mu}(x, y, z)$.

Figure 88 gives a simplified representation of the antiferromagnetic structure of hematite as it exists on the two sides of the low-temperature magnetic transition point. Dzyaloshinskii has shown that in the structure of Fig. 88b the magnetic symmetry permits the appearance of an uncompensated antiferromagnetism, since with the change of the magnetic symmetry there can be a "turning out" of the magnetic moments from their planes (Fig. 88b' shows the view from above) and as a result of this the geometrical sum of the magnetic moments is not zero. This causes the experimentally observed weak spontaneous magnetization in hematite. In the structure shown in Fig. 88a the resultant magnetic moment is zero in all possible positions of the magnetic moments that are allowed by the magnetic symmetry (Fig. 88 a'), and in this case there can be only compensated antiferromagnetism. On the basis of thermodynamic considerations Dzyaloshinskii has shown that the magnitude of the spontaneous magnetization in the structure shown in Fig. 88 b is small, because it is caused not by exchange forces but by a "relativistic" interaction (the magnetic forces of the lattice).

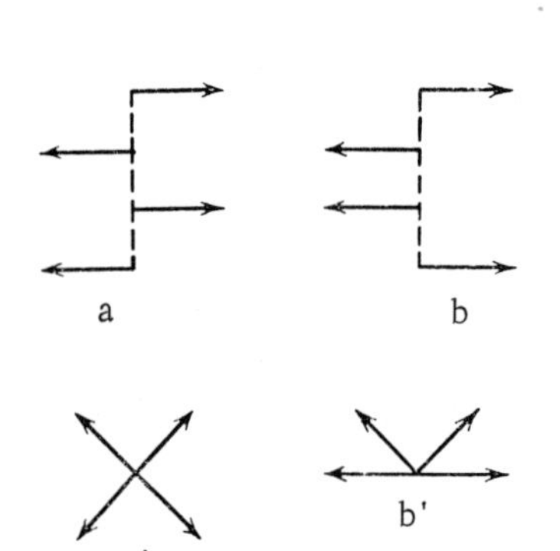


Fig. 88. For the explanation of the weak ferromagnetism in hematite.

In order of magnitude the energy of this interaction is a fraction $(v/c)^2 \sim \sim 10^{-2}$–$10^{-5}$ of the magnitude of the exchange interaction energy ($v$ is the speed of the electrons in the metal and $c$ is the speed of light), and this explains the small size of the spontaneous magnetization in hematite.

The theory of Dzyaloshinskii can be used to explain the nature of the weak spontaneous magnetization in the carbonates of manganese and cobalt which has been observed by Borovik-Romanov and Orlova [152]. They found that the magnetic properties of these substances at low temperatures can be regarded as a superposition of weak ferromagnetism and ordinary paramagnetism. For $H > 1000$ oe the magnetization curves of $MnCO_3$ (Fig. 89) and $CoCO_3$ obey the relation

$$M = M_s + \chi H, \quad (129$$

where $M_s$ is the spontaneous magnetization and $\chi$ is the susceptibility, which does not depend on the field. By extrapolating the straight lines to zero field one can determine the values of $M_s$. At 0°K the value of $M_s$ for $MnCO_3$ is 0.2% of the value that corresponds to complete ferromagnetic ordering, and for $CoCO_3$ it is 10% of this value. Figure 90 shows the temperature dependence of $M_s$ for $MnCO_3$.

The authors believe that antiferromagnetism appears at temperatures below $\theta = 31.5$°K for $MnCO_3$ and $\theta = 17.5$°K for $CoCO_3$. Unlike the usual situation in antiferromagnetic materials, however, the magnetic moments of the sublattices are not in exactly antiparallel directions, but are turned at a certain angle, so that as a result there is a nonvanishing spontaneous magnetization. In the case of hematite and of the carbonates of cobalt and manganese we thus encounter a curious phenomenon,

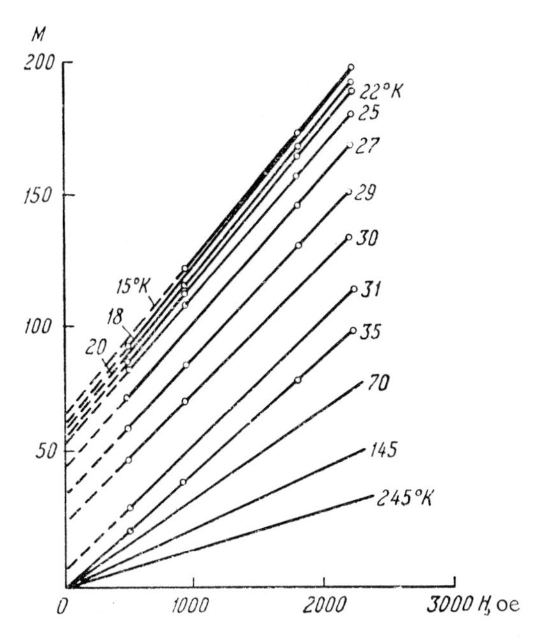


Fig. 89. Isotherms of the magnetization for $MnCO_3$.

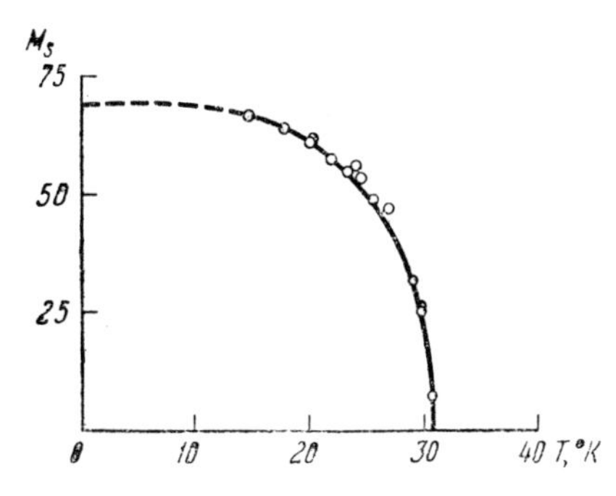


Fig. 90. Temperature dependence of the spontaneous magnetization for $MnCO_3$.

the appearance of a weak ferrimagnetic moment in pure antiferromagnetic materials which have only one type of magnetic ions.

An interesting conclusion from this theory is that in substances of the type of $\alpha$-$Fe_2CO_3$, $FeCO_3$, and others it is possible for there to exist a piezomagnetism (appearance of magnetization under the action of elastic deformations in the absence of an external magnetic field). Until very recently there have been assertions in the literature that it is entirely impossible for piezomagnetic substances to exist in nature. This conclusion was based on the fact that there are no terms in the thermodynamic potential of magnetic substances [Eq. (71) and (110)] that have a linear dependence on the magnetic field or on the magnetization. On the basis of an analysis of the magnetic symmetry of the substances $\alpha$-$Fe_2O_3$ and $FeCO_3$, Dzyaloshinskii [153] came to the conclusion that it is quite possible for there to be terms that are linear in the magnetizations in the thermodynamic potentials of these substances, that is, in other words, it is possible for piezomagnetism to occur in these substances (cf. also [154]). Borovik-Romanov has recently observed the phenomenon of piezomagnetism in fluorides of cobalt and manganese [see Zhur. Éksp. i Teor. Fiz. 36, 1954 (1959)].

Chapter V

# MAGNETIC TRANSITIONS IN FERRIMAGNETIC MATERIALS

Ferrimagnetic materials are substances in which the spontaneous magnetization of one sublattice considerably "outweighs" the magnetization of the second sublattice. Owing to this ferrimagnetic materials have a large resultant spontaneous magnetization: their properties recall those of ordinary ferromagnetic metals and alloys and therefore some such substances, for example ferrites, are used in technology as magnetic materials.

It would be more exact to call ferrimagnetic materials uncompensated antiferromagnetic materials [15], but this term has not received wide use in the literature. Uncompensated antiferromagnetism is usually observed in complex compounds in which sublattices can occur which are not equivalent magnetically. In the general case the lack of equivalence can consist in different values for the magnetic moments of the ions located at the sites of the two sublattices and also in there being different numbers of these ions in the two sublattices.

Ferrimagnetic materials include broad groups of oxides of the transition elements (both simple and complex oxides), which are called ferrites and manganites and which have the spinel structure, and also ferrites of the rare-earth elements and of yttrium with the structure of garnet. Ferrimagnetic properties are possessed by some compounds of transition metals with sulfur, tellurium, and selenium, for example:

$$Fe_{1-\delta}S\ (\delta \approx 0.12).\ \ Cr_{1-\delta}S\ (\delta \approx 0.16).\ \ CoS_2.\ \ CrTe$$

and by other sulfides, tellurides, and so on. Lotgering [155] has recently shown that there is a rather broad group of compounds with the spinel structure: $MeCr_2S_4$, sulfo-chromites; and $MeCo_2S_4$, sulfo-cobaltites (the symbol Me denotes a divalent metal). These compounds also possess uncompensated antiferromagnetism. Finally, certain alloys based on Mn and Cr which were earlier regarded as ferromagnetic materials are actually uncompensated antiferromagnetic materials (for example, $Mn_2Sb$ [156]).

The antiferromagnetic nature of ferrites and other ferrimagnetic materials is shown by neutron-diffraction experiments [157, 158], and also an analysis of the magnitude of their ionic magnetic moments [159].

In the present chapter we consider the temperature dependences of the magnetic and "nonmagnetic" properties of ferrimagnetic materials, which can be used as a basis for finding the features of the magnetic transitions in such materials.

## § 1. On the Theory of the Temperature Dependence of the Spontaneous Magnetization of Ferrites

Continuing the classical tradition in the theory of magnetism that was founded by Langevin and Weiss, Néel [159] gave the first explanation of the temperature dependence of the spontaneous magnetization of substances of the ferrite type. He extended the molecular-field theory of Weiss to a lattice consisting of magnetic ions of the same type but located at two types of sites, denoted by A and B.

Ferrites crystallize in the close-packed cubic lattice of the inverse spinel (Fig. 91). The elementary cell of this structure contains 32 oxygen ions, between which there are inserted 16 iron ions in octahedral positions (sites B) and 8 iron ions in tetrahedral positions (sites A). Furthermore at the sites B part of the iron ions can be in the trivalent state and part in the divalent state, whereas at the sites A the iron ions are only in the trivalent state.

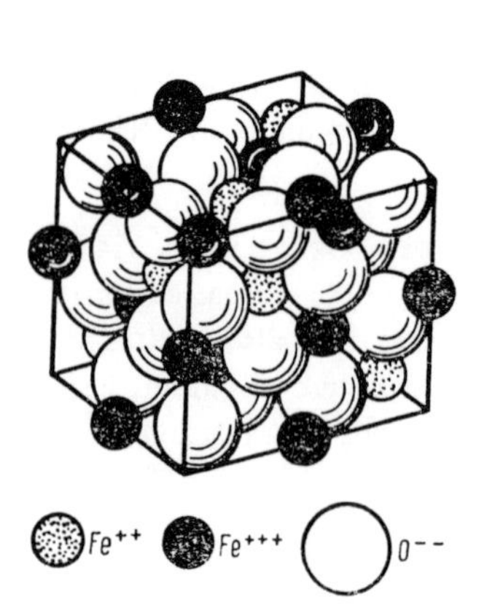


Fig. 91. The elementary cell of the inverse spinel $FeO \cdot Fe_2O_3$.

The sites A and B form the magnetic sublattices in ferrites. According to Néel the main part is played by the negative exchange interaction of sites A-B, while the interactions A-A and B-B are assumed to be small (they can be either positive or negative). The resultant spontaneous magnetization of a ferrite is the difference between the spontaneous magnetizations of the sublattices.

Néel made a theoretical study of the temperature dependence of the resultant spontaneous magnetization of the sublattices for various cases of distribution of ions over the sites A and B. To find the temperature dependence of the spontaneous magnetization of ferrimagnetic substances he used the Weiss equation of state in a modified form. For each sublattice one can write

$$\left.\begin{aligned} M_{sA} &= M_0 B_j\left[\frac{M_0 h_A}{kT}\right], \\ M_{sB} &= M_0 B_j\left[\frac{M_0 h_B}{kT}\right]. \end{aligned}\right\} \tag{130}$$

Here $M_{sA}$ and $M_{sB}$ are the spontaneous magnetizations of the sublattices per gram atom of material, $M_0$ is the saturation magnetization per gram atom at 0°K ($M_0 = Ngj\mu_B$ where N is Avogadro's number, $g$ is the Landé factor, $j$ is the quantum number, and $\mu_B$ is the Bohr magneton); $B_j$ is the Brillouin function, which has the form

$$B_j = \frac{j+\frac{1}{2}}{j} \operatorname{cth} \frac{\left(j+\frac{1}{2}\right)Ng\mu_B h}{kT} - \frac{\frac{1}{2}}{j} \operatorname{cth} \frac{Ng\mu_B h}{kT} -$$

(where $h$ can have the subscript A or B); $h_A$ is the molecular field acting on an ion that is at a site A; this field is equal to the sum of two molecular fields, one of which is the interaction of the adjacent ions of type A and is proportional to the magnetization $M_{sA}$ of the sublattice A and to the fractional number $\lambda$ of ions at site A, and the other is the interaction of ions of type B, proportional to $M_{sB}$ and to the fractional number $\mu$ of ions at site B. Thus one can write

$$h_A = n\,(\alpha\lambda M_{sA} - \mu M_{sB}), \tag{131}$$

where $n$ is a constant proportional to the sum of the exchange integrals of type A-B and $\alpha$ is the ratio of the energies of the exchange interactions A-A and A-B. For $h_B$ one can write the corresponding formula:

$$h_B = n\,(\beta\mu M_{sB} - \lambda M_{sA}), \tag{132}$$

where $\beta$ is the ratio of the energies of the exchange interactions B-B and A-B.

The resultant spontaneous magnetization per mole is given by

$$M_s = \mu M_{sB} - \lambda M_{sA}. \tag{133}$$

Equations (130) and (133) enable us to find the shape of the temperature dependence of the spontaneous magnetization of ferrites.

As Néel has shown, depending on the values of the quantities $\alpha$ and $\beta$ and of the ratio $\lambda/\mu$, one gets six possible types of curves for the temperature dependence of the spontaneous magnetization, which are shown schematically in Fig. 92.

The most interesting conclusion from the Néel theory is that under definite conditions there can be found in ferrites a so-called point of compensation $\theta_k$ (curves V and N in Fig. 92). The point $\theta_k$ is not a point of magnetic transition in the usual sense of this word. Its appearance is due to the fact that the spontaneous magnetizations of the sublattices A and B, which have different temperature dependences, completely compensate each other at $T = \theta_k$. When the temperature rises above $\theta_k$ the compensation is destroyed and there will again be a magnetization in the ferrite; it disappears only at the true Curie point $\theta$.

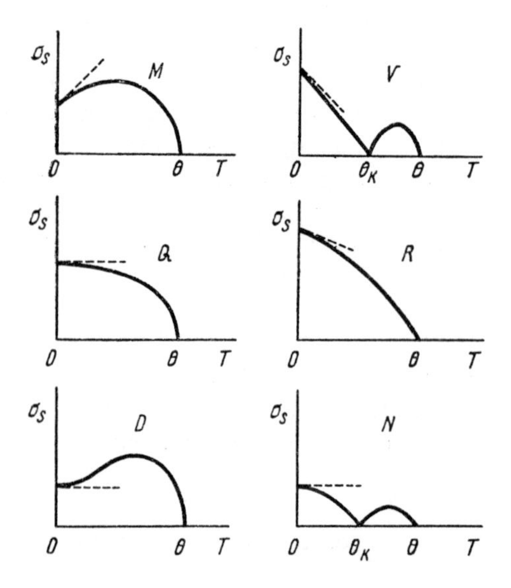


Fig. 92. Principal possible types of temperature dependence of the spontaneous magnetization according to Néel (schematic drawings). $\theta$ is the Curie point; $\theta_k$ is the point of compensation; M, Q, D, V, R, and N are different types of curves.

For the region above the Curie point one can expand the relation (130) in series and, including the effect of H, obtain the so-called Néel law for the paramagnetic susceptibility:

$$\frac{1}{\chi}=\frac{T}{C}+\frac{1}{\chi_0}-\frac{\delta}{T-\theta}, \tag{134}$$

where

$$\frac{1}{\chi_0}=n(2\lambda\mu-\lambda^2\alpha-\mu^2\beta),$$
$$\delta=n^2C\lambda\mu[\lambda(1+\alpha)-\mu(1+\beta)]^2,$$
$$\theta=nC\lambda\mu(2+\alpha+\beta)$$

(C is a constant).

Thus the Curie-Weiss law does not apply to ferrimagnetic materials; instead of a linear dependence of $1/\chi$ on T, which is observed in metals and alloys, for ferrimagnetic materials the dependence of $1/\chi$ on T has a hyperbolic shape. This conclusion from the theory is in qualitative agreement with experiment (see below).

In order to achieve quantitative agreement between theory and experiment Néel [32] introduced an additional parameter $\gamma$ to take account of a temperature dependence of the molecular field in the formulas (130). Such a "refinement" of the theory, however, as we have already pointed out, has no deep physical meaning, because the formula (134) is obtained from an extremely crude and approximate theory.

The next important step in the development of the theory of the temperature dependence of the spontaneous magnetization of ferrimagnetic materials was made by Vlasov and Ishmukhametov [160]. They constructed a quantitative theory (by the method of centers of gravity of energy levels) of the temperature dependence of the magnetization of ferrites. The formulas they obtained are of approximately the same form as those of the Néel theory:

$$\left.\begin{aligned}
J_1&=\operatorname{th}\left[\frac{\theta_1}{T}J_1+\left(\frac{N_2}{N_1}\right)^{1/2}\frac{\theta_{12}}{T}J_2\right],\\
J_2&=\operatorname{th}\left[\frac{\theta_2}{T}J_2+\left(\frac{N_1}{N_2}\right)^{1/2}\frac{\theta_{12}}{T}J_1\right],\\
J&=\frac{N_1J_1-N_2J_2}{N_1-N_2},
\end{aligned}\right\} \tag{135}$$

where $J_1$ and $J_2$ are the relative magnetizations of the sublattices, J is the resultant relative magnetization of the ferrimagnetic substance, $\theta_1$, $\theta_2$, and $\theta_{12}$ have the dimensions of temperature and are respectively proportional to the sums of the exchange integrals in the first and second sublattices and between the sublattices, $N_1$ is the number of spin magnetic moments in the first sublattice, and $N_2$ is the number of spin magnetic moments in the second sublattice. The authors show that near the Curie point, and also above it, the formulas (135) can be expanded in series (with effects of H included) for small values of $J_1$ and $J_2$. In this way they obtained the Néel law [a formula of the type of Eq. (134)] and the temperature dependence of the spontaneous magnetization in the immediate neighborhood of the Curie point, which has just the same form as for ordinary ferromagnetic materials

$$J=\frac{(N_1N_2)^{1/2}}{N_1-N_2}\frac{\theta^{1/2}\left[N_1^{1/2}(\theta-\theta_2)^{1/2}-N_2^{1/2}(\theta-\theta_1)^{1/2}\right](\theta-\theta')^{1/2}}{\theta^{1/2}\left[N_1(\theta-\theta_1)^2+N_2(\theta-\theta_2)^2\right]^{1/2}}\times\sqrt{3\left(1-\frac{T}{\theta}\right)}, \quad (136)$$

where $\theta$ is the Curie temperature and $\theta'$ is the second value of the root given by the expression

$$\theta=\frac{\theta_1-\theta_2}{2}\pm\sqrt{\frac{(\theta_1-\theta_2)^2}{2}\pm\theta_{12}^2}.$$

In determining the Curie point $\theta$ one takes the positive sign of the square root, and in determining $\theta'$ one takes the negative sign.

It must be noted that the theory of Vlasov and Ishmukhametov can not give quantitative agreement with experiment since it, like the Néel theory, is based on approximate assumptions about models. Nevertheless it has an advantage as compared with the Néel theory. The weak point of the Néel theory is that in it the dependence of the molecular field on the magnetization of the sublattices is essentially postulated, whereas in the quantum theory this dependence follows from the calculations. From this point of view the calculation of Vlasov and Ishmukhametov can serve as a quantum-mechanical foundation for the Néel theory.

As other papers [161, 162, 163] show, more exact quantum-mechanical calculations of the temperature dependence of the spontaneous magnetization of ferrites are possible only near the absolute zero of temperature. For the temperature dependence of the spontaneous magnetization one here obtains the same result ("the $T^{3/2}$ law") as for metals and alloys, and also a "$T^2$ law". The calculations show that if the absence of compensation of the magnetic sublattices is due to a difference of the moments one gets the "$T^2$ law" [161]. In the model of sublattices that are nonequivalent in the number of sites one gets the "$T^{3/2}$ law" [162, 163]. Experimentally, however, it is hard to distinguish between the two laws.

A further development of the theory of ferrites by the molecular-field method has been given in a paper by Jafet and Kittel [164]. In addition to the interaction A-B, these authors have taken into account the interactions A-A and B-B. They have shown that in cases in which the interaction within the sublattices is larger than the interaction between the sublattices the division into two sublattices may be unjustified; the lattice is then divided into a larger number of sublattices. Applying the same method they have shown that sublattice A in turn divides into sublattices A' and A", and the sublattice B into four sublattices: $B_1$, $B_2$, $B_3$, and $B_4$ (in the latter case one can assume approximately that there are two sublattices B' and B"). Jafet and Kittel have shown that as a result of the interaction of the sublattices A'-A", B'-B", and A-B the state that has the minimum energy of the magnetic sublattices at 0°K (with certain definite relations between the values of the exchange integrals) will be that for which the magnetization vectors of the sublattices A' and A" or B' and B" make a certain angle. In other words, even at 0°K it is possible that in a ferrite there is a distribution of the magnetizations of the sublattices that is different from the parallel position ("triangular" ordering). According to Jafet and Kittel the result is that in the curves of Fig. 92 there must be no "nonzero" slope of the tangents at the point 0°K (cf. curves M, V, R); at low temperatures all tangents must have "zero" slopes, which agrees with the Nernst theorem.

When the temperature is raised it is possible for there to be a change of the relative positions of the magnetization vectors, because of a change of the interaction. Figure 93, following Jafet and Kittel, shows the probable orientation of the magnetization in the sublattices A and B for various ratios between the interactions A-A, B-B, and A-B: a, with the interactions A-A and B-B small in comparison with A-B (the Néel case); b, with interaction A-A comparable with A-B and interaction B-B small in comparison with A-B; c, with interaction B-B comparable with A-B and interaction A-A small in comparison with A-B; d, interactions A-A and B-B large in comparison with A-B.

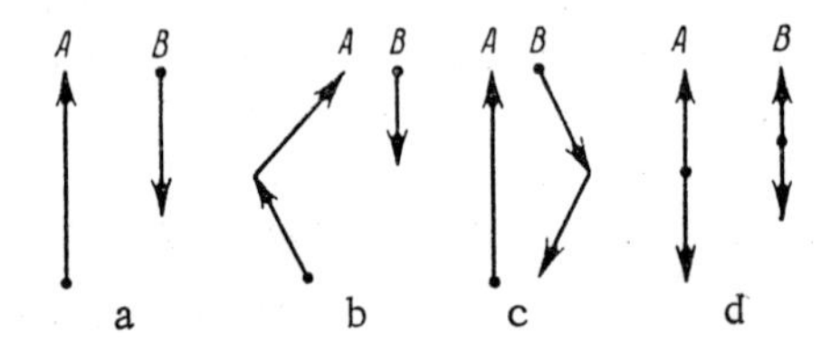


Fig. 93. Possible orientations of the magnetization vectors of the sublattices in uncompensated antiferromagnetic materials.

An analysis of the energies shows that the first three configurations are more stable than the fourth, which is almost nonexistent in practice. The authors have shown that a direct transition from configuration b (or c) to a chaotic distribution of the spins (paramagnetism) is impossible. At a certain temperature, lower than the true Curie point, the configuration b (or c) goes over into configuration a, and only after this, with further increase of the temperature, does it go into the paramagnetic state.

Thus according to Jafet and Kittel a single substance can have several points of magnetic transition (transitions from one type of magnetic ordering to another). It must be remarked however that up to the present no experimental confirmations of these conclusions of the theory have been found.

Both Néel and also Jafet and Kittel assumed that there are magnetic ions of a single type in the sublattices. If magnetic ions of different kinds interact in the sublattices, the theory is much more complicated. Niessen [165] has used the molecular-field method and developed the theory for mixed ferrites with two types of magnetic ions, with the ions of one type occupying both tetrahedral and octahedral sites, and the other kind of ions occupying only octahedral sites. According to Niessen, a change of temperature causes changes of the absolute magnitudes of the magnetic moments of all four sublattices, and also changes of the angles between the directions of the moments of the sublattices. The result is that there are various shapes of the temperature dependence of the spontaneous magnetization.

## § 2. Investigation of the Magnetization of Ferrites in the Neighborhood of the Curie Point

In this section we present the results of an experimental study [166] of the true magnetization curve and the temperature dependence of the spontaneous magnetization in ferrites near the Curie point. There are very few such data in the literature.* At the same time they are very necessary for the study of the nature of the ferromagnetic transition in ferrites, the details of which have not been completely cleared up. It is also interesting to ascertain to what extent the thermodynamic theory of the magnetic transition can be applied in the case of ferrites to describe the magnetization near the Curie point. It has been found in [166] that both in simple ferrites and in mixed ferrites the magnetization curves near

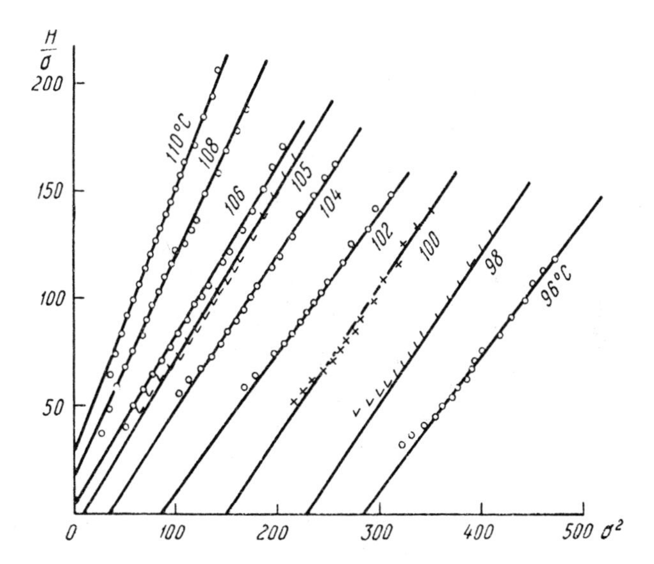


Fig. 94. Dependence of $H/\sigma$ on $\sigma^2$ for a ferrite of 28% MnO, 22.5% ZnO, 49.5% $Fe_2O_3$.

* The temperature dependence of the spontaneous magnetization of ferrites has mainly been studied at temperatures that are not very close to the Curie point [167, 168, 169].

the Curie point obey quite well the same thermodynamic equation which was used for the description of the para-process of metallic ferromagnetic substances (cf. Chapter III):

$$\alpha + \beta\sigma^2 = \frac{H}{\sigma},$$

where $\sigma$ is the resultant magnetization of the sublattices of the ferrites. For the case of ferrimagnetic materials the thermodynamic potential must be expanded in a series of even powers of this resultant magnetization, and therefore the final formulas are of the same form as in the case of ferromagnetic materials.

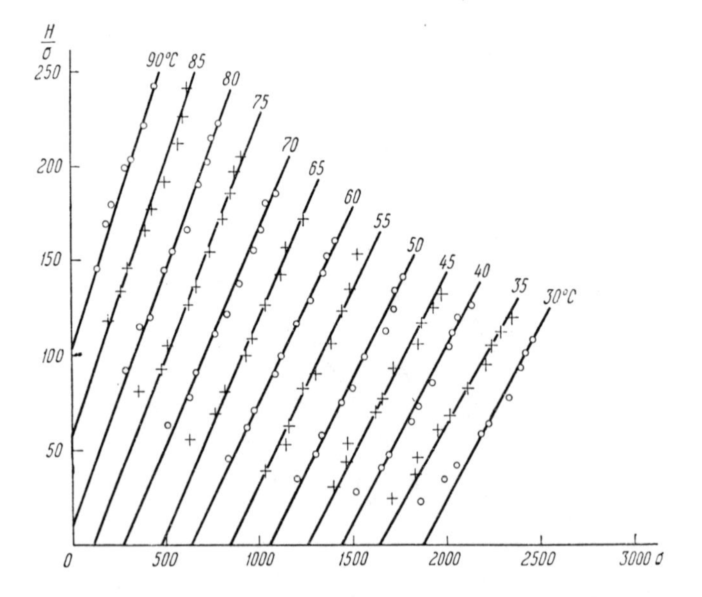


Fig. 95. Dependence of $H/\sigma$ on $\sigma^2$ for a ferrite 14.5% NiO, 36% ZnO, 49.5% $Fe_2O_3$.

As examples, we show in Figs. 94 and 95 curves of the dependence of $H/\sigma$ on $\sigma^2$ for ferrites Mn-Zn and Ni-Zn.

It is seen that in agreement with the equation just quoted the curves are straight lines. The deviations from the straight line shape in the region of weak fields, owing to effects of processes of technical magnetization, are extremely small. The equation is particularly well satisfied in the range of temperatures in the immediate neighborhood of the Curie point. Figures 96 and 97 show the temperature dependences of the thermodynamic coefficients $\alpha$ and $\beta$ determined graphically from the curves of the dependence of $H/\sigma$ on $\sigma^2$. The curves for pure nickel are drawn in these same diagrams for comparison. It can be seen that the nature of the temperature dependences of $\alpha$ and $\beta$ for ferrites are approximately the same as for metallic ferromagnetic materials.

One can carry out a comparison of the "intensities" or the para-process in ferrites near the Curie point by means of the coefficient K:

$$\sigma_i = \frac{\sigma_0}{(4b)^{1/3}} H^{1/3} = KH^{1/3}.$$

The larger the value of K, the steeper the curve of the para-process at the Curie point, and the greater the "intensity" of the para-process.

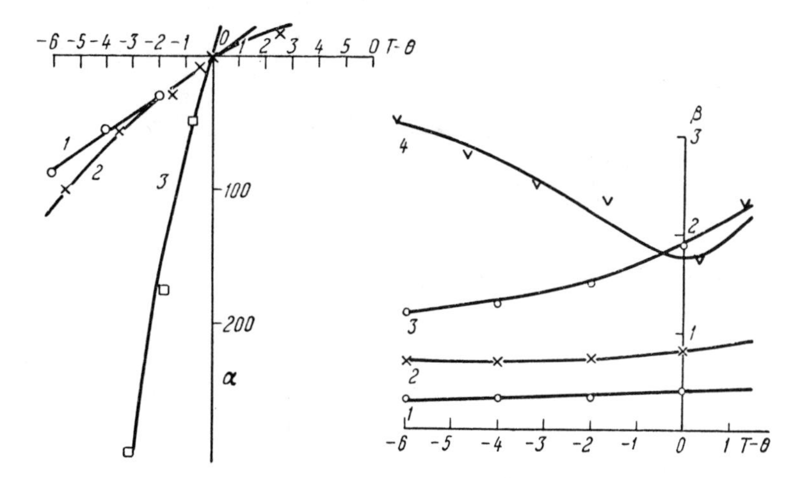


Fig. 96. Temperature dependence of the thermodynamic coefficient $\alpha$ for ferrites Mn-Zn and for nickel. 1) 23% MnO · 27.5% ZnO · 49.5% $Fe_2O_3$; 2) 28% MnO · 22.5 ZnO · · 49.5 $Fe_2O$; 3) Ni.

Fig. 97. Temperature dependence of the thermodynamic coefficient $\beta$. 1) 23% MnO · 27.5% ZnO · · 49.5 $Fe_2O_3$; 2) 28% MnO · 22.5% ZnO · 49.5% $Fe_2O_3$; 3) 35% MnO · · 15.5% ZnO · 49.5% $Fe_2O_3$; 4) Ni.

Investigations have shown that the coefficient K in ferrites is of the same order of magnitude as in metallic ferromagnetic materials. As was already pointed out in Chapter III, the "intensity" of the para-process is

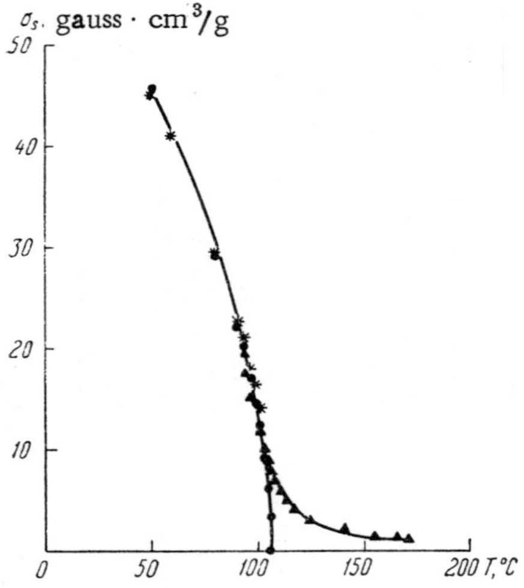

Fig. 98. Temperature dependence of the spontaneous magnetization in ferrite 28% MnO, 22.5% Zno, 49.5% $Fe_2O_3$, determined by different methods. ●) method of thermodynamic coefficients; ▲) method of lines of equal magnetization; * ) from magnetization isotherms.

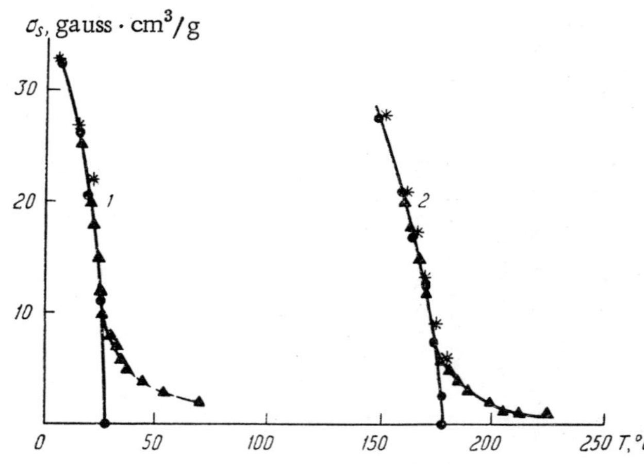


Fig. 99. Temperature dependence of the spontaneous magnetization, determined by various methods, for the ferrites: 23% MnO, 27.5% ZnO, 49.5% $Fe_2O_3$ (curve 1) and 35.5% MnO, 15.5% ZnO, 49% $Fe_2O_3$ (curve 2). ●) method of thermodynamic coefficients; ▲) method of lines of equal magnetization; * ) from magnetization isotherms.

determined by the magnitude of the absolute saturation $\sigma_0$, which is equal to the product of the magnitude of the atomic magnetic moment by the number of such moments.

Figures 98 and 99 show curves of the temperature dependence of the spontaneous magnetization determined by three methods: by the method of thermodynamic coefficients, by the method of "lines of equal magnetization," and by extrapolation of the magnetization isotherms. It can be seen that here, just as in alloys, there are "tails" of the spontaneous magnetization, which are probably due to fluctuations of the chemical composition through the volume of the ferrite specimen. Sücksmith and Clark [167] have found that in a simple ferrite ($MnO \cdot Fe_2O_3$) the "tail" is shorter than in a mixed ferrite ($0.5\ MgO \cdot 0.5\ ZnO \cdot Fe_2O_3$); it has been shown by Smith [72] that in a single crystal of magnetite there is almost no "tail."

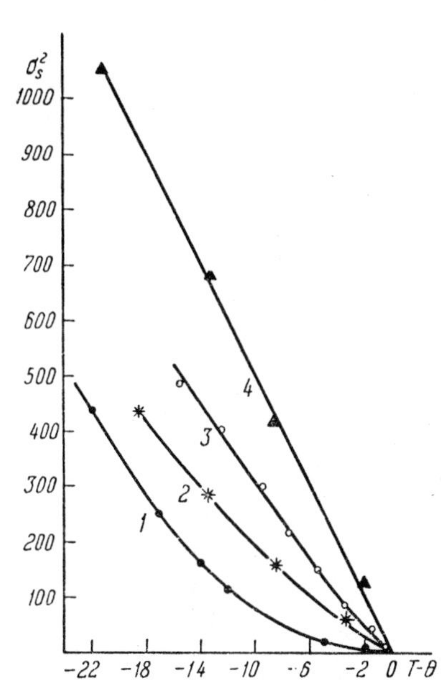


Fig. 100. Temperature dependence of $\sigma_s^2$ for ferrites Mn-Zn. 1) 40% MnO; 2) 35.5% MnO; 3) 28% MnO; 4) 23% MnO.

Figure 100 shows curves of the temperature dependence of $\sigma_s^2$ for ferrites Mn-Zn. It can be seen that the linear dependence of $\sigma_s^2$ that corresponds to the thermodynamic formula (9) and to Eq. (136), which follows from ideas about a model, is confirmed for ferrites Mn-Zn of two different compositions; for the other two compositions the linear dependence is not confirmed. There is a similar situation in alloys. For alloys the absence of agreement with the formulas is explained by the effects of inhomogeneity of concentration. Obviously this can also be the reason in ferrites.

K. B. Vlasov has made an attempt to estimate the value of the coefficient $\xi$ [i.e., the coefficient of the term $(1-T/\theta)$, cf. Eq. (63)] for

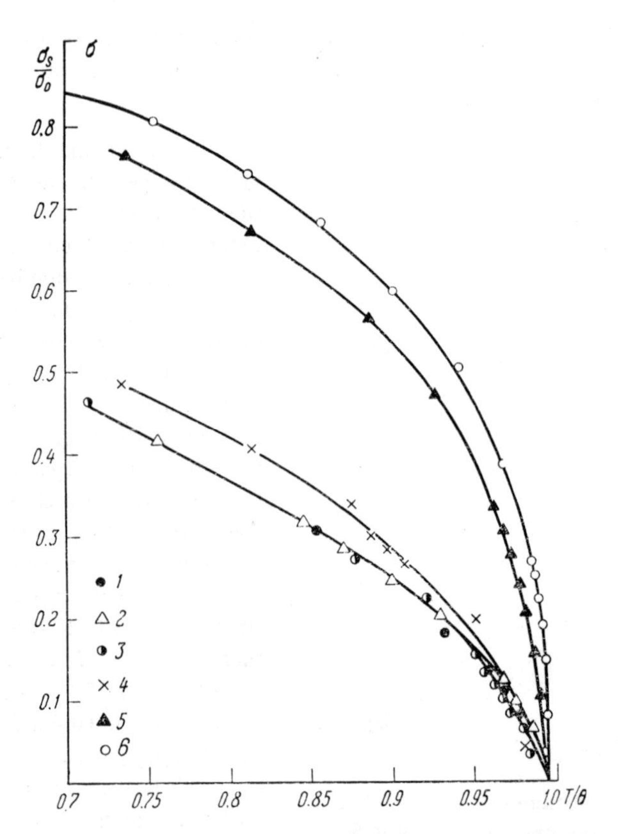


Fig. 101. Temperature dependence of the spontaneous magnetization for ferrites Mn-Zn. 1) 35.5% MnO; 2) 28% MnO; 3) 30% MnO; 4) 40% MnO; 5) 80% Ni, 20% Cu; 6) Ni.

ferrites by using the formula (136). He has found that whereas in metallic ferromagnetic substances the value of $\xi$ must larger than 3, for ferrites the calculation gives values of $\xi$ that are much smaller than 3. In fact, experiment shows that in ferrites Mn-Zn, for example, the values of $\xi$ lie in the range 0.1-0.7. This indicates that the magnetic transition in ferrites has a very diffuse character as compared with the transition in metallic ferromagnetic substances.

Figure 101 shows curves of the temperature dependence of the spontaneous magnetization for ferrites Mn-Zn, with ordinate $\sigma_s/\sigma_0$ and abscissa $T/\theta$. The figure also shows for comparison the curves for pure nickel and for an annealed alloy of 80% Ni and 20% Cu. It can be seen that the curve for the ferrites has a flatter shape. It must be noted that in ferrites the diffuseness of the transition is caused not only by the existence of fluctuations of the concentrations of the chemical components, but also by fluctuations of the sublattice structure [159, 160].

It follows from what has been said that the magnetic behavior of ferrites in the immediate neighborhood of the Curie point shows scarcely any difference from the behavior of metallic ferromagnetic substances.

## § 3. Study of the Temperature Dependence of the Magnetization of Ferrites That Have a Point of Compensation

Ferrites have an anomalous variation of the spontaneous magnetization with the temperature. The most interesting substances in this respect are ferrites that have points of compensation ($\theta_k$). Néel [159] has shown that a curve $\sigma_s(T)$ that has a point of compensation can be characteristic of ferrites in which the difference of the magnetization of the sublattices is close to 0 at 0°K

$$M_B - M_A \to 0.$$

If in the inverted ferrite $Fe^{3+}[Me^{2+}Fe^{3+}]O_4$ one partially replaces the iron ions in the sublattice B by a nonmagnetic ion or by a magnetic ion with a small magnetic moment, one can decrease the magnetization of this sublattice and thus produce a ferrite with only a small difference between the magnetizations of the sublattices. If the sublattices have different temperature dependences of their spontaneous magnetizations, then this is the type of ferrite for which curves that have points of compensation are most probable.

The first to succeed in preparing such ferrites was E. W. Gorter [170]. Figure 102 shows curves of the dependence of the magnetization $\sigma/\sigma_0$ on the ratio $T/\theta$ for ferrites $0.5Li \cdot (2.5 - a) Fe \cdot a CrO_4$, where a varies from 0 to 1.7. It can be seen that over a rather wide range of compositions (from a = 1 to a = 1.7) these ferrites have curves with points of compensation.

For clarity the values of the magnetization above the point of compensation $\theta_k$ are plotted in the negative direction in Fig. 102, so as to emphasize the "preponderance" of the sublattice with the opposite magnetization. Experimentally, however, in the presence of a field one measures a positive value of the magnetization.

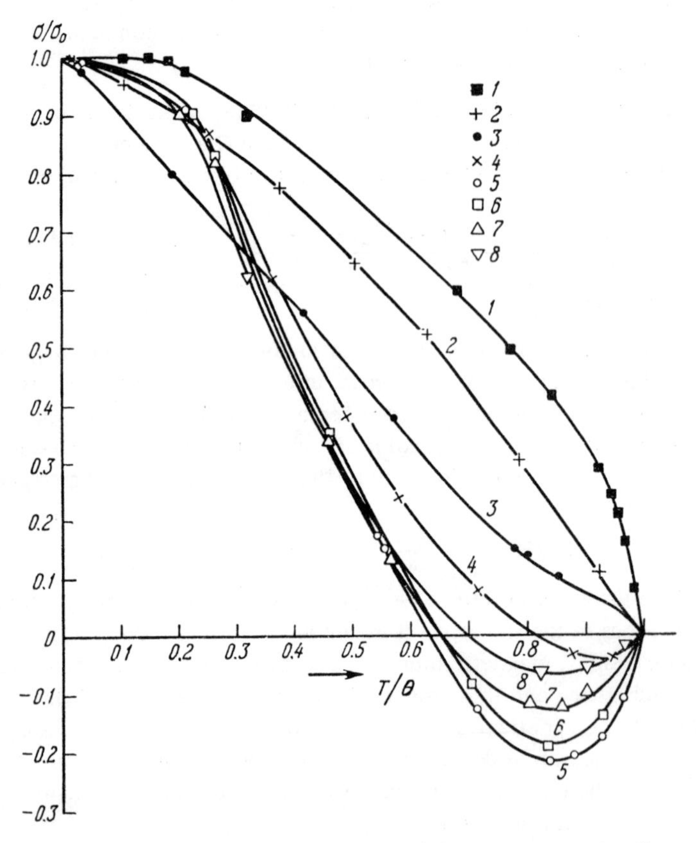


Fig. 102. Temperature dependence of the magnetization for ferrites 0.5Li · (2.5-a) Fe · a $CrO_4$. 1) a = 0; 2) a = 0.5; 3) a = = 0.75; 4) a = 1; 5) a = 1.25; 6) a = 1.5; 7) a = 1.6; 8) a = = 1.71.

To observe the reversed magnetization above the point $\Theta_k$ one can use the following elegant experiment described in [171].

A residual magnetization is produced in a specimen of ferrite which has a point of compensation; the specimen is suspended by a thread in a weak field and is then warmed up, for example in a water bath. After the passage through the point of compensation the residual magnetization reverses its direction, and as a result the specimen turns through 180°.

It must be stated that in other ferrites in which the condition $M_B - M_A \rightarrow 0$ was satisfied, the expected point of compensation has not been found. It is therefore interesting to study ferrites $0.5Li \cdot (2.5-a) Fe \cdot aCrO_4$, varying the composition and the heat treatment so as to find the conditions under which a point of compensation appears. Furthermore, since it is in these ferrites that the "antiferromagnetic" nature is most clearly manifested, it is also interesting to make a more detailed study of the peculiarities of the magnetization curves in the neighborhood of the compensation point and the Curie point.

In this research [172] lithium chromite ferrites were prepared with composition close to that for which, according to Gorter, points of compensation occur. Specimens of a high degree of purity were prepared from iron and chromium oxides and lithium carbonate by the usual powder technique. Measurements were made over the temperature range from 4°C to temperatures that exceeded the Curie temperature by 100 to 150°. The specimens were of large sizes, which made it possible to measure their magnetizations by the more precise differential ballistic method. The spontaneous magnetization was determined from the magnetization curves by extrapolating the curves of true magnetization to 0 field and by the method of thermodynamic coefficients (near the Curie point). The experiment showed that in all of the ferrites prepared there was incomplete compensation (at the point $\theta_k$ the magnetization $\sigma_s$ was of the order of 0.1-0.5 gauss · $cm^3/g$). Heat treatment did not lead to the disappearance of this magnetization (Fig. 103).

Let us examine in more detail the effects of heat treatment on the curves of the temperature dependence of the spontaneous magnetization. All of the specimens were subjected to quenching from 1000°C in air (treatment at 1000°C for 40 minutes), and then after measurement of their properties in the quenched state they were subjected to stepwise annealing under the following conditions: a) at 500°C for 5 hours, b) at 500°C for 24 hours, c) at 800°C for 8 hours.

All of these types of heat treatment caused sharp changes in the curve $\sigma_s(T)$. In all cases quenching led to suppression of the reverse magnetization (the magnetization in the range $\theta - \theta_k$) and to a decrease of $\theta$ as compared with its value for the specimen in the original state; on the other hand, the value of $\theta_k$ was increased, so that there was a decided decrease of the difference $\theta - \theta_k$.

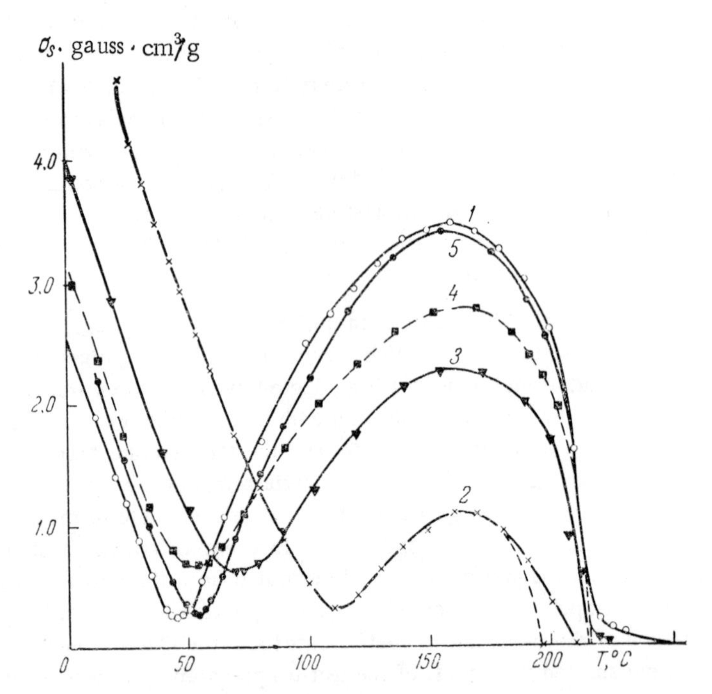


Fig. 103. Temperature dependence of the spontaneous magnetization in a ferrite $Li_2O \cdot 2.5\,Fe_2O_3 \cdot 2.5Cr_2O_3$ with various heat treatments. 1) original state; 2) quenched from 1000°C in air; 3) annealed for 5 hours at 500°C; 4) annealed for 24 hours at 500°C; 5) annealed for 8 hours at 800°C (the dashed curves in the neighborhood of the Curie point are calculated by the method of thermodynamic coefficients).

In the specimen with the smallest chromium content (a = 1.25) the decrease of the difference $\theta - \theta_k$ occurs because of a large displacement of the temperature $\theta_k$ (there is little change of $\theta$ as compared with the original state). In the specimen with the largest chromium content (a = = 1.6) the decrease of $\theta - \theta_k$ occurs exclusively because of a marked decrease of $\theta$, while the temperature $\theta_k$ is practically the same in the quenched and original states. In the specimen with intermediate chromium content (a = 1.5) the decrease of the temperature interval $\theta - \theta_k$ occurs both because of a change of $\theta$ and because of a change of $\theta_k$.

Measurements were also made on the absolute saturation at liquid-helium temperature. Quenching led to an increase of the atomic magnetic moment, in some cases by almost 50% (Table 11). According to the Néel theory this is in agreement with the fact that the reverse magnetization is decreased in the temperature interval $\theta - \theta_k$ and that the

TABLE 11. Compensation Temperatures, Curie Temperatures, and Mean Magnetic Moments of Lithium Chromite Ferrites

| Composition of ferrite | Compensation temperature, °C | Curie temperature, °C | Mean magnetic moment $\mu_B$ |
|---|---|---|---|
| $Li_2O \cdot 2.5Fe_2O_3 \cdot 2.5Cr_2O_3$ | 38[1]<br>45[2] | 214[1]<br>217[2] | 0.61[1]<br>0.68 (quenched state)[2]<br>0.74 (annealed state)[2]<br>0.91[3] |
| $Li_2O \cdot 2Fe_2O_3 \cdot 3Cr_2O_3$ | —16[1]<br>—6[2] | 119[1]<br>108[2] | |
| $Li_2O \cdot 1.8Fe_2O_3 \cdot 3.2Cr_2O_3$ | 11[1]<br>7[2] | 167[1]<br>147[2] | 0.42[1]<br>0.39 (quenched state)[2]<br>0.57 (annealed state)[2]<br>1.9[3] |
| $Li_2O \cdot 1.6Fe_2O_3 \cdot 3.4Cr_2O_3$ | 20[1]<br>15[2] | 155[1]<br>160[2] | 0.22[1]<br>0.24 (quenched state)[2]<br>0.31 (annealed state)[2]<br>3.7[3] |

[1]According to Gorter.
[2]According to Belov, Bol'shova, Elkina, and Zaitseva.
[3]According to the Néel theory.

length of the interval $\theta - \theta_k$ is diminished. It must be noted that the magnitude of the magnetization at the points $\theta_k$ remains practically unchanged after quenching.

For specimens annealed after quenching the curves of $\sigma_s(T)$ showed an approach to the curve for the material in its original state that was closer for higher annealing temperatures and for longer periods of annealing (cf. Fig. 103), i.e., as compared with quenching, annealing causes reverse changes in the curves of $\sigma_s(T)$. There is a small change in the amount of magnetization at the point $\theta_k$.

The very strong changes in the quantities $\theta$ and $\sigma_0$ that are produced in these ferrites by quenching and by annealing lead us to suppose that in these types of heat treatment there are redistributions of the cations (the degree of inversion of the ferrite is changed [173]). If the ferrite is at a high temperature the positions of the $Fe^{3+}$, $Cr^{3+}$, and $Li^{+}$ ions are close to each other energetically, and therefore their distribution among the sites of the A and B sublattices will be more or less random. This distribution can be fixed by sudden quenching. On the other hand, when there is slow cooling the $Fe^{3+}$, $Cr^{3+}$, and $Li^{+}$ ions are distributed in a more ordered way. Owing to this the values of $\theta$ and $\sigma_0$ will be different for specimens in the quenched and annealed states, and also the properties of the specimens will be different. Furthermore these properties can be changed more or less reversibly if we change the degree of annealing, as is shown by the measurements (cf. Fig. 103). This also leads to violation of the condition $M_B - M_A \rightarrow 0$, so that there is a change of the magnitude of the reversible magnetization in the range $\theta - \theta_k$, and the point $\theta_k$ is displaced.

Originally the hypothesis was put forward that the incomplete compensation is due to the presence of a magnetite impurity, which could be formed in the process of preparation of the ferrites. To test this hypothesis measurements were made on the magnetization of the specimen above the Curie point, up to the Curie point of magnetite (+ 578°C). These measurements, however, showed that there was no magnetite phase in the ferrites in question. The phenomenon of incomplete compensation can be explained by the effects of structural inhomogeneities of the ferrite specimen. In fact, in such a material there are regions with different compensation temperatures, though they differ only slightly from the main compensation temperature $\theta_k$; the result is that in the absence of a field there is always a magnetization that can be observed, which corresponds to neighboring regions whose compensation temperatures are displaced relative to $\theta_k$*.

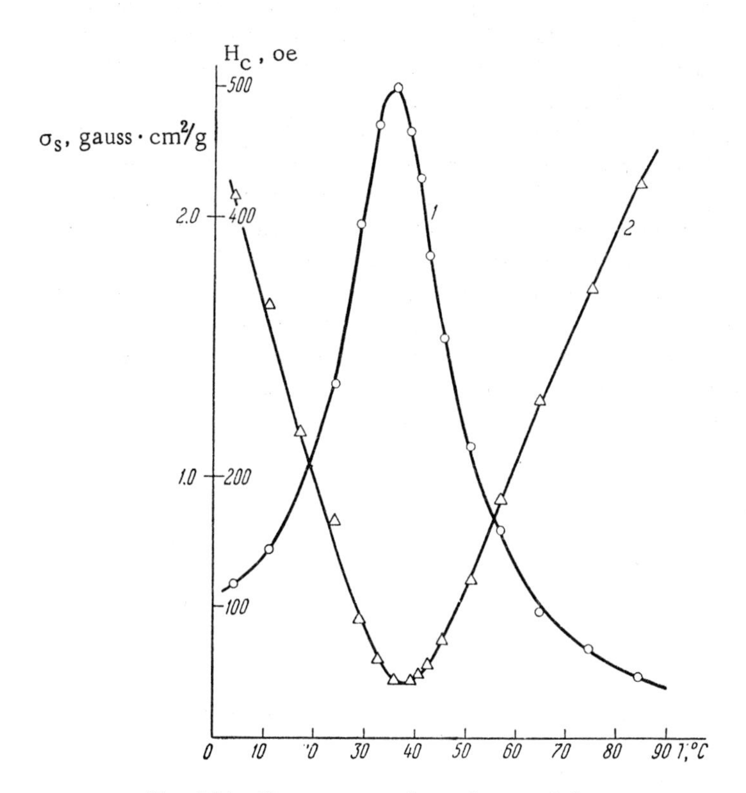


Fig. 104. Temperature dependence of the magnetic properties of the ferrite $Li_2O \cdot 2.5\,Fe_2O_3 \cdot 2.5\,Cr_2O_3$ near the point of compensation. 1) coercive force $H_c$; 2) spontaneous magnetization $\sigma_s$.

One further experimental result deserves attention: it was recently observed by Bol'sheva and Elkina [174] that in all the lithium chromite ferrites that were studied, both in the annealed and in the quenched

* It must be noted that Gorter [170] also did not succeed in getting complete compensation of the magnetization at the point $\theta_k$. This is brought out clearly if one redraws the curves of Fig. 102 in the manner of the curves of Fig. 103.

states, the coercive force increases in the neighborhood of the compensation point. Figure 104 shows an example of this in the results of measurement for the ferrite $Li_2O \cdot 2.5Fe_2O_3 \cdot 2.5Cr_2O_3$; it can be seen that at the point of compensation, where the spontaneous magnetization has a minimum, the coercive force shows a maximum. This phenomenon can evidently be explained in the following way. From the point of view of its magnetic structure a material that has an incomplete compensation at the point $\theta_k$ is a weak magnetic medium (approaching the antiferromagnetic state), in which there are "islands" of ferromagnetic "impurities," which correspond to regions with a compensation temperature difference from the compensation point $\theta_k$ of the main material. Here processes of magnetization and reversal of magnetization will occur with great difficulty, because they can be produced only by processes of rotation, i.e., the material will be magnetically hard in the neighborhood of the compensation point. This causes the increase of the coercive force in the neighborhood of the compensation point.

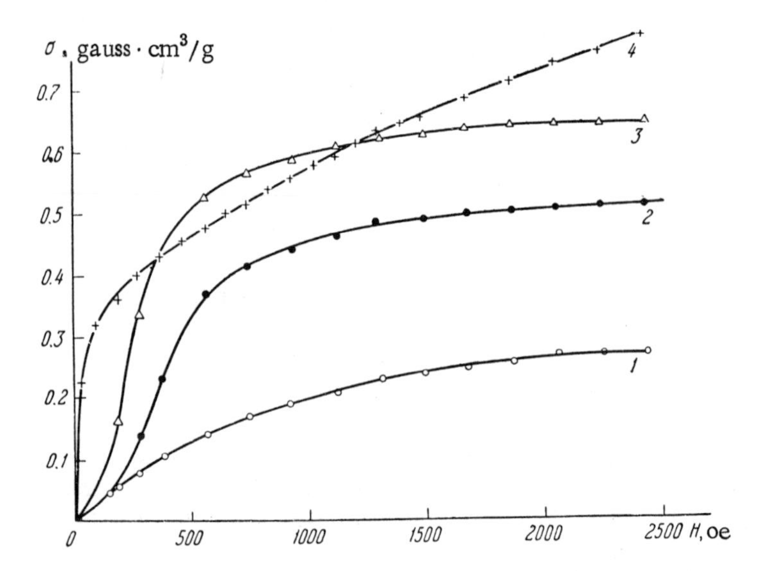


Fig. 105. Magnetization curves of the ferrite $Li_2O \cdot 2.5\ Fe_2O_3 \cdot 2.5Cr_2O_3$ in the neighborhood of the point of compensation. 1) $\theta_k = 44°C$; 2) $T = 36°C$; 3) $T = 55°C$; 4) $\theta = 217°C$.

For lithium chromite ferrites the experimental values of $\sigma_0$ and the values calculated from the cation redistribution according to the Néel theory (cf. Table 11) differ considerably from each other. This fact was pointed out by Gorter [170], who ascribes the difference to the fact that Néel neglects the interaction B-B in comparison with A-B. If, as in the treatment of Jafet and Kittel, we take into account the B-B (or the A-A) interaction, then the magnetic moments in the sublattices (in the ground state at 0°K) will be established at an angle with each other, which leads to a decrease of $\sigma_0$ for these ferrites.

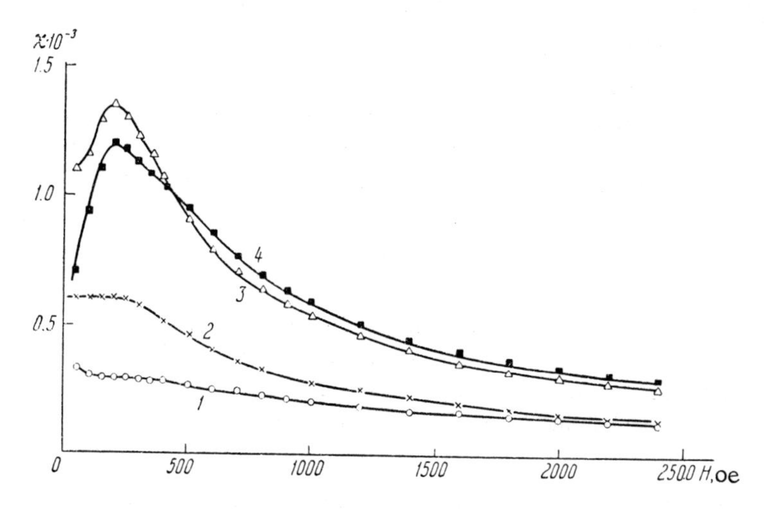


Fig. 106. Dependence of susceptibility on field at the point of compensation for the ferrite $Li_2O \cdot 2.5Fe_2O_3 \cdot 2.5Cr_2O_3$. 1) original state; 2) quenched in air from 1000°C; 3) annealed 5 hours at 500°C; 4) annealed 24 hours at 500°C.

It is interesting to compare the character of the magnetization curves in the neighborhood of the temperatures $\theta_k$ and $\theta$. Let us first examine the character of the magnetization in the neighborhood of the Curie point $\theta$. The behavior of ferrites that have a point of compensation, in comparison with that of ferrites that do not have such a point, is distinguished by the presence of a small para-process at the Curie point. As was noted in the preceding section, one can make a comparison of the size of the para-process for various materials from the slopes of the curves of $\sigma_\theta(H^{1/3})$ right at the Curie point (from the values of K). The measurements showed that the coefficient K for the first type of ferrites is much smaller than it is for the second. This is in agreement with the values of their atomic magnetic moments.

Figure 105 shows magnetization curves for the ferrite $Li_2O \cdot 2.5$ $Fe_2O_3 \cdot 2.5$ $Cr_2O_3$ taken at the compensation temperature $\theta_k = 44°C$, somewhat below and somewhat above the temperature $\theta_k$, and also for comparison a curve taken near the Curie point (217°C). It can be seen that the curve for the neighborhood of $\theta_k$ differs sharply from the curve for the neighborhood of $\theta$. In the neighborhood of $\theta_k$ the curves have a clearly marked "ferromagnetic" character (see the initial sections of the curves).

Figure 106 shows curves of the dependence of the susceptibility on the field (at the point $\theta_k$ these curves have the same general character as the curves of Stoletov). All of the facts that have been mentioned indicate that the point $\theta_k$ is not a point of magnetic transition in the usual sense of the word.

## § 4. Ferrite Garnets

The phenomenon of compensation of the magnetic moments of the sublattices at definite temperatures is particularly characteristic of ferrites with the garnet structure. Since there has so far been very little said in the literature describing the properties of this type of ferrimagnetic material, we will first give some general information about these materials.

The interest that is shown in the new class of magnetic materials, ferrite garnets, is due to the fact that they display properties which can be used in the technology of ultrahigh frequencies (175). The main advantage of certain ferrites with the garnet structure as compared with ferrites with the spinel structure is the extraordinarily narrow line width of the ferromagnetic resonance absorption. Crystals of certain ferrite garnets give an absorption line a few tenths of an oersted wide [176], whereas crystals of the spinel ferrites give resonance line widths of some tens of oersteds.

Besides the practical considerations, the study of ferrite garnets is of great interest for the theory of magnetism and crystal chemistry, because the ferrite garnets differ completely in their structure from the well-known spinel ferrites. Knowledge of the peculiarities of their ferromagnetic properties gives additional information about the nature of the spontaneous magnetization and its connection with the structure of a substance.

The properties of ferrite garnets were studied in 1956 by Bertaut and Forrat [177] and by Pauthenet [178], and independently of these authors by Geller and Gilleo [179] in 1957.

The ferrite garnets have the following composition:

$$3Me_2O_3 \cdot 5Fe_2O_3 \text{ ( or } Me_3Fe_2 \cdot Fe_3O_{12}),$$

where Me is a conventional notation for a rare-earth element (or for yttrium).

The preparation of this type of compound is carried out by the usual ceramic technology, with iron oxide and oxides of the rare-earth elements as the raw materials. The crystals are grown from the melt by slow cooling from 1325 to about 900°C, the solvent being lead oxide [180]. Sometimes one obtains instead of ferrite garnet, either in part or in whole, ferrites with the perovskite structure ($Me_2O_3 \cdot Fe_2O_3$), which are antiferromagnetic materials with a weak "parasitic" ferromagnetism, and also sometimes nonmagnetic oxides of the rare-earth elements. This leads to a "heterogeneous" structure of the specimens, which results in a marked distortion of the magnetic properties of the specimens. The crystal lattice of a ferrite garnite is a cubic lattice; it contains a very large number of ions, which are located in various crystallographic positions. Because of the complexity of the distribution of anions and cations it is hard to picture such a lattice. The cations $Fe^{3+}$ and $Me^{3+}$ occupy the gaps between the oxygen ions, and there can be 24 fourfold sites of the $\underline{d}$ type (tetrahedral spaces) 16 sixfold $\underline{a}$ sites (octahedral spaces) and 24 eightfold $\underline{c}$ sites. The $Fe^{3+}$ ions are located at the $\underline{d}$ and $\underline{a}$ sites and the $Me^{3+}$ ions at the $\underline{c}$ sites.

To explain the magnetic properties of ferrite garnets Néel [181] suggested that one should regard the crystal lattice of these substances as consisting of three sublattices (unlike the spinels, in which one usually considers two sublattices, there being more octahedral sites than tetrahedral sites). In two of the sublattices ($\underline{a}$ and $\underline{d}$) there are $Fe^{3+}$ ions, and there are more tetrahedral sites than octahedral. In the third sublattice (c) there are $Me^{3+}$ ions. According to Néel there is a strong negative interaction between the first two sublattices ($\underline{a}$ and $\underline{d}$), and owing to this there is a resultant magnetization (on account of the excess of tetrahedral magnetic moments). The $Me^{3+}$ ions are magnetized by the weak field of the sublattices $\underline{d}$ and $\underline{a}$; the magnetization in the sublattice $\underline{c}$ is directed opposite to the magnetization in the sublattice $\underline{d}$. The arrangement of the magnetizations of the sublattices can be thought of schematically in the following way (the length of the arrow represents the relative magnitude of the magnetic moment of the sublattice):

$$\underset{Me^{3+}}{\xrightarrow{\quad c \quad}} \; \underset{Fe^{3+}}{\xleftarrow{\;\; d \;\;}} \; \underset{Fe^{3+}}{\xrightarrow{\;\; a \;\;}} .$$

This scheme provides a possible way to calculate the magnetic moments of ferrite garnets at 0°K. For example, for the case of gadolinium garnet $3Gd_2O_3 \cdot 5Fe_2O_3$ we have (taking account of the fact that $Me_c = 7\,\mu_B$ and $Me_d = Me_a = 5\,\mu_B$):

$$6Me_c - (6Me_d - 4Me_a) = 6 \times 7\mu_B - (6 \times 5\mu_B - 4 \times 5\mu_B) = 32\mu_B$$

(experiment gives $30\,\mu_B$). In the case of yttrium garnet $3Y_2O_3 \cdot 5Fe_2O_3$, since Y is nonmagnetic, we have:

$$6Me_d - 4Me_a = 10\mu_B,$$

which also agrees with experiment. Thus an analysis of the values of the magnetic moments in ferrite garnets confirms the Néel "three-sublattice" hypothesis. Quite recently this hypothesis has been confirmed by experiments on the diffraction of neutrons [182].

In the case of ferrite garnets we encounter an uncompensated antiferromagnetism that arises because of lack of equivalence between three magnetic sublattices.

In the very recent literature [183] there are a rather large number of papers on the replacement of iron ions by other ions in stoichiometric ferrite garnets $3Me_2O_3 \cdot 5Fe_2O_3$. These papers pursue two purposes: a search for ferrite garnets with new magnetic properties, and the elucidation of the part played by the sublattices in ferrimagnetism (which is accomplished by changing the numbers of iron ions introduced into the sublattices of nonmagnetic or other magnetic ions).

If one introduces into the sublattice ions with a different electron configuration and atomic radius, then these ions will have a preference for the fourfold, sixfold, or eightfold sites, and consequently one can thus change the position of the atoms in the garnet structure and study the part they play in the process of magnetization. Experiments have been made on the replacement of iron in yttrium garnet by the ions $Al^{3+}$, $Ga^{3+}$, $Cr^{3+}$, $Sc^{3+}$, and $In^{3+}$. The introduction of $Al^{3+}$ and $Ga^{3+}$ decreases the magnetic moment of yttrium ferrite. This is explained by the fact that the

$Al^{3+}$ and $Ga^{3+}$ ions place themselves in tetrahedral sites (in the sublattice d), with the result that the resultant magnetic moment is decreased. The $Al^{3+}$ and $Ga^{3+}$ ions have smaller ionic radii than the $Fe^{3+}$ ions, and therefore these ions try to occupy tetrahedral positions. The ions $Sc^{3+}$ and $In^{3+}$, with larger radii than the $Fe^{3+}$ ions, preferentially occupy octahedral positions, and therefore the magnetic moment of the ferrite is increased. Although the $Cr^{3+}$ ion has a smaller radius than the $Fe^{3+}$ ion, nevertheless it can occupy octahedral positions, possibly because of its specific electronic configuration. This leads to a complex behavior of the magnetic moment in the ferrite.

Thus one can increase the moment of a ferrite garnet if one replaces an iron ion by some nonmagnetic ion in the sublattice a, and can decrease the magnetic moment by replacing an iron ion by a nonmagnetic ion in the sublattice d.

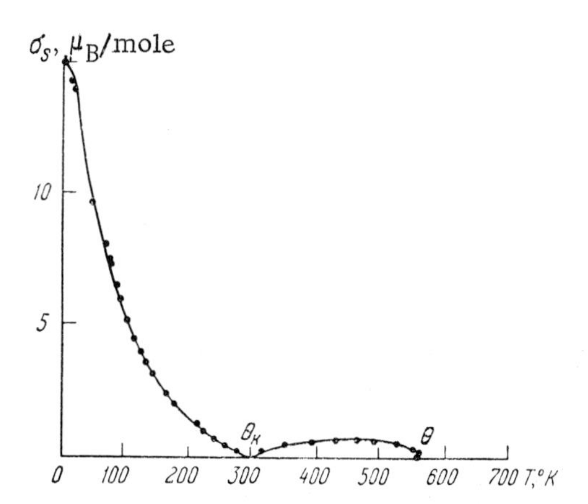


Fig. 107. Temperature dependence of the spontaneous magnetization for gadolinium ferrite garnet.

It must be noted that in all cases in which one replaces an iron ion by another ion the Curie temperature of the yttrium ferrite garnet is decreased. This is a consequence of the fact that the number of magnetic interactions $Fe^{3+}$-$O^{2-}$-$Fe^{3+}$ per magnetic ion is decreased.

Concerning the magnetic properties of ferrite garnets one has the following data available [178]. The temperature dependence of the spontaneous magnetization has been studied by the ponderomotive method in the range from 2.2 to 750°K for the ferrite garnets $3Me_2O_3 \cdot 5Fe_2O_3$ (where Me denotes the elements Gd, Tb, Dy, Ho, Er, Tu, Yb, Lu, Sm, Eu, and Y).

In the majority of ferrites the dependence of the magnetization on the field is described by the following equation:

$$\sigma_H = \sigma_S + \chi H,$$

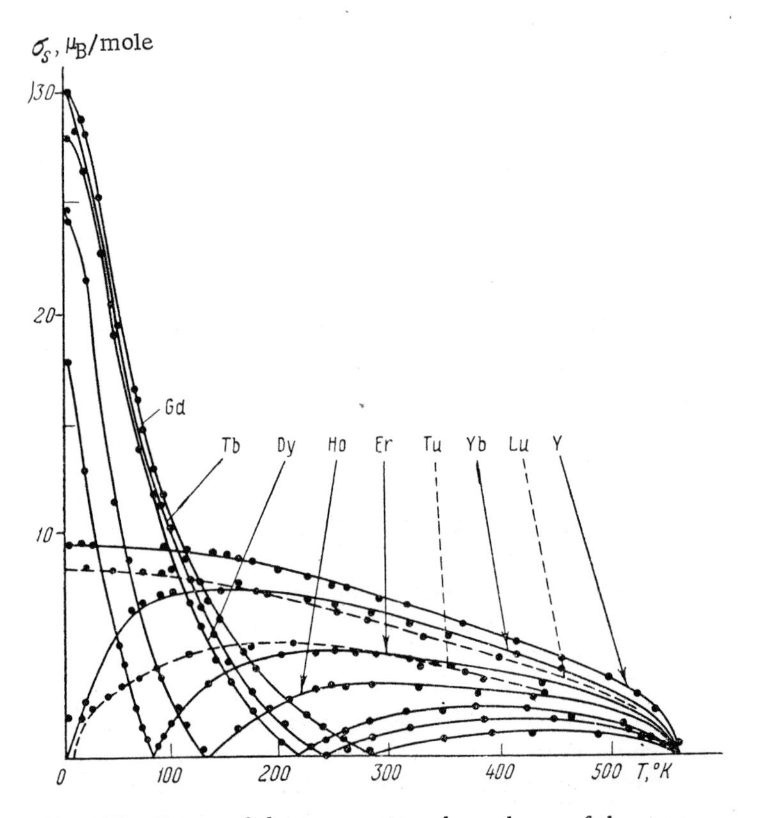


Fig. 108. Curves of the temperature dependence of the spontaneous magnetization for ferrite garnets of the rare-earth elements.

where $\chi$ is the susceptibility in strong fields, which does not depend on the field. The spontaneous magnetization $\sigma_s$ has been determined by extrapolation of the straight-line part of the curve in strong fields to zero field.

Figure 107 shows the curve of the temperature dependence of the spontaneous magnetization for gadolinium ferrite garnet. This ferrite has the point of compensation $\theta_k = 290°K$ (the Curie point is $\theta = 564°K$). The curve of $\sigma_s(T)$ obtained in the early work of Pauthenet for gadolinium ferrite showed two points of compensation; this is evidently explained by the fact that the ferrite being studied was a mixture of $3Cd_2O_5 \cdot 5Fe_2O_3$ and $Cd_2O_3 \cdot Fe_2O_3$.

Studies of other rare-earth ferrites of the garnet type have shown that for the majority of these substances (with the exception of the ferrite garnets of the rare-earth elements Y, Lu, Sm, and Eu) the curves of $\sigma_s(T)$ have points of compensation (Fig. 108). Table 12 gives the values of the compensation temperature $\theta_k$, the Curie point $\theta$, and the mean magnetic moment $\sigma_0$ (in Bohr magnetons per mole) for several rare-earth ferrite garnets.

TABLE 12. Compensation Temperatures $\theta_k$, Curie Points $\theta$, and Mean Magnetic Moments $\sigma_0$ (in $\mu_B$/mole) of Several Rare-Earth Ferrite Garnets

| Characteristic quantity | Me | | | | | | | |
|---|---|---|---|---|---|---|---|---|
| | Tb | Dy | Ho | Er | Tu | Yb | Lu | Y |
| $\theta_k$ °K | 246 | 220 | 136 | 84 | $4 < \theta_k < 20.4$ | | | |
| $\theta$°K | 568 | 560 | 567 | 556 | 549 | 548 | 549 | 560 |
| $\sigma_0$ | 28.3 | 29.6 | 24.7 | 18.7 | 2.0 | 0 ± 0.3 | 8.3 | 9.7 |

It is interesting that all of the ferrite garnets whose characteristics are given in Table 12 have approximately the same Curie temperature, whereas the compensation temperatures and mean magnetic moments at 0°K vary over rather wide ranges. The small difference in the values of the Curie point is explained by the fact that the $Me^{3+}$ ions play a small part in the phenomenon of ferromagnetism; the interaction of sublattice c with the sublattices d and a is very small, and therefore the value of the Curie point is mainly determined by the size of the interaction between the iron ions (which are present in about the same number in all of these ferrite garnets).

A. V. Pel'ko and the writer have observed an anomalous increase of $H_c$ (Fig. 109) in the neighborhood of the point $\theta_k$ (and of the point $\theta$) in gadolinium ferrite garnet. The cause of this anomaly is probably the same as in lithium-chromite ferrite.

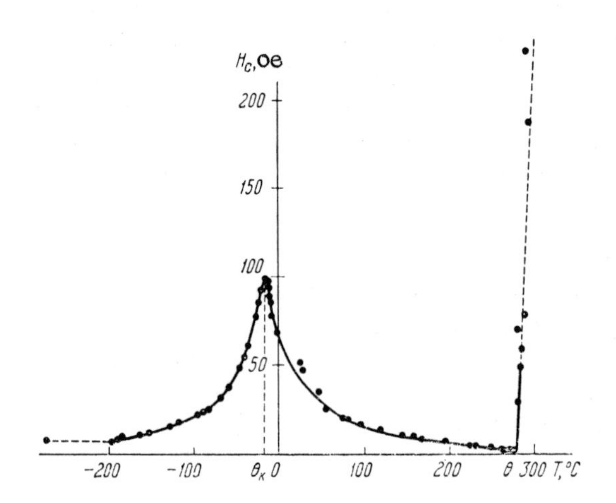


Fig. 109. Anomalous variation of the coercive force with the temperature near the compensation point $\theta_k$ and the Curie point $\theta$ in the ferrite garnet $3Gd_2O_3 \cdot$ $\cdot\, 4.8\, Fe_2O_3 \cdot 0.2Y_2O_3$.

In summarizing what has been said about the magnetic properties of ferrite garnets, we must point out that up to now we have only scanty data on the magnetic properties of these materials (in particular on the characteristics of the magnetic transitions). Up to the present little is known about the temperature dependence of the hysteresis, magnetostriction, electrical, and other characteristics of ferrite garnets. Information about these properties is necessary for an understanding of the nature of the spontaneous magnetization of ferrite garnets.

## § 5. A Study of Magnetic Transitions in Pyrrhotite

In recent times there has been much interest in the study of the magnetic, electric, and other properties of compounds of the transition elements with sulfur, tellurium, and selenium [184, 185, 186, 155]. This is due to the fact that many of these compounds belong the the class of substances in which antiferromagnetism or ferrimagnetism appears under certain conditions (ferrimagnetism appears in substances whose composition differs from the stoichiometric proportions).

The most detailed data on magnetic properties are available for the sulfides of iron.

Iron sulfide has a lattice of the Ni-As type. The cations are located in hexagonal layers perpendicular to the C axis. Therefore the lattice can be divided into two sublattices, A and B, formed by the odd and even layers. There is an antiferromagnetic interaction between cations in adjacent layers. In FeS of stoichiometric composition the sublattices are equivalent, and as a result this compound is antiferromagnetic. In the compound FeS the iron is divalent ($Fe^{2+}$) and the sulfur ions are also divalent ($S^{2-}$). When an excess of sulfur is added to FeS ($FeS_{1+\delta}$ or $Fe_{1-\delta}S$) a subtraction solid solution is formed, i.e., not all of the metal sites are filled; vacancies appear in the proportion $\delta$. Moreover, when there is an excess of sulfur there will inevitably be $Fe^{3+}$ ions (by the rule of conservation of valence). In fact, if we write the formula for ion sulfide (with an excess of sulfur) in the form $(Fe_{1-\delta}\square_{\delta})S$, where the sign $\square$ denotes the vacancies, it is seen that the $1-\delta$ ions $Fe^{2+}$ cannot compensate the charge of the $S^{2-}$ ions. Consequently for compensation of the valence there must appear a certain fraction of $Fe^{3+}$ ions and the number of $Fe^{2+}$ ions is decreased. A computation shows that when one takes into account the valences of the iron ions, one can write the formula for iron sulfide with an excess of sulfur in the form $\left(Fe^{2+}_{1-3\delta}Fe^{3+}_{2\delta}\square_{\delta}\right)S$.

Thus in the general case the iron sulfide lattice is very complicated, containing vacancies among the cation sites in which $Fe^{2+}$ and $Fe^{3+}$ ions are located. Depending on the way the ions are distributed in the A and B sites in the sublattices there will be antiferromagnetism or uncompensated antiferromagnetism. Since with changes of the temperature the ions will be displaced on the vacancies, or the vacancies will be displaced, we can expect a very complex temperature dependence of the magnetic properties in iron sulfide.

Figure 110 shows the temperature dependence $\chi(T)$ for $FeS_{1.11}$ (natural pyrrhotite) according to the data of [186]. Similar behavior of the curves was obtained in [155] for synthetic iron sulfide (with composition close to that of pyrrhotite). Beginning at room temperature and up to 200°C the susceptibility decreases somewhat, and at about 220°C it rises sharply, forming a so-called λ peak. With further increase of the temperature the magnetization falls along the usual curve (Weiss curve) to the Curie point. Up to 200°C there is a temperature hysteresis of the magnetic properties of pyrrhotite; the shape of the curve of susceptibility against temperature and the size of the λ peak depend on the rate of heating or cooling. It can be seen from Fig. 110 (curve 4) that with very rapid cooling the λ peak is absent and the curve starting from room temperature and going down to the Curie point has the ordinary "Weiss" character. The cause of the hysteresis is the redistribution of the vacancies

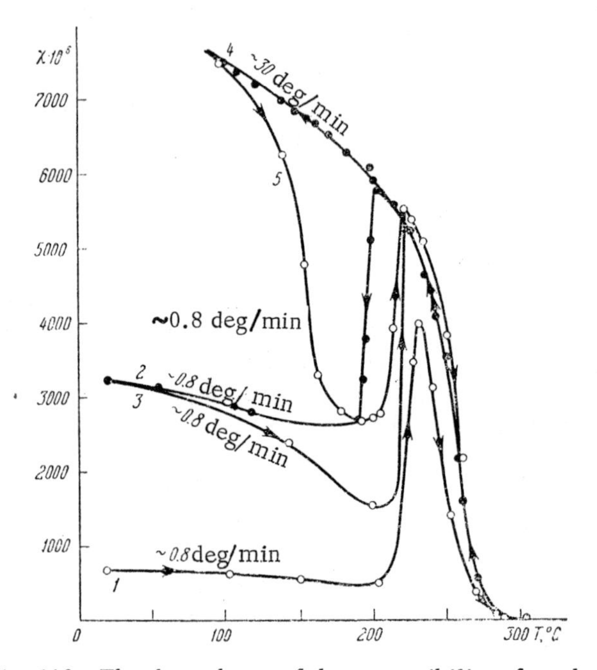


Fig. 110. The dependence of the susceptibility of pyrrhotite on the temperature in the range 20-300°C (H = 1340 oe). The arrows show the direction of change of temperature and the numbers 1 to 5 indicate a succession of heatings and coolings. The rate of change of the temperature is also indicated on the curves.

that occur in the pyrrhotite lattice below the temperature 220°C. This redistribution is of the nature of a diffusion process. A convincing proof of the diffusion nature of the redistribution is found in the curves shown in Fig. 111. Because there is a finite relaxation time necessary for a change in the positions of the vacancies in the passage from one distribution to another, in the case of rapid cooling the new distribution does not have time to be established completely and the old distribution remains partly "frozen in." This explains the absence of the λ peak for

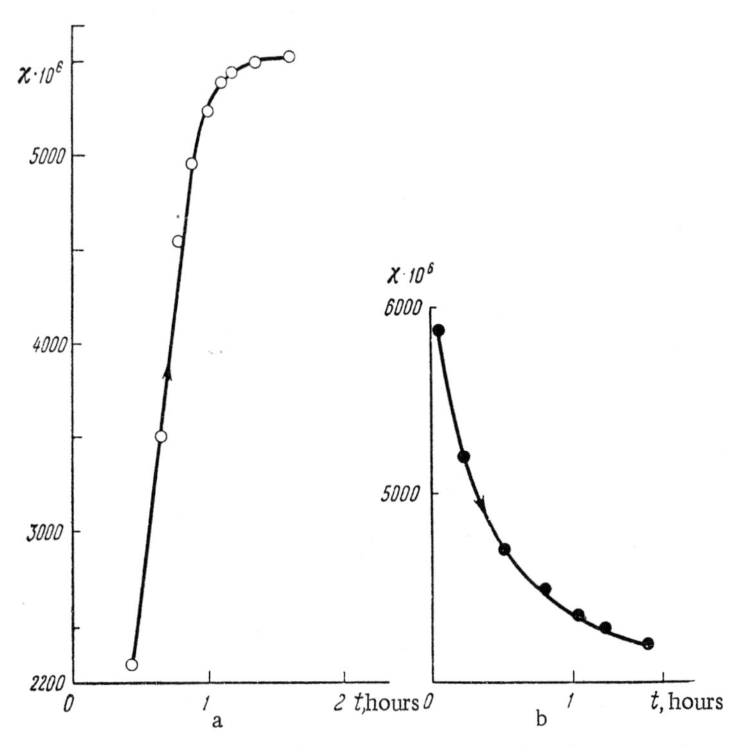


Fig. 111. Dependence of the susceptibility of pyrrhotite on the time during isothermal annealing in a field of 1340 oe. a) annealing at 221°C during the process of heating; b) annealing at 280°C during the process of cooling.

rapid cooling (cf. Fig. 110, curve 4). The degree of formation of the new distribution was so slight that the substance consisted practically entirely of the "frozen in" old distribution. In the next heating, carried out more slowly (cf. Fig. 110, curve 5), the diffusion process occurs more freely and the transition of the "frozen in" old distribution to a new distribution is accelerated.

The behavior of pyrrhotite above the Curie point has been studied in a paper by Benoit [187], who found a sharp drop of the magnetic susceptibility of pyrrhotite at 570°C. Néel [188] and other authors [189] have proposed a hypothesis according to which the ordered structure of the vacancies disappears at this temperature. Subsequent measurements showed, however, that the sharp change of the susceptibility at 570°C is evidently due to a side effect [186, 155].

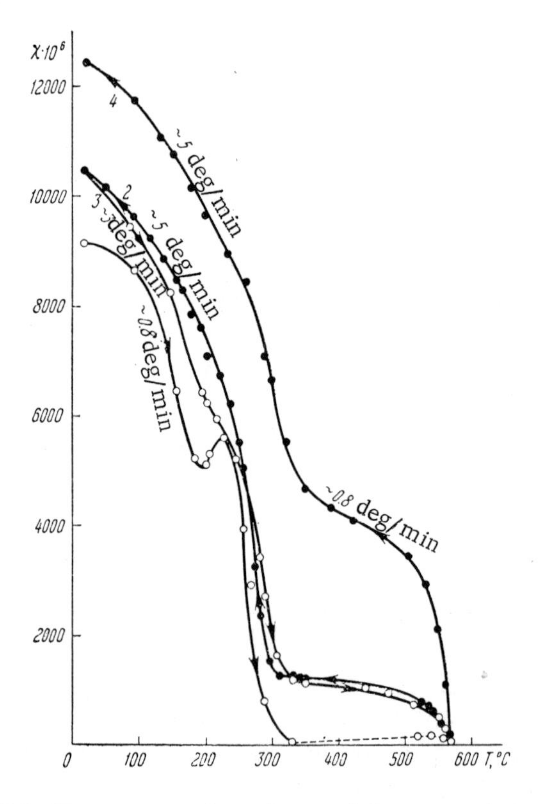


Fig. 112. Temperature dependence of the susceptibility of pyrrhotite when heated in air (H = 1340 oe). The arrows show the direction of change of temperature and the numbers 1 to 5 indicate the succession of heatings and coolings. The rates of change of temperature are also indicated on the curves.

During measurements of the temperature dependence of the magnetic properties of pyrrhotite in air, the pyrrhotite becomes oxidized, and this affects its magnetic behavior. During the original heating above 300°C (Fig. 112) the susceptibility rises in a number of cases, and then falls at 570°C. After annealing at about 600°C the curve found in the cooling process lies above the curve for the previous heating, and has the shape typical of the curve of a two-phase state with two Curie points. One gets the impression that at high temperatures the pyrrhotite becomes saturated with oxygen and forms a second ferromagnetic phase with a Curie point at 570°C. This phase could be $Fe_3O_4$, i.e., a magnetite phase, for which the Curie point is approximately that observed. The masking effect of a magnetite-like phase has been observed in FeTe, which belongs to the same group of compounds as FeS.

To test this hypothesis a study was made of the behavior of the curves of $\chi_2(T)$ in the temperature range 20-600°C with specimens heated and cooled in a bulb without exposure to air. In this case the curves corresponding to successive heatings and coolings do not have the characteristic point at 570°C.

Several attempts have been made to explain the temperature dependence of the magnetization in pyrrhotite [188, 189]. In this connection one usually considers four different temperatures: $\theta_N$, $\theta_V$, $\theta_C$, and $\theta_n$. It is assumed that when pyrrhotite is cooled an antiferromagnetic transition occurs at a temperature $\theta_N$ of 330-340°C, i.e., below the point $\theta_N$ an antiferromagnetic ordering of the spins occurs in the substance. With further cooling, at a temperature of approximately $\theta_V \approx 320$°C, there begins to be ordering of the vacancies. When the ordering has occurred to a certain degree the substance changes from the antiferromangetic state to a state of uncompensated antiferromagnetism with a Curie point $\theta_C \approx$ $\approx 300$°C. At a temperature $\theta_n \approx 220$°C, however, the ordering in the distribution of the vacancies begins to be destroyed, and there is a sharp decrease of the uncompensated antiferromagnetism.

It remains unclear why the vacancies lose their ordering at the point $\theta_n$. Lotgering [155] has put forward the hypothesis that the processes of ordering of the spins and ordering of the vacancies cannot occur independently of each other. The existence of a connection between these processes is theoretically possible in his opinion, if only for the reason that both in the process of ordering of the spins and also in the process of ordering of the vacancies there is a change of the lattice parameter, which must lead

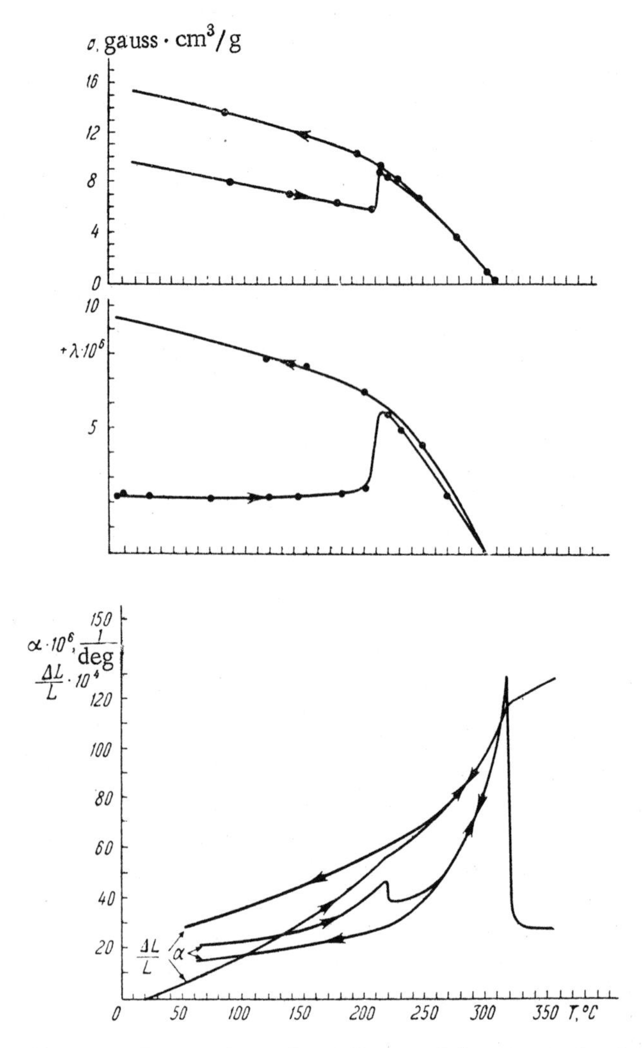


Fig. 113. Temperature dependences of the magnetization, the magnetostriction, and the thermal expansion coefficient for pyrrhotite.

to changes both in the exchange interaction and in the structure of the substance. The correctness of this explanation should be checked by measurements of the temperature dependence of the specific heat and the thermal expansion of pyrrhotite, which could provide a basis for estimating the magnitude of the ordering energies for the spins and the vacancies and the extent of their influence on each other at the points $\theta_N$, $\theta_V$, $\theta_c$, and $\theta_n$.

A study of the temperature dependences of the thermal expansion, the magnetostriction, and the magnetization of pyrrhotite was undertaken in [190]. Figure 113 shows curves of the temperature dependence of these properties (H = 1000 oe). The arrows indicate the processes of heating and cooling. The scale of temperature is the same for all of the curves, so that it is easy to compare the positions of the points $\theta_n$, $\theta_c$, $\theta_V$, and $\theta_N$.

The curve of the magnetostriction approximately reproduces the shape of the curve of $\sigma(T)$; the magnitude of the magnetostriction is small, and its occurrence is evidently mainly due to the effects of processes of technical magnetization. In the region of the Curie point one does not find any characteristic maximum (or minimum) on the curve, which would correspond to the volume magnetostriction of the paraprocess. It follows from this that the anomaly of the thermal expansion (caused by the spontaneous magnetization) at the Curie point must also be small. The observed sharp peak of the thermal expansion coefficient evidently corresponds entirely to the disordering of the vacancies at the point $\theta_V$; the small peak at ~ 220°C corresponds to the beginning of the ordering of the vacancies at the point $\theta_n$.

It must be noted that no peak on the curve of $\alpha$(t) corresponding to the point $\theta_N$ (~ 360°C) was found, although it is known that in antiferromagnetic substances the anomaly of the thermal expansion can reach large values.

From all of this we can draw the conclusion that the energy of disordering of the vacancies is much larger than the energy of disordering of the spins. Therefore in pyrrhotite there can be only an effect going in one direction: there is an effect of the energy of disordering of the vacancies on the magnetic state of pyrrhotite (and not conversely).

## § 6. The Role of Magnetic Anisotropy in Ferrites in the Neighborhood of the Curie Point

In Chapter IV we noted that in antiferromagnetic substances near the point of the antiferromagnetic transition magnetically anisotropic forces

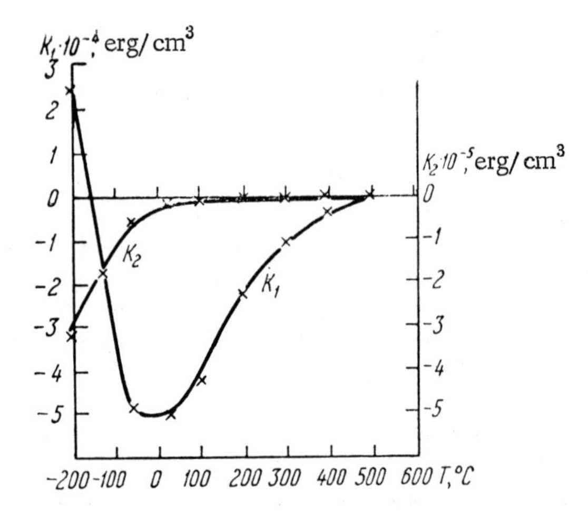


Fig. 114. Temperature dependence of the anisotropy constants $K_1$ and $K_2$ for a crystal of the ferrite $NiO \cdot Fe_2O_3$.

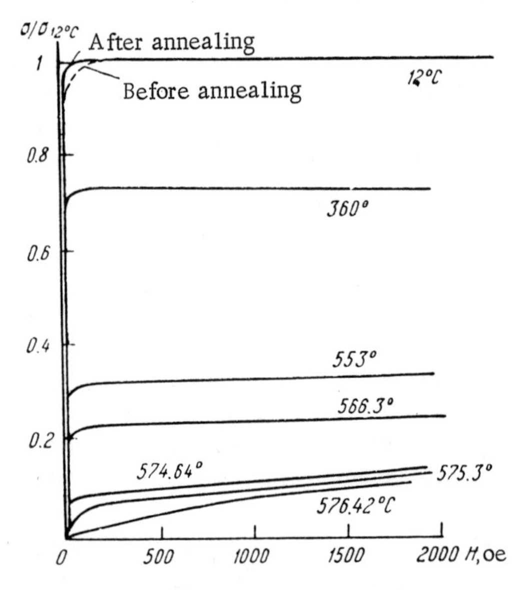


Fig. 115. Isotherms of the magnetization in a crystal of synthetic magnetite in the [111] direction.

can play a large role. Since ferrites are uncompensated antiferromagnetic substances, it is interesting to estimate the role of the magnetic anisotropy in ferrites near the Curie point. There are extremely few data in the literature on the temperature dependence of the magnetic-anisotropy constant of ferrites.

Figure 114 shows curves of the temperature dependence of the magnetic-anisotropy constants $K_1$ and $K_2$ obtained from measurements of the ferromagnetic resonance [191] in a single crystal of $NiO \cdot Fe_2O_3$. It is seen that far from the Curie point $K_1$ and $K_2$ have different signs. In the immediate neighborhood of the Curie point, however, the signs of the two constants are the same and they are both very small.

Okamura and his co-workers have used the method of ferromagnetic resonance to determine the temperature dependence of the constant $K_1$ in a single crystal of cobalt ferrite. For this ferrite $K_1$ decreases continuously with increase of the temperature right up to the Curie point. A similar result has recently been obtained by Dillon [176] for a crystal of yttrium ferrite garnet. Experiments made by Smith [72] to measure the temperature dependence of the magnetization curves in a crystal of synthetic magnetite $FeO \cdot Fe_2O_3$ have shown that near the Curie point along all the axes of the crystal the isotherms of the magnetization are identical with almost complete "damping" of the processes of displacement and rotation. The observed curvature of the isotherms of the magnetization near the Curie point is almost entirely due to the para-process (Fig. 115). In other words, in magnetite at the point of the ferromagnetic transition the energy of magnetic anisotropy does not play any important role.

It follows from what has been said that the behavior of ferrites as regards the temperature variation of the magnetic anisotropy near the Curie point evidently differs very little from the behavior of metallic ferromagnetic materials.

## § 7. The Temperature Dependence of Ferromagnetic Resonance in Ferrites

The results of resonance measurements in the ferrite $NiO \cdot Fe_2O_3$ [191], in both the single-crystal and the polycrystalline states, has shown that with increase of the temperature up to the Curie point the width of the resonance absorption line becomes smaller; this is in agreement with the temperature dependence of the anisotropy constants $K_1$ and $K_2$ in these ferrites. The g factor remains practically unchanged as the temperature is raised (the measurements were made in the centimeter wavelength range).

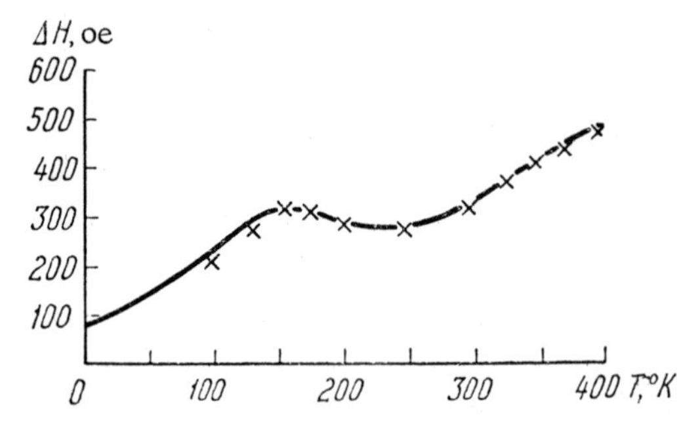


Fig. 116. Temperature dependence of the width of the resonance absorption line in a crystal of $0.75NiO \cdot 0.25FeO \cdot F_2O_3$ in the [111] direction.

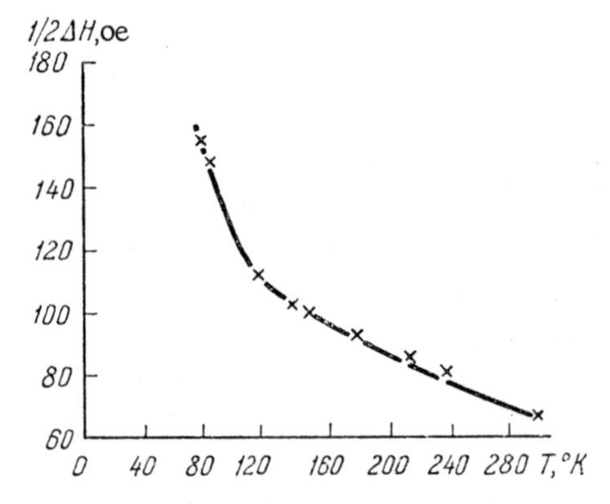


Fig. 117. Temperature dependence of the half-width of the resonance line in a crystal of $0.98\,Mn \cdot 1.86\,FeO_4$.

In [193] the temperature dependence of the width of the absorption line* in a crystal of the ferrite $0.75NiO \cdot 0.25FeO \cdot Fe_2O_3$ was measured

* The term "half-width of the line" is sometimes used in the literature.

at the frequency 24,000 Mc in the [111] direction. It was found that the widths of the absorption lines increase as the temperature is raised (Fig. 116). The increase of the line width with the temperature is ascribed by the authors to eddy current losses, since the specific resistance of this ferrite decreases rapidly as the temperature is raised. The fact that the increase of the line width is slower in the temperature range 150-200°K (Fig. 116) is ascribed to the relaxation time for the establishment of short-range order in the positions of the divalent and trivalent iron ions (electronic ordering, for further details see Section 9 of this Chapter). The existence of such a transition in these ferrites is confirmed by the data from measurements of the elastic constants.

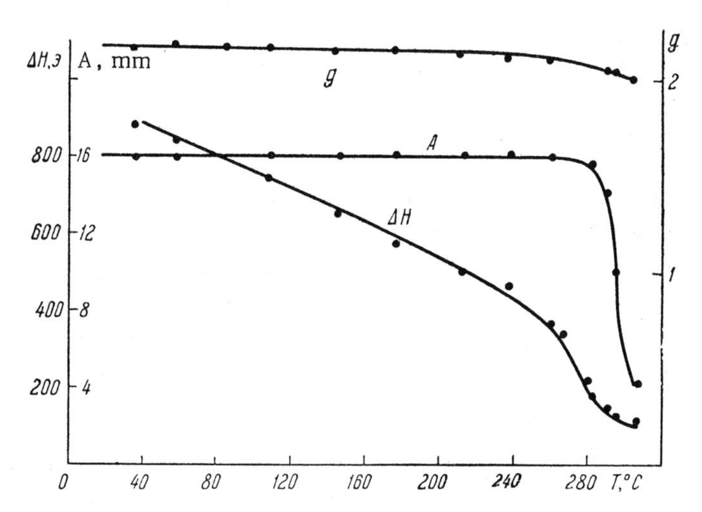


Fig. 118. Temperature dependences of the width ΔH of the resonance absorption line, the g factor, and the amplitude A of the resonance maximum for polycrystalline yttrium ferrite garnet $3Y_2O_3 \cdot 5Fe_2O_3$.

In [194] a study was made of the ferromagnetic resonance in a crystal of $0.98\,Mn \cdot 1.86\,FeO_4$ in the temperature range from 80 to 300°K. Figure 117 shows the results of measurements on the temperature dependence of the half-width of the line. It is seen that for this ferrite the width of the line decreases as the temperature is raised. An analogous result has been obtained for Mn-Zn ferrites [195] at frequencies 24,000, 9100, 5600, 2800 Mc.

In a ferrite which has a low electric resistance (which is due to the presence of divalent Fe ions or trivalent and tetravalent Mn ions), on the other hand, the width of the resonance line increases with the temperature, which is in agreement with [193, 196].

It is very interesting to study ferromagnetic resonance in the new ferrimagnetic materials, rare-earth ferrite garnets and yttrium ferrite garnet.

Dillon [176] has made measurements of the temperature dependence of the width of the resonance line with a single crystal of yttrium garnet at frequency 9300 Mc in the temperature range from 285 to 540°K. At room temperature the observations showed a very narrow line along the [100] direction, with a width of about $\Delta H = 13$ oe. The width of the line decreased with increasing temperature, and was 8 oe at 540°K. The existence of such a narrow resonance line opens up great possibilities for microwave applications of ferrite garnets. The use of ferrite garnets is of great importance for the construction of high-frequency amplifiers which are sensitive to signals and not noisy over the whole range of frequencies. Therefore it is natural that there are more and more papers in the literature on the resonance properties of ferrite garnet.

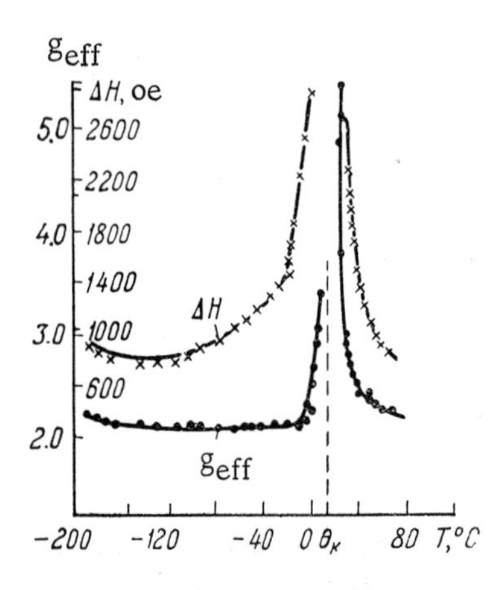


Fig. 119. Temperature dependence of the width ΔH of the resonance absorption line and of $g_{eff}$ in polycrystalline gadolinium ferrite garnet ($\nu$ = 9479 Mc).

Simultaneously with the studies of the resonance and magnetic properties of single-crystal specimens there have been studies of these same properties with polycrystalline specimens. It has been found that polycrystalline ferrite garnets which have a density smaller than the x-ray density have rather wide resonance lines, with widths exceeding 200 oe.

Figure 118 shows curves of the temperature dependences of the width ΔH of the absorption line, the g factor, and the amplitude A of the resonance maximum for a polycrystalline specimen of $3Y_2O_3 \cdot 5Fe_2O_3$ according to the data obtained by I. A. Malevskaya. At room temperature ΔH is ~ 850 oe (density ~3), and ΔH decreases rapidly with increase of the temperature. The reason for this is to be found in the porosity of the specimen. For polycrystalline specimens which have larger densities (~ 5 g/cm$^3$), $\Delta H(T)$ is the same as for single-crystal yttrium ferrite (cf. Kristallografiya 5, 732 (1960)).

The quantity A begins to show a change only near the Curie point; the g factor also decreases somewhat as the Curie point is approached.

In [197] measurements were made on the temperature dependence of the ferromagnetic resonance in polycrystalline gadolinium ferrite garnet (compensation point at 13°C) in the temperature range from 192 to 72°C (Fig. 119). Near the compensation point there is a maximum of the line width and the g factor decreases again with increasing temperature.

An increase of the g factor as the compensation point is approached has also been observed in other researches. In lithium chromite ferrite, for example, the value $g_{eff} \approx 7$ has been found [198], and in gadolinium ferrite $g_{eff} \approx 11$ [199].

A complete explanation of this phenomenon has not yet been found, but it is clear that the increase of the g factor above the value two is only an apparent one; it is not caused by an effect of the orbital magnetic moments on the g factor, but is due to a complex effect of the sublattice structure of the ferrite on its resonance properties. It must be noted that the temperature dependence of the resonance and also the temperature dependences of other frequency properties of ferrimagnetic substances have not been studied much up to the present (cf. [200]).

## § 8. "Nonmagnetic" Properties of Ferrimagnetic Materials in the Neighborhood of the Curie Point

Up to the present there are few data on the various "nonmagnetic" properties in the neighborhood of the Curie point for materials of the ferrimagnetic type (properties such as the specific heat, the thermal expansion, the electric conductivity, galvanomagnetic effects, etc.). Meanwhile these data are of great interest, because by using such data one could obtain additional information about the peculiarities of magnetic transitions in ferrimagnetic materials. A matter of the greatest interest is the study of electric phenomena in the neighborhood of the magnetic transition in ferrites which are electronic semiconductors. In the neighborhood of the Curie point, where the energy of the spontaneous magnetization undergoes great changes, one can expect that it has a particularly strong influence on the electronic state of a ferromagnetic semiconductor.

A careful study of the various electrical effects in the region of the Curie temperature is thus extremely important from the point of view of determining the effects of the ferrimagnetic and antiferromagnetic states on the energy spectrum of the electrons in a ferrimagnetic semiconductor.

Let us examine the nature of the changes of shape of the curve of the temperature dependence of the specific electric resistance in ferrites in the neighborhood of the Curie point. The temperature dependence of the specific resistance near the Curie point can be described by the function

$$\rho = Ae^{\frac{\Delta E}{kT}},$$

where $\Delta E$ is the activation energy [201, 202]. Figure 120 shows the curve of $\rho(T)$ from the data of [203] for a polycrystalline ferrite of 14.5 mole % NiO, 36 mole % ZnO, and 49.5 mole % $Fe_2O_3$. The same figure shows the curve of lg $\rho$ (1/T) for this material. At the Curie point there is a perceptible kink in the line of lg $\rho$ (1/T). Similar kinks in the straight-

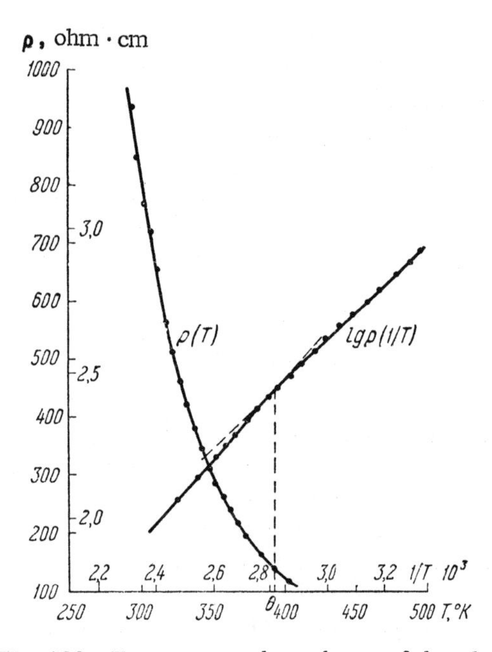


Fig. 120. Temperature dependence of the electronic resistance of a ferrite: 14.5 mole % NiO, 36 mole % ZnO, 49.5 mole % $Fe_2O_3$.

line plots of lg $\rho$ (1/T) at the Curie point have been obtained in [204] and [205]. The existence of these kinks is explained in a theoretical paper by Irkhin and Turov [206]. On the basis of the simplest many-électron model, in which the magnetic and electric properties of a crystal are described as the properties of a single system of many interacting electrons, these authors derived the result that the activation energy and the effective mass of the current-carrying excitons in ferromagnetic semiconductors depends on the spontaneous magnetization because of a "magnetizing" exchange interaction of the outer and inner electrons. This leads to an additional temperature dependence of the electric resistance which is especially strong near the Curie point. The straight line of lg $\rho$ (1/T) should have a kink when it passes through the Curie point.* The kink will be larger for cases in which there is a stronger exchange interaction between the outer and inner electrons.

The size of this effect can be smaller or larger in various ferrites, depending on their structural peculiarities, and also on the value of the electric resistance. The experiments show that the largest effects are characteristic for ferrites which have small specific resistance, because in these materials the activation energy $\Delta E$ is comparable with the magnitude of the energy of the spontaneous magnetization which is "released" as a result of the magnetic transition. According to the theory of Irkhin and Turov the slope of the straight line of lg $\rho$ (1/T) should increase as we go from the paramagnetic region to the ferrimagnetic region. This result of the theory is confirmed by experiment (cf. Figs. 120, 121).

It follows from the theoretical arguments that there can also be cases in which on passing from the paramagnetic to the ferrimagnetic or antiferromagnetic state a semiconductor goes into a "degenerate" electronic state and becomes similar to a metal in some respects [208], and thereafter again becomes a semiconductor. Evidently this must be the explanation of the complex nature of the kinks (the presence of "steps") which is observed in the curves of the temperature dependence for some ferrites.

---

* Yudin [207] has arrived at this same conclusion from somewhat different concepts.

Figure 121, based on the data of [205], shows the curve of lg ρ (1/T) for a single-crystal specimen of manganese ferrite of nearly stoichiometric composition (50 mole % MnO, 50 mole % $Fe_2O_3$). It can be seen that in the region of the Curie point there is a complicated kink with a "step." These more complicated kinks, accompanied by changes of the sign of the temperature coefficient of the electric resistance, are observed in such ferrimagnetic materials as chromium sulfide [209] and strontium manganite [210].

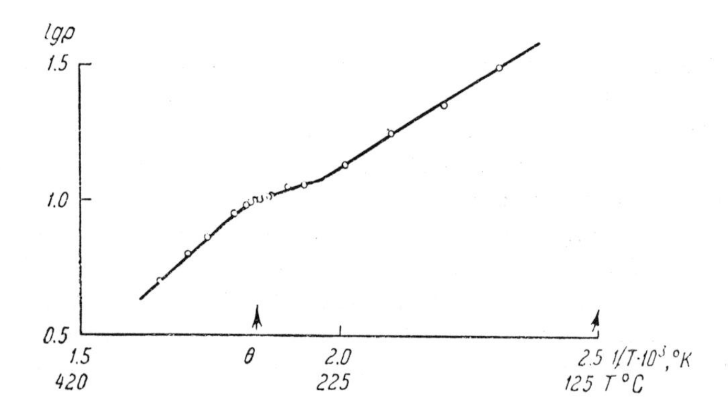


Fig. 121. Temperature dependence of the electric resistance for a single-crystal specimen of the ferrite 50% MnO, 50% $Fe_2O_3$.

The existence of sharp anomalies of the temperature dependence of the electric resistance at magnetic transitions in ferrites is confirmed by measurements of the galvanomagnetic effect ΔR/R [211]. Figures 122 and 123 show curves of the temperature dependence of the longitudinal

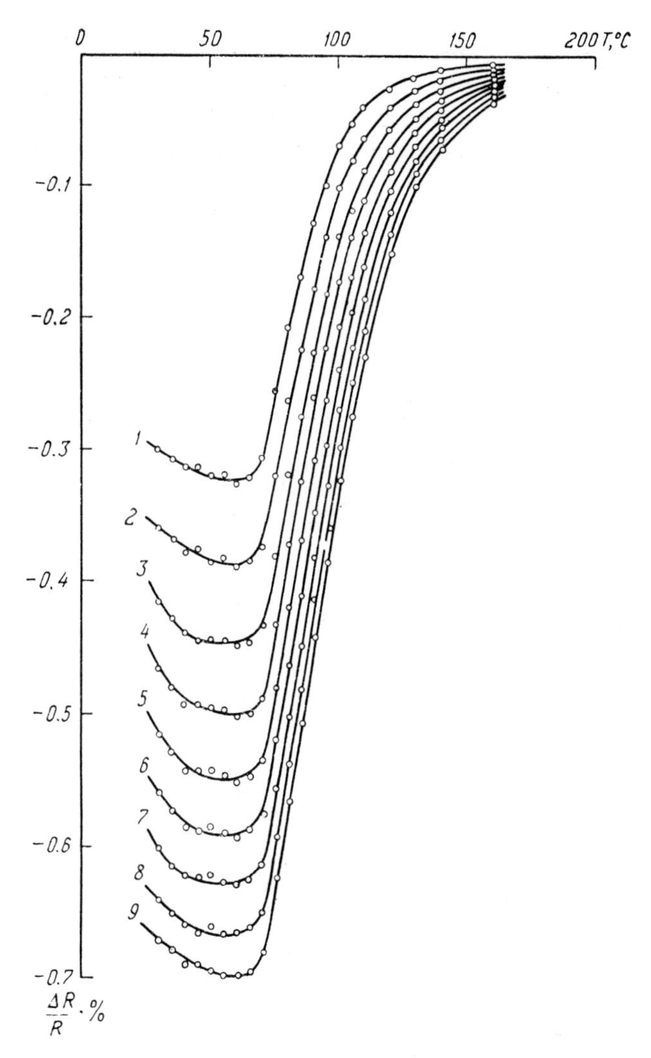


Fig. 122. Temperature dependence of the galvanomagnetic effect in the ferrite 14.5% NiO, 36% ZnO, 49.5% $Fe_2O_3$ at various magnetic fields. 1) H = 2000 oe; 2) H = 2500 oe; 3) H = 3000 oe; 4) H = 3500 oe; 5) H = = 4000 oe; 6) H = 4500 oe; 7) H = 5000 oe; 8) H = 5500 oe; 9) H = 6000 oe.

galvanomagnetic effect obtained in the neighborhood of the Curie point for a polycrystalline ferrite 14.5% NiO, 36% ZnO, 49.5% $Fe_2O_3$ [203] and for single-crystal manganese ferrite [211] of nearly stoichiometric composition. The galvanomagnetic effect (accompanying the para-process) shows a strong increase, and has a sharp maximum near the Curie point.

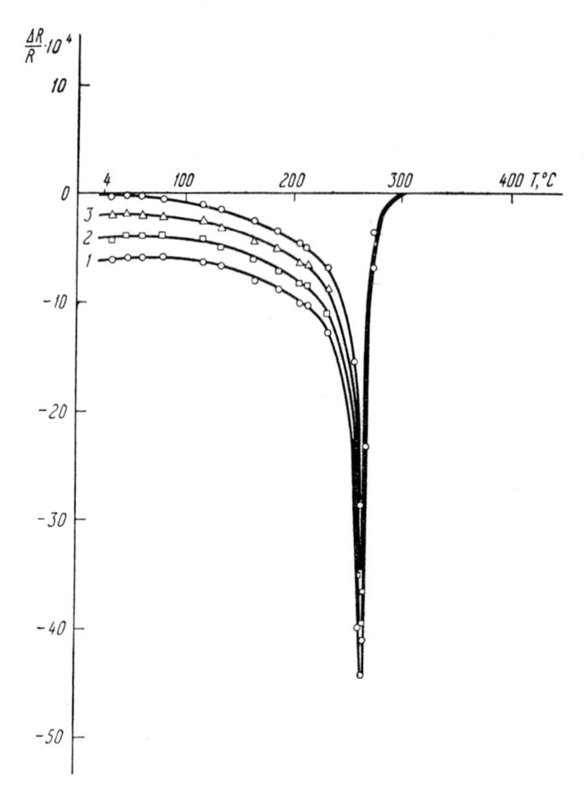


Fig. 123. Temperature dependence of the galvanomagnetic effect in a single crystal of manganese ferrite. 1) H = 1960 oe; 2) H = 1700 oe; 3) H = 1439 oe; 4) H = 1178 oe.

This increase of $\Delta R/R$ corresponds to the fact that there is a kink in the straight line lg $\rho$ $(1/T)$. Both phenomena are of the same nature: an influence of a change of orientation of the spins on the conductivity; in the first case the orientation is produced by an external field and in the second case by the internal molecular field.

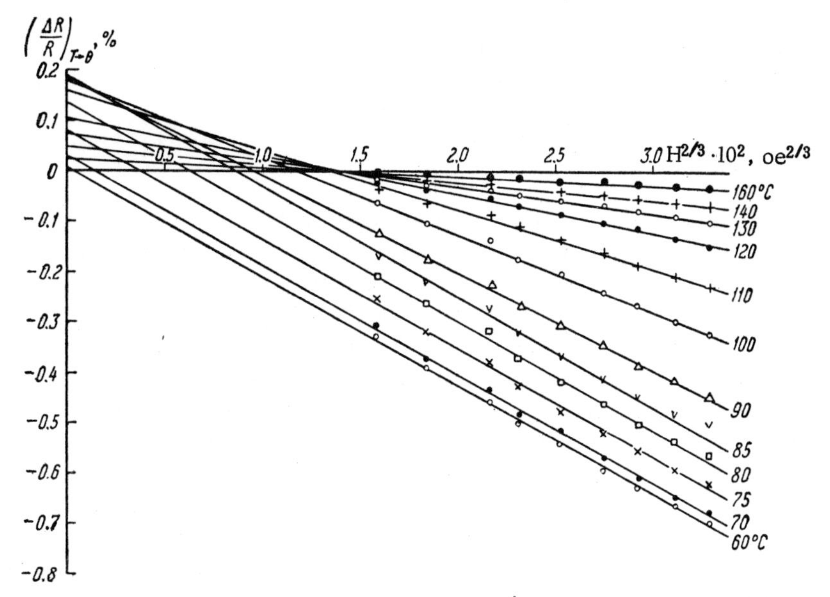


Fig. 124. Dependence of $(\Delta R/R)_{T \to \theta}$ on $H^{2/3}$ for the ferrite 14.5% NiO, 36% ZnO, 49.5% $Fe_2O_3$.

It must be noted that the size of the maximum of the curve of $(\Delta R/R)_\theta(T)$ at the Curie point is for ferrites of the same order of magnitude as for metallic ferromagnetic substances, or even somewhat larger. For single-crystal specimens the maximum is much sharper than in polycrystalline ferrites, since in single crystals the magnetic transition occurs in an extremely narrow temperature range, whereas in polycrystalline specimens it is more or less smeared out over a range of temperatures. In other respects the dependence of $\Delta R/R$ on H, σ, and T in the neighborhood of the magnetic transition is of the same general nature in ferrites as it is in metallic ferromagnetic material (cf. Chapter III, Sect. 13). As an example, Fig. 124 shows curves of $(\Delta R/R)_\theta (H^{2/3})$ for nickel-zinc ferrite [203]. In this case there is a good straight-line dependence of $(\Delta R/R)_\theta$ on $H^{2/3}$.

As for the other "nonmagnetic" anomalies in ferrites near the Curie point, there have been observations of the anomaly of the specific heat [212], the anomaly of the thermoelectric emf [213], and the anomaly of the thermal expansion [214].

An analysis of the behavior of the "nonmagnetic" properties of ferrites is difficult because of the scarcity of experimental data.

## § 9. Low-Temperature Transitions in Magnetite and Other Ferrites

In the low-temperature region (usually in the range from the ice point to the temperature of liquid nitrogen) certain ferrites show anomalies in the temperature dependence of the permeability, the electric conductivity, the elastic modulus, and other "nonmagnetic" properties. These anomalies have been studied in greatest detail in iron ferrite-magnetite, $Fe_2O_3$. Figure 125 shows the results of measurements of the initial permeability as a function of temperature in polycrystalline magnetite [215]. The maximum of the permeability at high temperatures is at the Curie point, and the maximum at low temperatures usually lies at temperatures 111-117°K (from -162 to -156°C). In this same temperature range there is a sharp variation of the electric conductivity [216, 217] (Fig. 126), the specific heat, the thermal expansion, and the elastic and other properties.

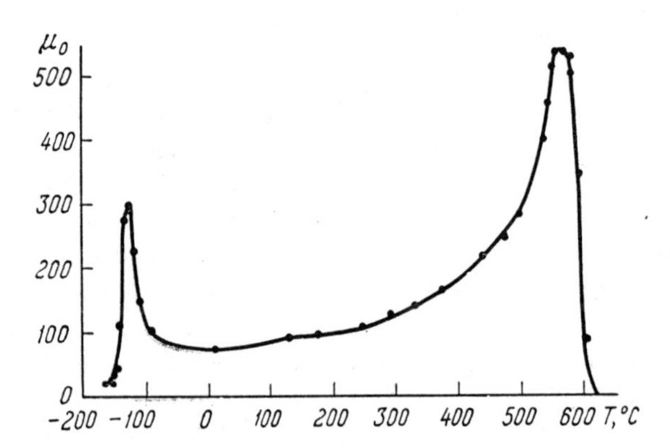


Fig. 125. Temperature dependence of the initial permeability $\mu_0$ in magnetite.

Figures 127 and 128, based on the data of [218], show the variation of Young's modulus and of the internal friction coefficient for a crystal of magnetite in the neighborhood of the temperature -160°C. It can be seen that in certain directions in the crystal the changes of these characteristics show maxima and minima. Furthermore these changes are practically unaffected by a magnetic field, i.e., they are not due to mechanical striction processes.

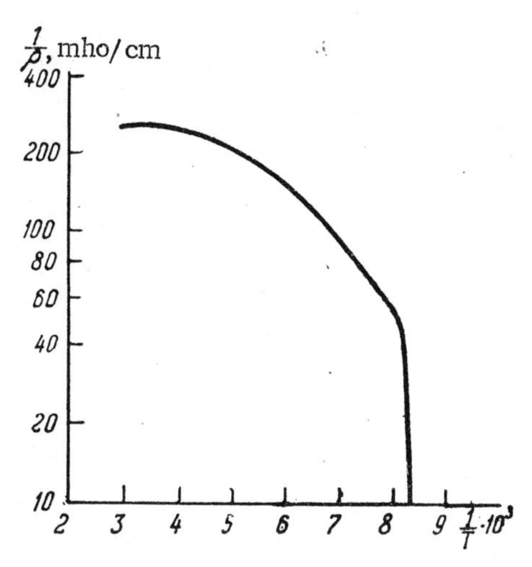


Fig. 126. Electric conductivity of magnetite near the low-temperature transition.

It is interesting to note that all of the anomalies that have been mentioned are spread over a certain range of temperatures and occur without thermal hysteresis on heating and cooling. In other words it would seem that we have here a phase transition of the second kind.

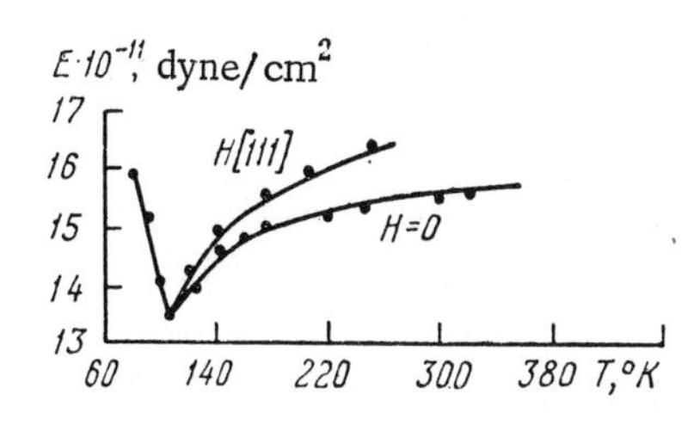


Fig. 127. Temperature dependence of Young's modulus for a crystal of magnetite in the [111] direction.

It must be noted that for a long time it was not possible to detect changes of the configuration of the lattice of magnetite at the low-temperature phase transition.

Eventually it was shown by careful x-ray studies [219] that below the transition point the spinel cubic lattice goes over into an orthorhombic lattice. After this it was easier to understand earlier observations of extremely peculiar magnetically anisotropic properties of magnetite in the region of the low-temperature transition. These properties are as follows.

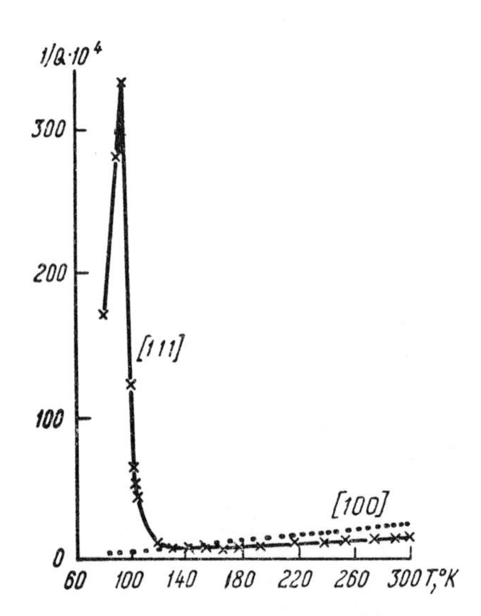


Fig. 128. Temperature dependence of the internal friction coefficient of a crystal of magnetite in the [111] and [100] directions.

On being cooled below the transition temperature (~ -160°C) in a strong magnetic field, a single crystal of magnetite acquires a uniaxial magnetic anisotropy (above the transition point the anisotropy is triaxial, corresponding to the spinel cubic lattice). The $\underline{c}$ axis of the orthorhombic crystal coincides with an edge of the original cubic lattice (the edge nearest to the direction of the field) and becomes the axis of easy magnetization. The $\underline{a}$ and $\underline{b}$ axes of the orthorhombic crystal coincide with face diagonals of the original cube; they are perpendicular to the $\underline{c}$ axis and are not axes of easy magnetization.

Thus when the crystal is cooled below the transition point in the presence of a magnetic field, the $\underline{c}$ axis is established in the crystal along the direction of the field. Furthermore the $\underline{c}$ axis can be displaced to a new position by a strong magnetic field.

Work done by Bickford [220] has revealed an effect of a unilateral pressure which is analogous to the effect of a field. He showed that a specimen of a magnetite crystal in the shape of a rod with its axis parallel to the [100] axis can be more easily magnetized in the region below the transition point if during the cooling through the transition temperature it is compressed along the axis of the rod. This effect is not observed in rods cut along the [110] and [111] directions.

The anisotropic properties of magnetite in the neighborhood of the low-temperature transition have been studied in detail in [221, 222, 223, 224]. A qualitative interpretation of the character of the low-temperature transition in magnetite was first given by Verwey and his collaborators [225, 226].

Magnetite belongs to the group of ferrites that have the inverse spinel lattice. A characteristic feature of this structure is that the atoms of divalent and trivalent iron ($Fe^{2+}$ and $Fe^{3+}$) in the elementary cell are distributed in such a way that half of all the $Fe^{3+}$ ions occupy crystallographic sites of one category (tetrahedral sites) and the other half of the $Fe^{3+}$ ions and all of the $Fe^{2+}$ ions occupy sites of the other category (octahedral sites).

Verwey suggested that above the transition temperature exchanges of electrons can easily occur between the $Fe^{3+}$ and $Fe^{2+}$ ions that are at the octahedral sites. This is due to the fact that the $Fe^{3+}$ and $Fe^{2+}$ ions are distributed at random over these sites and their positions are practically equivalent from the energetic point of view. He assumed further that at the transition temperature the statistical distribution of the $Fe^{2+}$ and $Fe^{3+}$ ions over the octahedral site is replaced by an ordered distribution and that the exchange of electrons is decidedly hindered. Thus according to Verwey the low-temperature transition in magnetite is accompanied by a new type of ordering-an electronic ordering in which the ions do not have to change their location in the lattice, but have only to exchange electrons. As a result of this transfer of electrons the distribution of the $Fe^{2+}$ and $Fe^{3+}$ ions in the lattice becomes an ordered one, i.e., the ions of a particular type are distributed in a regular way in the lattice plane. At the same time the lattice structure changes and there comes into existence a uniaxial symmetry (the lattice becomes orthorhombic). The ordered distribution of the iron ions in magnetite below the transition point is the cause of the appearance of the peculiar anisotropic magnetic and "nonmagnetic" properties noted above. An external field that acts during the cooling can assist the directed transfer of electrons between the $F^{2+}$ and $Fe^{3+}$ ions, and thus can produce an additional magnetic anisotropy.

It is very interesting to study the electric properties at the point of the low-temperature transition in magnetite, because one can thus obtain data to confirm the correctness of Verwey's hypothesis. It is well known that magnetite, unlike other ferrites, has a very high conductivity ($\sigma \approx \approx 200$ mho/cm) in the region above the transition point, whereas in other ferrites the conductivity is smaller by several orders of magnitude. The high conductivity of magnetite can be explained by the transfer of electrons between the $Fe^{2+}$ and $Fe^{3+}$ ions that are at the octahedral sites. When the material is cooled below the transition point, and the transfer of electrons is hindered (the mobility of the electrons is diminished), the conductivity falls sharply (cf. Fig. 126); moreover, one now finds a sharp anisotropy of the conductivity.

In [217] a detailed study was made of the anisotropy of the conductivity of magnetite below the transition poing (119.4°K) as a function of the crystallographic directions and the direction of the magnetic field that was applied during the cooling of the specimen. The results obtained fully confirmed the hypothesis of Verwey.

There has so far been very little study of low-temperature transition in other ferrites. There are indications that anomalies of the magnetic properties occur in cobalt ferrite in the temperature range from 85 to 93°K (from -180 to -188°C) [227]. Anomalies are also found in this region in the curve of the temperature dependence of the electric resistance. The authors of [227] believe that these anomalies are of a nature similar to that observed in magnetite.

Low-temperature anomalies have also been observed in nickel and manganese ferrites [228]. In manganese ferrites the transition region is very wide; it begins at room temperature and ends at a temperature -200°C. This is indicated by the data from measurements of the magnetization of manganese ferrites in weak fields (Fig. 129). In this case the magnetization does not increase as the temperature is lowered, but decreases sharply. Studies have also been made [229] on the temperature dependence of the elastic modulus E and of the internal friction coefficient (by an acoustical method) in single crystals of Mn-Zn ferrites. Peaks of the coefficient of internal friction were found in the crystallographic directions [111] and [110] at 11.4°K (for 5% Zn) and at 14°K (for 2.6% Zn); at these same temperatures the curves of E(T) have kinks, and the specific magnetization becomes smaller below the kinks (at lower temperatures). The authors suggest that the transition they have found in Mn-Zn ferrites is due to electronic ordering.

It must be remarked that whereas the nature of the low-temperature transition in magnetite has been studied in detail, the studies of low-temperature transitions in other ferrites are still inadequate.

## § 10. Ferrites in the Region above the Curie Point

In the region above the Curie point ($T > \theta_p$) ferrites show a very complex temperature dependence of the magnetic susceptibility, which is described by the Néel law. The presence of the term $\delta/(T - \theta)$ in the expression for the Néel law turns the linear dependence of the reciprocal of the magnetic susceptibility (which is found in metals and alloys) into a hyperbolic dependence in ferrites.

The reason that the temperature dependence of the susceptibility of ferrites is more complicated than that given by the Curie-Weiss law is that ferrites have a more complex magnetic structure than metals and alloys, namely the structure of uncompensated antiferromagnetism.

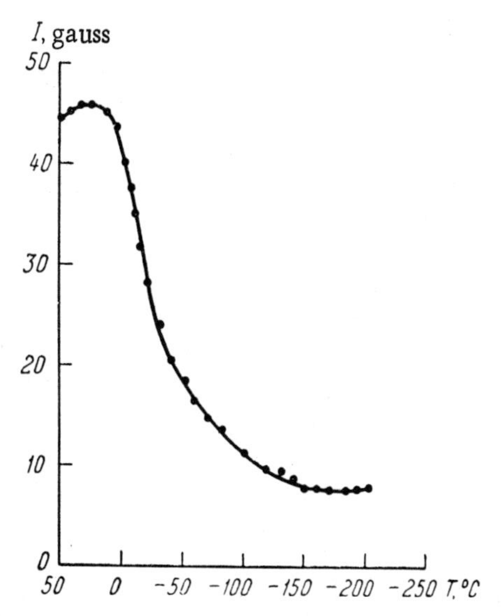


Fig. 129. Temperature dependence of the magnetization of manganese ferrite in a weak field in the low-temperature region.

For a suitable choice of the parameters $\delta$, $\theta$, $\chi_0$, and C [cf. Eq. (134)] the Néel law gives a satisfactory description of the experimental results for both simple and mixed ferrites.

The Néel law has been confirmed experimentally for magnetite [230], cobalt ferrite [231], yttrium ferrite garnet [232], and other simple and mixed ferrites [233].

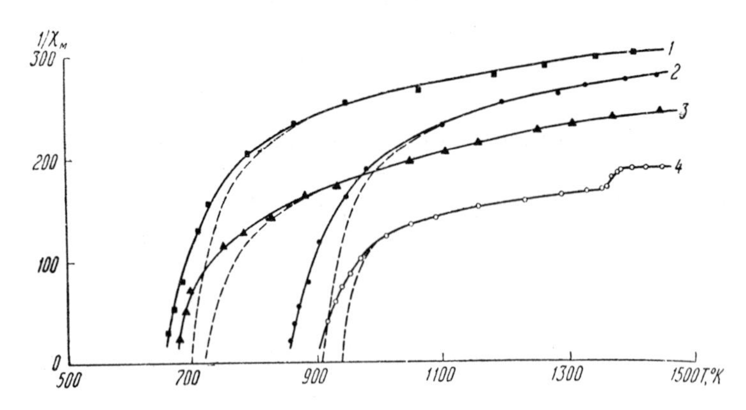


Fig. 130. Temperature dependence of the reciprocal of the magnetic susceptibility for various ferrites. 1) $MgO \cdot Fe_2O_3$; 2) $NiO \cdot Fe_2O_3$; 3) $MnO \cdot Fe_2O_3$; 4) $Li_2O \cdot Fe_2O_3$. The dashed lines show theoretical curves plotted from Eq. (134).

Figures 130 and 131 show curves of $(1/\chi_M)(T)$ ($\chi_M$ is the molar susceptibility] for several ferrites. The constants $\delta$, C, $\theta$, $1/\chi_0$ must be chosen by the method of successive approximations. The constant C can be found from the equation of the asymptote, $1/\chi_M = 1/\chi_0 + T/C$, and the other constants are determined by the method indicated in Néel's paper [159]. The values of these constants for several ferrites are given in Table 13.

It can be seen from the table that the values of the constants are very different for the different ferrites.

It follows from Figs. 130 and 131 that the Néel law holds over a wide range of temperatures, with the exception of a region immediately adjacent to the Curie point. In ferrites, as in ordinary ferromagnetic materials, one finds at the magnetic transition a transition region $\theta_f < T < \theta_p$ in which the magnetization depends not only on T but also on H (Fig. 132). The existence of the transition region can also be seen from the strong

TABLE 13. Values of the Constants for the Néel Formula

| Ferrite | $C$ | $\frac{1}{\chi_0}$ | $\delta$ | $\theta$, °K | $\theta_p$, °K | $\theta_f$, °K | $\theta_p-\theta_f$ |
|---|---|---|---|---|---|---|---|
| $Fe_3O_4$ | 14.2 | 103.2 | 15100 | 777 | 869 | 847 | +22 |
| $NiO \cdot Fe_2O_3$ | 23.2 | 231 | 11200 | 868 | 905 | 843 | +62 |
| $5Fe_2O_3 \cdot 3Y_2O_3$ | 50.0 | 30 | 990 | 570 | — | — | — |
| $0.3NiO \cdot 0.7ZnO \cdot Fe_2O_3$ | 10.0 | 143 | 49500 | 320 | 570 | 295 | +275 |

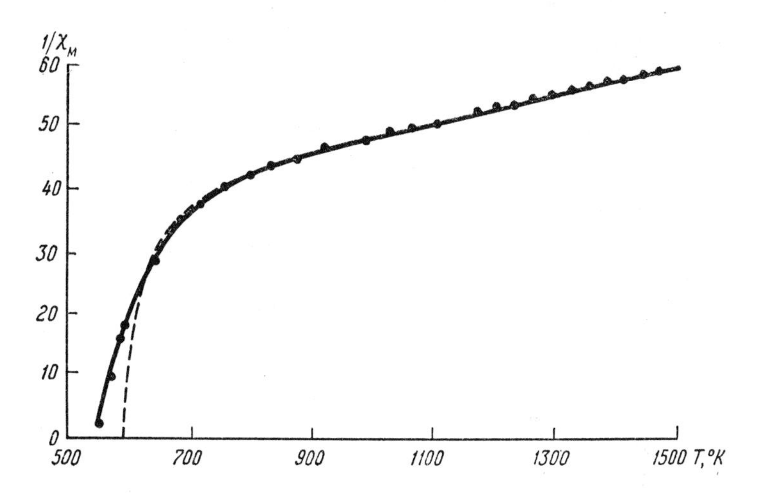


Fig. 131. Temperature dependence of the reciprocal of the paramagnetic susceptibility for yttrium ferrite garnet (the dashed curve is the Néel law).

deviation of the temperature dependence of the susceptibility from the Néel law (Fig. 133, from the data of [233]). The dependence of $\sigma$ on H becomes linear only when the temperature exceeds the value $\theta_f$ by a sufficient amount.

Volkov and Chechernikov [233] have made a detailed study of the transition region in simple and mixed ferrites and have found that in this region the magnetization curves can be described with good accuracy by

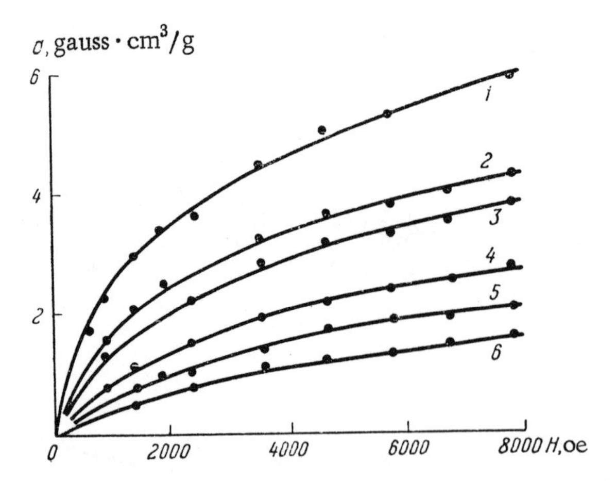


Fig. 132. Isotherms of the magnetization for the ferrite $MnO \cdot Fe_2O_3$ in the region $\theta_f < T < \theta_p$. 1) T = 631°C; 2) T = 640°C; 3) T = = 646°C; 4) T = 654°C; 5) T = 668°C; 6) T = 672°C.

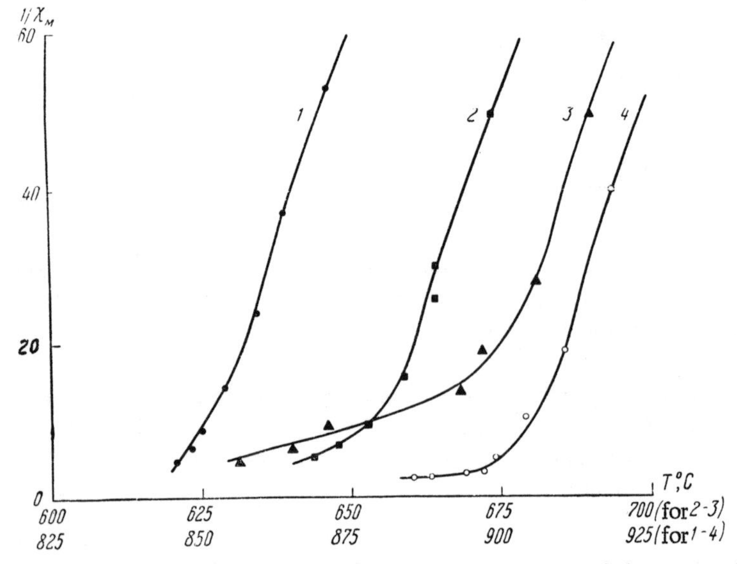


Fig. 133. Temperature dependence of the reciprocal of the susceptibility in the region $\theta_f < T < \theta_p$. 1) $NiO \cdot Fe_2O_3$; 2) $MgO \cdot Fe_2O_3$; 3) $MnO \cdot Fe_2O_3$; 4) $Li_2O \cdot Fe_2O_3$.

the empirical relation

$$A\sigma + B\sigma^3 + C\sigma^5 = H,$$

where A, B, C are constants.

As in the case of metallic ferromagnetic materials, the existence of a transition region is mainly due to inhomogeneities in the composition of the specimens that were studied. The width of the transition region can be characterized by the difference $\theta_p - \theta_f$. Values of $\theta_p - \theta_f$ for several ferrites are given in Table 13; the transition region is especially wide in mixed ferrites [233].

Chapter VI

# ON METHODS FOR MEASURING MAGNETIC AND "NONMAGNETIC" PHENOMENA IN THE NEIGHBORHOOD OF THE CURIE POINT

Near the Curie point the magnetization and the various "nonmagnetic" phenomena which accompany it are usually small in magnitude, and therefore there is a need to develop special and very precise methods for measuring them. One must also impose more stringent requirements on the properties of the heating furnace and the system for controlling the temperature. The point is that in the neighborhood of the Curie point, where the spontaneous magnetization disappears, the slightest temperature gradient along the length of the specimen can lead to falsification of the results of measurements of the temperature dependence of the magnetization and of the "nonmagnetic" properties (in the case of ferromagnetic materials different parts of the specimen can be in the ferromagnetic and the paramagnetic states). In the case of ferrites, which usually have small thermal conductivity, it is also easy for temperature gradients to occur if means are not used to establish stationary thermal conditions during the heating of the specimen. For these materials a much longer time is required to establish a given thermal condition than for metallic ferromagnetic materials.

## § 1. Methods for Measuring the Magnetization

The Induction Method. Figure 134 shows a schematic diagram of an apparatus [234] for measuring the temperature dependence of the magnetization and the susceptibility of ferromagnetic and ferrimagnetic materials near the Curie point. The specimen 1, in the form of a rod, is placed in the electric furnace 5, which has a bifilar winding, inside a water jacket 4, around which is placed a system of measuring windings 7, connected for differential measurements; these windings provide high sensitivity for measurements of small changes of the magnetization. The windings are placed one over the other and have different numbers of turns. Owing to a special choice of the cross sections these coils do not react to changes of the field of the magnetizing solenoid (without the specimen). When the specimen is placed in the windings a differential induced pulse of emf appears in them and is measured by a ballistic galvanometer and serves as a basis for calculating the magnetization of the specimen.

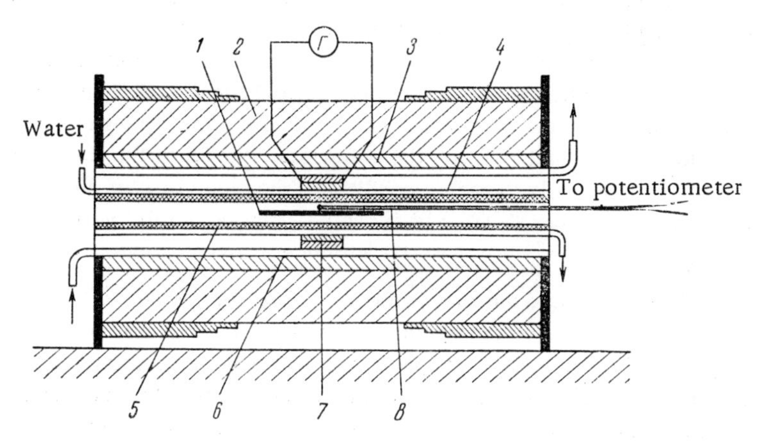


Fig. 134. Schematic arrangements for measuring the temperature dependence of the magnetization and susceptibility by the induction method. 1) specimen; 2) solenoid; 3) supplementary winding; 4) water jacket; 5) furnace; 6) water jacket of solenoid; 7) system of ballistic coils; 8) thermocouple.

In the neighborhood of the Curie point, owing to anomalies of the thermal expansion and to volume magnetostriction, the cross section of the specimen changes in a way which is hard to control (the change of the cross section can be particularly large in invar alloys, in which the volume effects in the neighborhood of the Curie point are extraordinarily large). To eliminate the influence of volume effects on the results of measurements of the magnetization it is necessary to refer the magnetic moment of the specimen to its mass instead of to the volume.

With the differential connection of the induction windings the magnetization per gram of the substance can be calculated by the following formula

$$\sigma = \frac{C'\rho l}{4\pi m (n_1 - n_2)} \alpha,$$

where C' is the ballistic constant of the apparatus, $\rho$, $l$, and $\underline{m}$ are respectively the density, length, and mass of the specimen, and $n_1 - n_2$ is the difference of the numbers of turns in the measuring coils, which usually is several thousand.

The system of measuring windings is placed (cf. Fig. 134) between the water jackets 4 and 6 (the latter is the water jacket of the magnetizing solenoid 2); this protects the windings from heating by the furnace and by the solenoid. Heating of the coils would not only lead to a change of their electric resistance, but would also cause a thermal change of their dimensions which would destroy the compensation. Since the two coils 7 are in approximately the same conditions, the phase shift of the induced emf in them is usually slight, and it can be eliminated relatively easily by connecting a capacity in parallel with one of the windings.

It must be pointed out that strictly speaking the method of "coils placed one inside the other" can be applied only to measure the magnetizations of sufficiently long specimens. For short specimens it would be incorrect to calculate the magnetization in the specimen by means of the usual formulas, since the flux in the air from the ends of the specimen will "cut" the turns of the measuring coils; the result of this is that the magnetization of the specimen calculated from the usual formula is smaller than the true value. Therefore it is necessary to carry out a calibration of the apparatus, i.e., to find experimentally the proportionality coefficient between the ballistic throw of the galvanometer and the magnetization of the specimen. For this purpose one uses a single-layer air-core coil: a single wire wound on a blank of the same shape and dimensions as the specimen. It is placed in precisely the position to be occupied by the specimen and a known current is passed through it.

The magnetic moment of the coil can be calculated and thus one can obtain a calibration of the apparatus.

The differential susceptibility $\chi = \Delta\sigma/\Delta H$ is measured in the following way. One first turns on the field H, and then by means of a bias winding (cf. Fig. 134) one applies a further field $\Delta H$ and measures $\Delta\sigma$. For measurements of small changes of the magnetization one can also use a vacuum-tube voltmeter with suitable amplifiers [69]. Particular care must be taken to assure that the temperature gradient along the length of the specimen is as small as possible. The temperature field inside the furnace is equalized by means of supplementary heating windings in the furnace, by placing copper cylinders in the furnace, and by regulating the flow of water through the water jacket. The current is ordinarily applied to the furnace from an alternating-current circuit through a voltage stabilizer (of the ferromagnetic resonance or of the electronic type), which assures constancy of the temperature to accuracy 0.1°C. The fractional error in measurements of the magnetization by this method is 1.5 to 2%.

The Ponderomotive Method. This method possesses high sensitivity, but is inferior in accuracy to the induction method. It is usually used for measurements on weak ferrimagnetic materials and also on antiferromagnetic materials, and is indispensable for measurements of the paramagnetic susceptibility (in the region $T > \theta_p$). Specimens in the shape of ellipsoids, disks, and cylinders with dimensions of a few millimeters are hung from a quartz fiber in a furnace with bifilar windings, which in turn is placed between the poles of an electromagnet or in a solenoid, which produces an inhomogeneous magnetic field. The value of the magnetic susceptibility is determined from the force of attraction of the specimen into the inhomogeneous field, by the formula

$$\chi = \frac{F}{mH\frac{dH}{dx}},$$

where F is the force of attraction, $m$ is the mass of the specimen, and dH/dx is the gradient of the field.

The force of attraction can be determined by means of a microbalance, a torsion balance, or a special spring dynamometer. The value of the product H(dH/dx) can be calibrated from substances with known susceptibility. The field strength is determined by means of a small coil connected to a ballistic device. In the neighborhood of the Curie point, where the magnetization is small, the demagnetizing field of the specimen is negligibly small and in practice one does not need to take it into account.

The fractional error in measurements of the susceptibility of ferromagnetic materials by the ponderomotive method is usually about 5%. Because of the smallness of the specimen the requirements on the homogeneity of the temperature field of the furnace are much less stringent than in the case of measurements made on long specimens by the induction method.

## § 2. Thermal Expansion and Magnetostriction

The literature contains descriptions of numerous methods for measuring thermal expansion and magnetostriction: the mechanical-optical, dilatometer, interference, and radiotechnical methods, a method based on a hydraulic device for magnifying displacements, and so on. Many of these methods, however, are of limited usefulness in measurements in the region of a magnetic transition, since they do not give the necessary accuracy. Other methods may give the required accuracy but are complicated to use.

A method which has recently come into wide use for measurements of magnetostriction and thermal expansion is that of attaching wire sensing elements to the specimen. This method is extremely simple, but has important shortcomings: the spread in the characteristics of the sensing elements leads to ambiguities in the readings, and such sensing elements cannot be used for high-temperature measurements. These shortcomings make it impossible to secure the necessary accuracy and sensitivity.

A method of wire tension sensors has recently been perfected for use in measurements of temperature-dependence quantities. Use has been made of the so-called "extension" wire sensor [235]. In this method the wire tension sensor is connected to the specimen being tested not directly but through an intermediate rod so that the sensor is not heated. Figure 135 shows schematically the arrangement of the apparatus. The specimen 2 is placed in the quartz tube 1 and the top of the specimen is pressed on by a second quartz tube 3 which carries a weight 4. The weight is necessary so that the specimen shall be firmly pressed against the bottom of the tube 1. Between the points a and b a nichrome wire of diameter 15-20 μ is attached by soldering to metal shackles. The ends of the wire are connected to a sensitive bridge circuit. The entire arrangement is placed in the furnace and solenoid. When the field is turned on the length of the specimen changes, the wire is stressed, and the change of its resistance is measured with the bridge. The fractional elongation on the application of the field or on heating (thermal expansion) can be calculated from the formula

$$\frac{\Delta l}{l} = \frac{R_{э}}{kR\alpha_{э}} \frac{L}{l} \alpha,$$

where k is the sensitivity to tension, R is the resistance of the wire, $R_s$ is the resistance of a calibrated standard resistance connected in series with

R, $\alpha_s$ is the deflection of the galvanometer connected in the null circuit when the resistance $R_s$ is short-circuited, and $\alpha$ is the deflection of the galvanometer when H is turned on; L is the length of the wire and $l$ is the length of the specimen. With this apparatus a sensitivity of $1 \cdot 10^{-8}$ has been achieved in the measurement of fractional elongation, with an error of 5%.

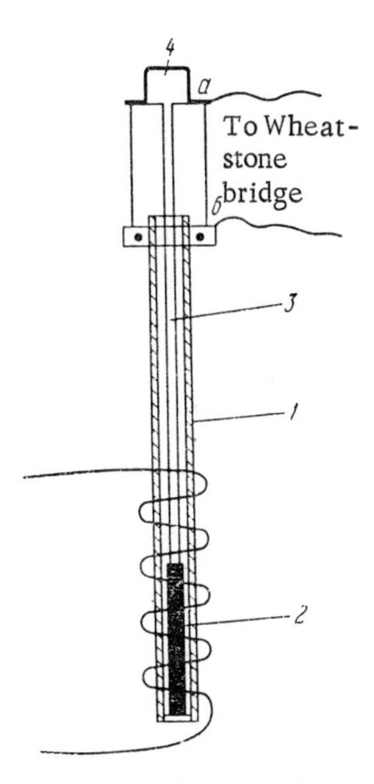


Fig. 135. Schematic arrangement for use of extension wire sensor.

A further improvement of the method of the extension sensor has been made in a paper by Levin [236]; he constructed a special apparatus for the measurement of magnetostriction and thermal expansion over a wide range of temperatures with an extremely sensitive "extension" wire sensor. Figure 136 shows the schematic arrangement of the apparatus. Inside the magnetizing solenoid 2 is mounted the electric furnace 4 with bifilar winding 3. To equalize the temperature a brass tube 5 is placed inside the furnace. The specimen 7 is placed inside the quartz tube 6. The lower end of the specimen is rigidly connected by means of a collar, a brass nut 9, a brass tube 10, and a nut 11 to the lower part of the tube 6. The upper end of the specimen is fastened with another collar and a nut 9 to a brass tube 14, which in turn is connected to the tension gauge contained in the head 1. The upper part of the quartz tube 6 is rigidly connected to the head. At the middle of the specimen are placed differential ballistic windings 8 (to measure the magnetization) and a thermocouple 13 (to measure the temperature). Water circulates between the walls of the solenoid and the furnace. The lower end of the furnace is closed by a plug 12.

For measurements at low temperatures the magnetostriction apparatus is mounted in a special cryostat (Fig. 137). To produce a continuous range of temperatures, for example from liquid-nitrogen temperature to room temperature, one uses a heating spiral 8, which is placed inside the Dewar flask 14 which contains the liquid nitrogen.

By means of a pump 15 one can produce various degrees of vacuum in the space where the specimen 10 is located, so as to regulate the passage of heat (from the spiral) to the specimen and thus establish any required intermediate temperature. The Dewar flask and heater are placed inside a magnetizing solenoid (not shown in the diagram).

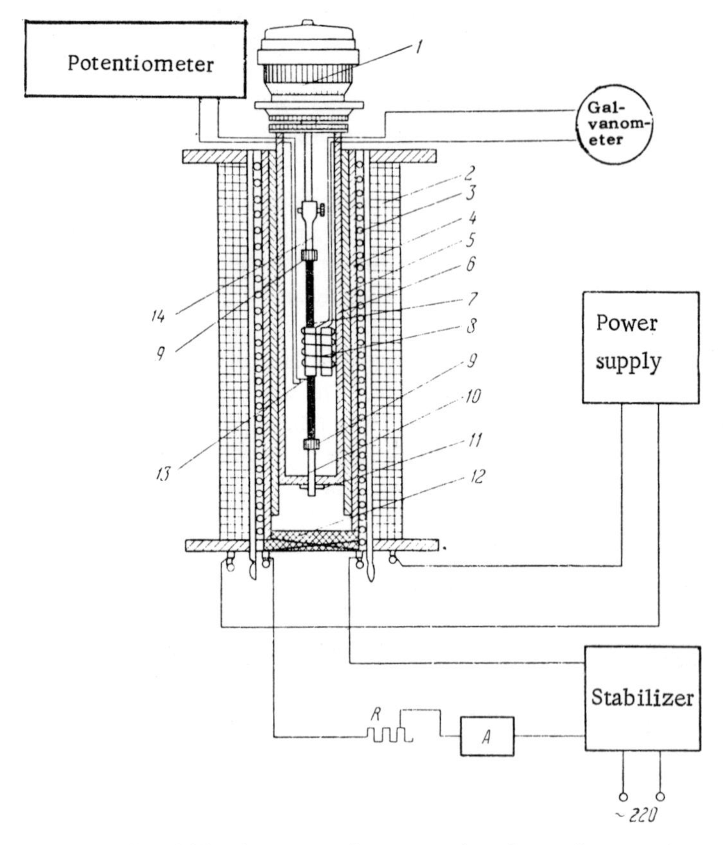


Fig. 136. Apparatus for measuring thermal expansion and magnetostriction by the method of the "extension" wire sensor.

A similar cryostat can be used for the study of the temperature dependence of the susceptibility of antiferromagnetic substances [129,

152]. In this case one mounts inside the cryostat one of the devices for measuring the force with which the specimen is attracted into an inhomogeneous magnetic field (the cryostat is placed between the poles of an electromagnet), and from the magnitude of this force one calculates the magnetic susceptibility.

## § 3. Elastic Moduli and Internal Friction Coefficient

To study the anomalies in the temperature dependence of the elastic properties of ferromagnetic, antiferromagnetic, and ferrimagnetic materials at the Curie point one must measure the moduli with greater accu-

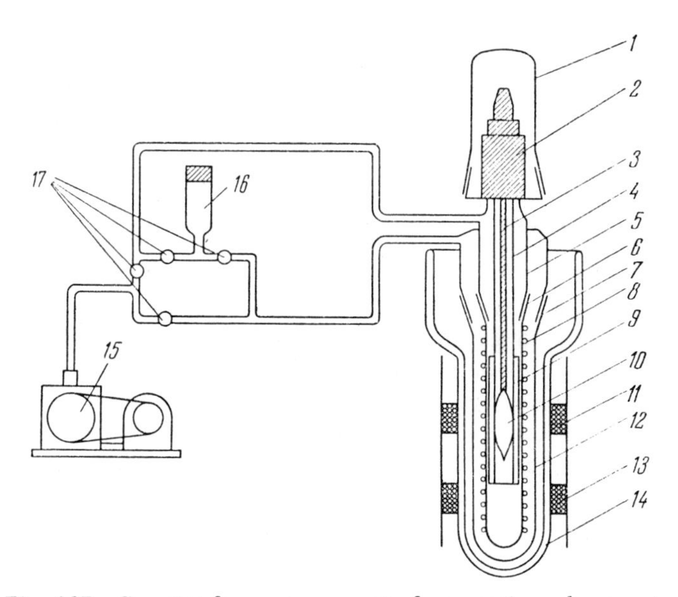


Fig. 137. Cryostat for measurement of magnetic and magnetostriction properties of ferromagnetic and antiferromagnetic materials. 1) Glass cover; 2) magnetostriction head; 3) quartz rod; 4) quartz bulb; 5) glass tube; 6,7) ground joints; 8) heating spiral; 9) copper tube; 10) specimen; 11) ballistic coil; 12) glass tube; 13) compensating ballistic coil; 14) Dewar flask; 15) vacuum pump; 16) hot-wire gauge for measuring vacuum; 17) vacuum stopcocks.

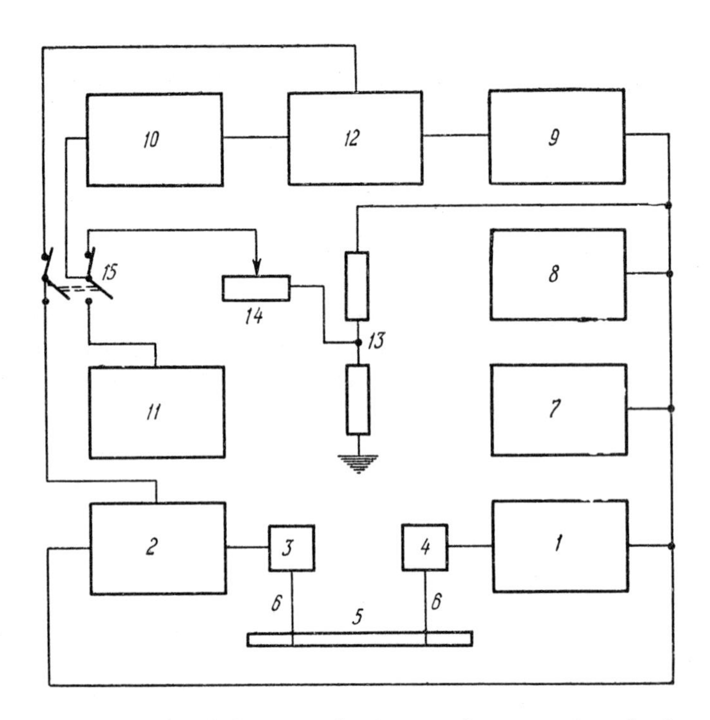


Fig. 138. Block diagram of apparatus for measuring elastic moduli and internal friction by using counting devices. 1) Amplifier with gain coefficient $10^5$-$10^6$ (with tunable filter); 2) cathode follower; 3) electrodynamic excitor; 4) piezoelectric sensor; 5) specimen; 6) suspension wires; 7) cathode-ray oscilloscope; 8) vacuum tube voltmeter; 9) counter; 10) counter of "quartz clock"; 11) quartz crystal oscillator, 50 kc; 12) electronic switch; 13) output voltage divider; 14) variable resistance for equalizing thresholds of counters; 15) double throw switch (position shown is that for measurement of the damping decrement).

racy than is provided by the apparatus that exists at present. We described below an apparatus which makes it possible to measure E(T) with increased accuracy [237]. The main difficulty in the use of resonance methods to measure elastic properties is in fixing the point at which resonance occurs. It is preferable to use the method of exciting vibrations of the specimen itself, since in this case the vibrations are automatically set up exactly under the conditions for the characteristic oscillations, however the stateof the specimen may vary. The greatest part of the error in measurements of elastic moduli is due to inaccuracy in determining the frequency, since wavemeters and frequency meters do not give high accuracy. New possibilities are provided by the use of counting devices which have been designed for counting the number of electric pulses. This method was first used for the measurement of elastic moduli in [238].

A block diagram of the apparatus is shown in Fig. 138. The output of the audio-frequency amplifier 2 is connected to the electrodynamic excitor 3 (electrodynamometer), and to the axis of the movable coil of this device there is attached a suspension of fine nichrome wire 6. The other end of the (cylindrical) specimen 5 is suspended from a similar wire 6 attached to the element of a barium titanate vibration sensor 4, which is attached to the input of the amplifier 1. When the voltage amplitude at the amplifier output is sufficiently large, the specimen becomes gradually excited from small accidental disturbances to bending vibrations at its fundamental natural frequency, and a stationary condition of vibrations is established. The amplitude of the fundamental vibrations is checked with a cathode-ray oscilloscope 7, which is also connected to the output of the amplifier. The output is also connected to a counting device 9 which has four decades of neon-lamp indicators and a mechanical counter (counting factor 10,000, type LP). This device counts harmonic frequencies in the kilocycle range with an accuracy of a single (incomplete vibration).

To calculate the frequency of the vibrations it is necessary to know the time and the number of vibrations. For measurements, however, it is far from being accurate enough to take the time of the vibrations of the specimen from a stop watch unless this time is extremely long. Therefore the apparatus includes another counter 10, whose input is connected to a quartz oscillator which gives a definite fixed frequency (50 kc). The inputs to the counters can be blocked with a constant voltage. A special electronic switch (type LS) 12 serves for the simultaneous blocking and unblocking of the inputs of the two counters. Thus during precisely the same time the counter 10 counts $n'$ vibrations given by the quartz oscillator (frequency $f'$), and the counter 9 gives $\underline{n}$ vibrations of the unknown frequency $f$. From this we have

$$f = \frac{n}{n'} f'.$$

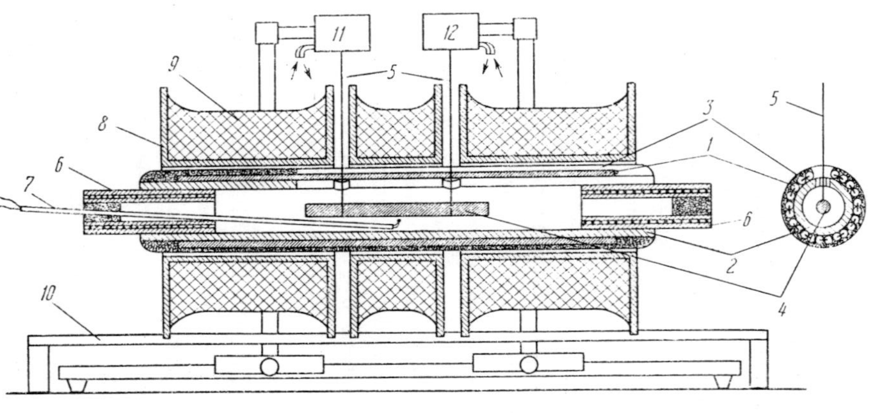


Fig. 139. Heating furnace and solenoid for the apparatus for measuring elastic moduli and internal friction coefficients. 1) Heating coil of the furnace in porcelain tubes; 2) brass tube with longitudinal slit; 3) adhesive coating and asbestos heat insulation of the furnace; 4) specimen in the loops of the suspensions placed near the nodes of its bending vibrations; 5) wire suspensions, diameter 0.1-0.05 mm; 6) supplementary heating windings; 7) copper-constantan thermocouple; 8) brass frames of three-section magnetizing coils; 9) magnetizing coils with equalizing layers in heat-stable silicone insulation; 10) guide frame for magnetizing coils; 11, 12) casings of excitor and detector.

Young's modulus E for a circular cylindrical specimen is calculated from the formula

$$E = 1\ 6388 \cdot 10^{-8}\left(\frac{l}{d}\right)^4 \frac{m}{l} f^2 \text{ km/mm}^2,$$

where $l$ is the length, d is the diameter, m is the mass of the specimen, and s is the resonance frequency.

For measurements at various temperatures the specimen is placed in a furnace (Fig. 139) with longitudinal slits for the suspension wires. Around the furnace there is a solenoid made up of three sections. In the furnace there is a copper screen and also special supplementary windings for equalizing the temperature of the furnace. With this apparatus the precision of measurements of elastic moduli is 0.1%, and in measurements of changes of a modulus the precision is 0.004%.

This apparatus can also be used for measuring the temperature dependence of the internal friction coefficient. For this purpose it is necessary to count the number of vibrations after the amplifier has been turned off, i.e., the number of vibrations during the damping process.

## § 4. Galvanomagnetic Effects

Methods for studying galvanomagnetic effects in metallic ferromagnetic substances have been repeatedly described in the literature (cf., e.g., [63]). Here we shall only touch on the question of measuring these effects in ferrimagnetic semiconductors. The study of galvanomagnetic effects in materials of this type is really only beginning.

Both longitudinal and transverse galvanomagnetic effects (including the Hall effect) are at present measured mostly for ferrimagnetic semiconductors which have relatively small electric resistance (magnetite, manganese ferrite, strontium manganite, etc). In this case the method used for the measurements are almost exactly the same as those used in the study of metallic ferromagnetic substances (direct-current potentiometer and bridge methods). The most diffi-

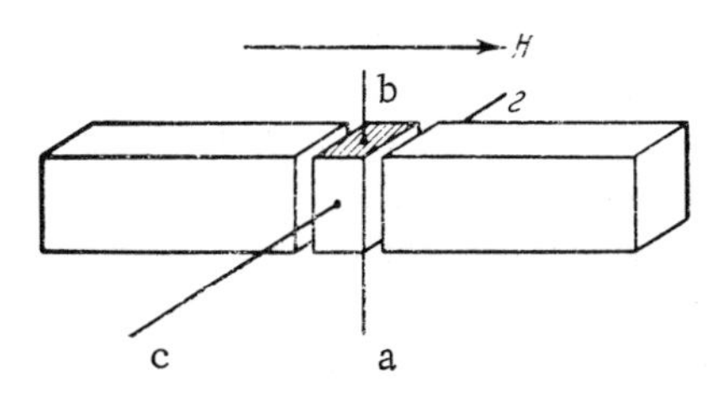


Fig. 140. "Cut" specimen for measurement of Hall effect in a ferromagnetic semiconductor.

cult problem is that of developing reliable electric contacts for supplying the current.

There are several methods for applying contacts to the ends of ferrite specimens: burning-in of silver paste, cathode sputtering of a metal in vacuum, the electrolytic method, etc. Experience with the use of these methods has shown that the most reliable is the method of burning-in a silver paste, although it has some inconvenient features (heating the specimen to 500°C) [205, 211].

As has already been noted, in work with ferrimagnetic semiconductors it is very important to anneal the specimen for a long time at each temperature before making the measurements, because this is necessary in order to establish a stationary thermal condition. In the case of measurements of the Hall effect there are two main requirements to be considered in choosing the shape of the specimen: the specimen must have the smallest possible demagnetizing factor in the direction of the field, and one must make sure that the lines of the electric field are uniformly distributed in the specimen, because this is necessary for correct calculation of the current density $\underline{j}$ (which occurs in the formulas for calculating the Hall effect).

Experience has shown that the most rational shape for a specimen for the study of the Hall effect in ferrites is that of a rod with "cuts." Figure 140 represents schematically the shape of such a specimen (of ferrite). The field is directed along the length of the specimen, because for this case the specimen has the smallest demagnetizing factor. The electric current is fed through the surfaces $\underline{a}$ and $\underline{b}$ of a parallelepiped cut from the specimen. Thin sheets of mica are placed in the gaps, and the specimen is firmly glued together (with silicone adhesive). In this way one secures electrical insulation of the parallelepiped from the other parts of the specimen, and the magnetic contact and demagnetizing factor remain practically unchanged (experiments have shown that the magnetization curve is practically the same before the specimen is cut and after it is glued together). Silver paste is burned into the upper and lower surfaces of the parallelepiped and then the current leads $\underline{a}$ and $\underline{b}$ are soldered to them. The Hall emf is measured through the wires $\underline{c}$ and $\underline{d}$; they are also attached to the specimen by burning-in silver.

A similar method for measuring the Hall effect in metallic ferromagnetic materials (with a "cut" specimen) has been described in [239].

## 5. Resonance Absorption

A block diagram of an apparatus for studying the temperature dependence of ferromagnetic resonance is shown in Fig. 141. The specimen to be studied is subjected to a weak radio-frequency field and a strong constant magnetic field. The source of the radio-frequency field is the klystron generator 2. The energy passes through a waveguide into the absorption cell 7, which consists of a short-circuited waveguide section, with the specimen in the shape of a small sphere fastened to its end wall by means of the holder 6. The specimen is fixed on the end of a rod and inserted through a hole in the "short-circuited" wall. The constant magnetic field produced by an electromagnet is directed perpendicular to the magnetic vector of the radio-frequency field; in this case one has the optimal

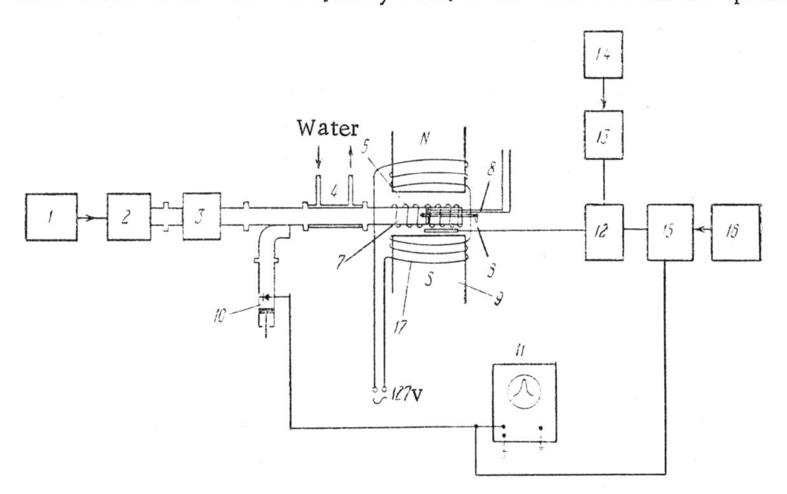


Fig. 141. Block diagram of apparatus for studying the temperature dependence of ferromagnetic resonance. 1) Power supply; 2) klystron generator; 3) valve; 4) waveguide section with cooled jacket; 5) heating spiral; 6) holder with sphere of ferrite to be studied; 7) absorption cell; 8) thermocouple; 9) electromagnet; 10) detector; 11) oscilloscope; 12) proton resonance system for measuring field intensity; 13) generator; 14) power supply; 15) amplifier; 16) power supply; 17) modulating windings on poles of electromagnet.

conditions for the resonance absorption of energy. The radio-frequency field energy reflected from the short-circuited section passes through a directional coupler into the detector section 10, from which it is fed to the oscilloscope 11. At resonance parts of the high-frequency power in the short-circuited section is absorbed by the specimen, and the detector and oscilloscope show a fall in the power. The valve 3, whose operation is based on the Faraday effect, serves to eliminate the effect of the reflected wave on the generator. In this apparatus the generator is tuned to a fixed frequency, and the resonance absorption line is made to pass through this frequency by varying the external magnetic field. For this purpose one superposes on the constant magnetic field an alternating field of low frequency (50 cps) so that the resonance absorption line undergoes periodic displacement relative to the source of the radio-frequency field. This modulation of the magnetic field is produced by supplementary windings 17 placed on the poles of the electromagnet. The absorption line can be observed directly on the screen of the oscilloscope, since the sweep is synchronized with the frequency of the modulating field.

The magnitude of the constant field is determined by a field-strength measuring device 12, which operates on the principle of proton magnetic resonance. The proton sensor (a substance containing hydrogen, for example, water or paraffin) is placed in the field of the electromagnet. The resonance signal that arises is fed through the amplifier 15 to the same plate of the oscilloscope as the reflected signal from the specimen being studied. By measuring the frequency of the proton resonance one can determine the intensity of the magnetic field with very high accuracy (to $10^{-4}$-$10^{-5}$ oe).

For measurements of the resonance at various temperatures the short-circuited waveguide section is placed in a bifilar heating spiral 5 or in a Dewar flask with liquid nitrogen (or liquid hydrogen or helium). The spiral is located so that the specimen is precisely at its center. So that the waveguide system may not get heated up, a waveguide section 4 with a water jacket is placed between the directional coupler and the short-circuited section.

The temperature measurements are made by means of the thermocouple 8, which has one junction in contact with the outside of the end wall of the short-circuited waveguide section. The good heat conductivity of the walls of the waveguide permits the use of this method for measuring the temperature.

For studying the resonance absorption in single crystals the rod 6 to which the specimen is attached is provided with a graduated circle; this makes it possible to turn the single-crystal specimen in various directions relative to the constant magnetic field and the perpendicular high-frequency field.

# MATERIAL ADDED IN PROOF

Chapter III, Section 15. Calculations made very recently on the basis of the general theory of phase transitions of the second kind with effects of relaxation phenomena included [240] (see also [241]) have shown that in a single-domain ferromagnetic material near the Curie point Young's modulus E and the logarithmic decrement $\delta$, which characterizes the absorption of energy in elastic vibrations, can be expressed by the following relaxation formulas:

$$E = E_0\left(1 - \frac{\Delta_E}{1+\omega^2\tau^2}\right); \qquad \delta = \pi\Delta_E \frac{\omega\tau}{1+\omega^2\tau^2}.$$

Here $E_0$ is Young's modulus without the effects of the ferromagnetic interaction; $\omega$ is the angular frequency of the vibrations; $\tau$ is the relaxation time; $\Delta_E$ is the degree of relaxation of the modulus; and $\tau$ and $\Delta_E$ are expressed in terms of the magnetic parameters of the ferromagnetic material in the following way:

$$\tau = \frac{1}{\gamma_0\left(\frac{H}{\sigma} + 2\beta\sigma^2\right)}; \qquad \Delta_E = \frac{E_0\gamma^2\sigma^2\rho}{\frac{H}{\sigma} + 2\beta\sigma^2}.$$

From these expressions it follows that in the static case $\omega = 0$ one should find at the Curie point with $H = 0$ a discontinuity of Young's modulus given by

$$\frac{\Delta E}{E} = \frac{\gamma^2\rho}{2\beta}E_0.$$

Application of a magnetic field, and also increase of the frequency of the vibrations, lead to a decrease of the discontinuity of Young's modulus and a "smearing out" of its temperature dependence; at the Curie point itself the discontinuity of Young's modulus decreases with increasing field according to the following law:

$$\frac{1}{\Delta E} = \frac{3\beta}{\gamma^2 E_0^2\rho} + \frac{\omega^2\beta^{1/3}}{3\gamma^2\gamma_0^2 E_0^2\rho} H^{-4/3}.$$

For the condition $\omega\tau = 1$ the internal friction has a maximum somewhat below the Curie point. When a field is applied this maximum should flatten out and move closer to the Curie point.

These effects should be large in substances with a sharp dependence of the exchange interaction on the interatomic distance, i.e., in substances which have a large magnetostriction constant $\gamma$ of the para-process (in alloys of invar and elinvar type). Experiment gives results which qualitatively confirm this theory.

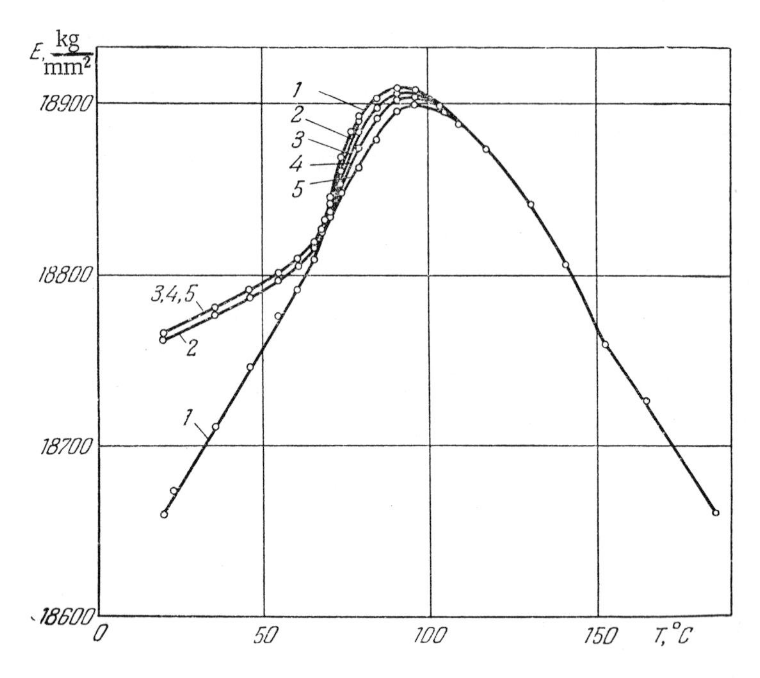


Fig. 142. Temperature dependence of Young's modulus for an alloy of 33.1% Ni, 7.4% Cr, 59.5% Fe. 1) Without field, 2) H = 84 oe, 3) H = 252 oe, 4) H = 503 oe, 5) H = 1006 oe.

Figure 142 shows the temperature dependence of Young's modulus taken for the demagnetized specimen and in various fields for an annealed alloy of 33.1% Ni, 7.4% Cr, 59.5% Fe. In the neighborhood of the Curie point (about 75°C) there is a clearly visible smeared-out discontinuity of the modulus (approximately 0.5% of E) and a decrease of the modulus in a magnetic field [240].

In Figure 143 one sees that near the Curie point (~ 110°C) there is a sharp maximum of the internal friction of an annealed alloy of 53.5% Co,

8.7% Cr, 37.8% Fe; this maximum decreases with increase of the magnetic field [240].

Chapter IV, Section 8. Using the Landau theory of phase transitions and the most general expression for the magnetic energy permitted by the symmetry of the crystal, Turov [242] has recently made a theoretical study of the weak ferromagnetism of the crystals $\alpha$-$Fe_2O_3$ and $MnCO_3$ far from the Curie point (at low temperatures). He considered the cases of "transverse" and "longitudinal" weak ferromagnetism (in the first case the spontaneous magnetization is perpendicular to the axis of

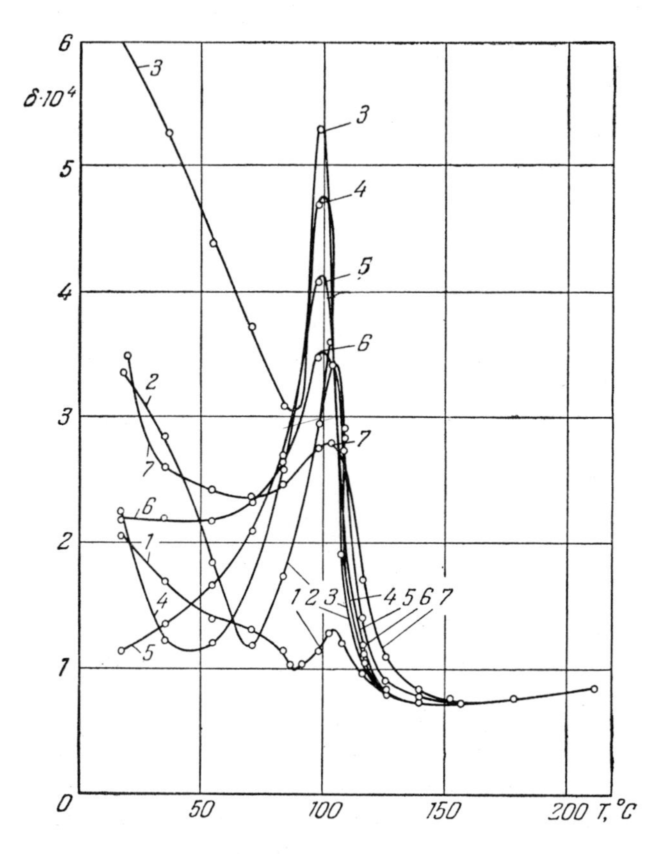


Fig. 143. Temperature dependence of the internal friction ($\delta = \pi/Q$) in the alloy: 53.5% Co, 8.7% Cr, 37.8% Fe. 1) Without field, 2) H = 4.2 oe, 3) H = 8.4 oe, 4) H = 34 oe; 5) H = 63 oe, 6) H = 168 oe, 7) H = 503 oe.

the antiferromagnetism and in the second case it is parallel to this axis) and calculated values of the energy of the spin waves, the magnetization as a function of the temperature, and the spin part of the specific heat.

Chapter V, Section 4. Studies made quite recently [243] have revealed new interesting features in the magnetic behavior of gadolinium ferrite with the garnet structure. Figure 144 shows isotherms of the longitudinal magnetostriction ($\lambda_{\parallel}$). It was found that whereas in the region above the compensation point ($\theta_k$) the magnetostriction curves behave "normally," i.e., display a saturation, in the region below $\theta_k$ the picture changes and a large positive component of the magnetostriction appears;

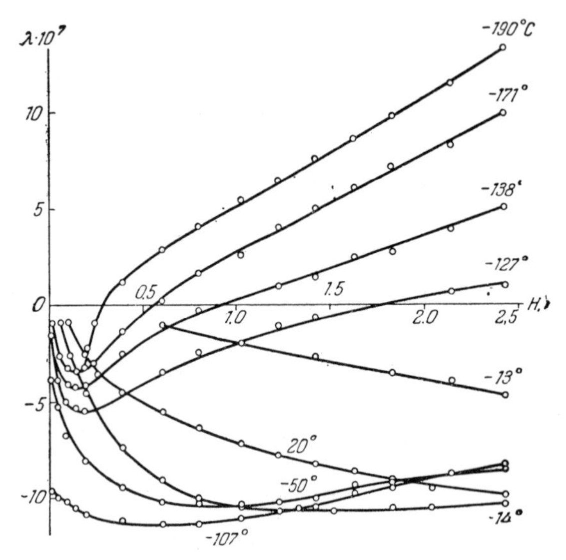


Fig. 144. Isotherms of magnetostriction in the ferrite garnet $3Gd_2O_2 \cdot 0.2\,Gd_2O_3 \cdot 4.8\,Fe_2O_3$.

the curves show no saturation in strong fields. It is clear that as the temperature is lowered (below $\theta_k$) there is a strong increase of the exchange magnetostriction of the para-process. These experimental data make us think that the Gd sublattice (sublattice c) and the Fe sublattices (sublattices a and d) manifest themselves differently in the magnetostriction. The large magnetostriction of the para-process is peculiar to the Gd sublattice (evidently this is due to the fact that the exchange interaction between the Gd ions depends very strongly on the interatomic distance). On the other hand the Fe sublattices are characterized by a very small magnetostriction of the para-process. When the temperature is lowered (below $\theta_k$) there is an increase of the fractional share of magnetization of the Gd sublattice in the total magnetization of the ferrite garnet, and therefore there is an increase of the magnetostriction of the para-process, which is the anomaly in question (not previously observed in ferromagnetic materials).

In a number of specimens of gadolinium ferrite garnet one finds in the region of nitrogen temperatures a peculiar magnetic hyperviscosity. The time for establishment of equilibrium magnetization amounts to hundreds of minutes. Evidently the cause of this phenomenon is also connected with a special behavior of the Gd ions in sublattice c.

Chapter V, Section 8. Up to the present there are very few data on the Hall effect in ferrites. Meanwhile the study of this effect is of great interest from the point of view of learning the nautre of the conductivity of ferrites and the connection between their magnetic and electric properties. In [244] measurements were made of the Hall emf as a function of the magnetization and the temperature in the neighborhood of the Curie point in nickel-zinc and manganese ferrites (with polycrystalline and single-crystal specimens). The expression used to describe the Hall effect near the Curie point was

$$E = R_0 H + R_s I_s + R_i I_i,$$

where $R_0$ and $R_s$ are the "ordinary" (or classical) and "spontaneous" Hall constants, $R_i$ is the Hall constant corresponding to the para-process, and $I_s$ and $I_i$ are the spontaneous and true magnetizations. Differentiating this relation with respect to H, we have:

$$\frac{\partial E}{\partial H} = R_0 + R_i \frac{\partial I_i}{\partial H},$$

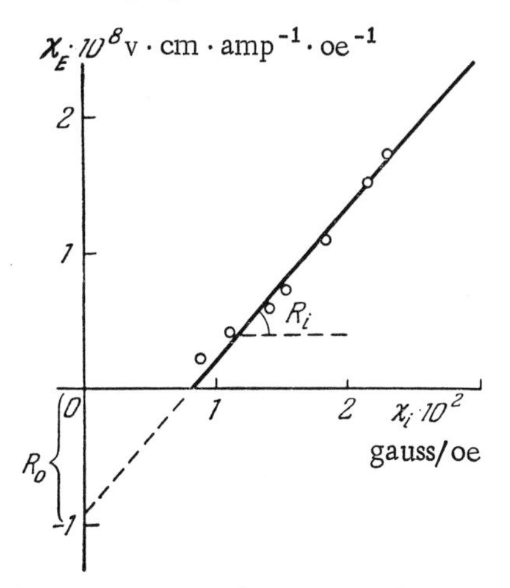


Fig. 145. Dependence of the "susceptibility" of the Hall emf on the susceptibility of the para-process (in the neighborhood of the Curie point) for the ferrite 37.5% NiO, 12.5% ZnO, 50% $Fe_2O_3$.

where $\partial E/\partial H = \chi_E$ is the "susceptibility" of the Hall emf [as determined from curves E(H)] and $\partial I_i/\partial H = \chi_i$ is the susceptibility of the paraprocess. Figure 145 shows the dependence of $\chi_E$ on $\chi_i$ for one of the nickel-zinc ferrites (at 12°C). The intercept on the vertical axis gives the quantity $R_0 \approx -0.9 \cdot 10^{-8}$ v · cm · amp$^{-1}$ · oe$^{-1}$, and the slope of the straight line gives the constant $R_i = +1.10^{-6}$ v · cm · amp$^{-1}$· gauss$^{-1}$. The negative sign of $R_0$ indicates that there is electronic conductivity in nickel-zinc ferrite. An estimate of the number of carriers of electricity can be made from the formula $R_0 = -3\pi/8$ en, where n is the concentration of electrons. For nickel-zinc ferrite $n = 1 \cdot 10^{19}$ cm$^{-3}$. Knowing the concentration n and the specific electric resistance (at 12°C), we can estimate the mobility, and for the given ferrite it is 0.08 cm$^2$ · v$^{-1}$ · sec$^{-1}$. Approximately the same values have been found in other ferrites. These values agree with those that have been found for nonferromagnetic oxide semiconductors. Thus the use of this method for processing the results of measurements of the Hall effect near the Curie point gives a possibility for analyzing the electric properties of ferromagnetic semiconductors.

# LITERATURE CITED


1. P. Curie, Journ. de Phys. 4, 197, 263 (1895).
2. W. Gilbert, Amsterdam (1651); J. Hopkinson, Proc. Roy. Soc. 44, 317 (1888).
3. P. Weiss and R. Forrer, Ann. d. Phys. 5, 153 (1926).
4. W. Gerlach, Z. Elektrochem. 45, 151 (1939); Usp. Fiz. Nauk 23, 368 (1940).
5. D. A. Rozhanskii, Zhur. Ross. Fiz. Khim. Obshch. 7, 25 (1926).
6. H. Potter, Proc. Roy. Soc. Lond. A 146, 362 (1934).
7. W. Sücksmith, J. Phys. Radium 12, 430 (1951).
8. R. Becker and W. Döring, Ferromagnetismus, Berlin (1939).
9. L. Landau and E. Lifshits, Statistical Physics [in Russian], Gostekhizdat (1951); L. D. Landau, Zhur. Éksp. i Teor. Fiz. 7, 19, 627 (1937); E. M. Lifshits, Zhur. Éksp. i Teor. Fiz. 11, 269 (1941).
10. S. V. Vonsovskii, Izv. Akad. Nauk SSSR (Ser. Fiz.) 11, 485 (1947).
11. V. L. Ginzburg, Zhur. Éksp. i Teor. Fiz. 17, 833 (1947).
12. V. K. Semenchenko, Zhur. Fiz. Khim. 21, 1461 (1947); 25, 121 (1951).
13. S. V. Vonsovskii and Ya. S. Shur, Ferromagnetism [in Russian], Gostekhizdat (1948).
14. N. S. Akulov, Ferromagnetism [in Russian], General Science and Technology Press (ONTI) (1939).
15. Ya. G. Dorfman, Magnetic Properties and Structure of Matter [in Russian], Gostekhizdat (1955).
16. P. Ehrenfest, Comm. Leiden Suppl. 756 (1933).
17. V. L. Ginzburg, Zhur. Éksp. i Teor. Fiz. 15, 739 (1945).
18. G. A. Smolenskii and N. V. Kozhevnikov, Doklady Akad. Nauk SSSR 76, 519 (1951).
19. Yu. B. Rumer, Usp. Fiz. Nauk 53, 245 (1954).
20. K. P. Belov, Fiz. Met. i Metalloved. 11, 447 (1956).
21. A. G. Samoilovich, Thermodynamics and Statistical Physics [in Russian], Gostekhizdat (1953).
22. L. D. Landau, Zhur. Éksp. i Teor. Fiz. 7, 1232 (1937).
23. Ya. I. Frenkel', Statistical Physics [in Russian], Acad. Sci. USSR Press (1948).
24. G. M. Bartenev, Zhur. Fiz. Khim 23, 1077 (1949); 24, 1437 (1950).

V. Yu. Urbakh, Candidate's Dissertation, Physics Faculty, Moscow State University (1955).

25. L. D. Landau and I. M. Khalatnikov, Doklady Akad. Nauk SSSR 96, 469 (1954).
26. J. Frenkel, Z. Physik 49, 31 (1928).
27. W. Heisenberg, Z. Physik 49, 619 (1928).
28. H. Potter, Phil. Mag. 13, 233 (1932).
29. M. Kornetzki, Z. Physik 98, 289 (1935).
30. W. Jellinghaus and H. Schlechtweg, Ann. Physik 2, 161 (1948).
31. C. Guillaud, Compt. Rend. 233, 1110 (1946); C. Guillaud and M. Roux, Compt. Rend. 229, 1133 (1949).
32. L. Néel, J. Phys. Radium 12, 258 (1951); M. Fallot and P. Maroni, J. Phys. Radium 12, 256 (1951).
33. W. Sücksmith and R. Pearse, Proc. Roy. Soc., Lond. A 167, 189 (1938).
34. F. Bloch, Z. Physik 61, 206 (1936); T. Holstein and H. Primakoff, Phys. Rev. 58, 1098 (1940).
35. N. N. Bogolyubov and S. V. Tyablikov, Zhur. Éksp. i Teor. Fiz. 19, 251, 256 (1949).
36. E. I. Kondorskii and A. S. Pakhomov, Doklady Akad. Nauk SSSR 106, 1139 (1954).
37. F. J. Dyson, Phys. Rev. 102, 1217, 1230 (1956) (also Probl. Sovr. Fiz., No. 2, 1950).
38. H. Kramers and G. Wannier, Phys. Rev. 60, 252 (1941).
39. F. Kaner, Zhur. Éksp. i Teor. Fiz. 10, 670 (1940).
40. E. Montroll, J. Chem. Phys. 9, 706 (1942).
41. P. R. Weiss, Phys. Rev. 74, 1493 (1948).
42. L. S. Stil'bans, Zhur. Éksp. i Teor. Fiz. 9, 432 (1939).
43. S. V. Vonsovskii and K. B. Vlasov, Zhur. Éksp. i Teor. Fiz. 25, 327 (1953).
44. K. B. Vlasov and S. V. Vonsovskii, Fiz. Met. i Metalloved. 2, 403 (1956).
45. F. Bitter, Phys. Rev. 54, 79 (1938).
46. V. Vonsovskii, Zhur. Tekh. Fiz. 18, 131 (1948).
47. A. P. Komar, Izv. Akad. Nauk SSSR (Ser. Fiz.) 11, 497 (1947).
48. E. I. Kondorskii and A. S. Pakhomov, Zhur. Éksp. i Teor. Fiz. 32, 323 (1957).
49. K. P. Belov and A. N. Goryaga, Fiz. Met. i Metalloved. 2, 441 (1956).
50. K. P. Belov and I. K. Panina, Doklady Akad. Nauk SSSR 111, 985 (1956).

51. Ya. Paches, Candidate's Dissertation, Physics Faculty, Moscow State University(1956); Czech. Phys. J. 7, 729 (1957).
52. K. P. Belov and Ya.Paches, Fiz. Met. i Metalloved, 4, 48 (1957).
53. A. N. Goryaga, Candidate's Dissertation, Physics Faculty, Moscow State University (1958).
54. R. Forrer, J. Phys. 1, 49 (1930); 4, 109, 86, 427, 501 (1933).
55. J. Went, Physica 17, 596 (1951).
56. W. Sücksmith, J. Phys. Radium 12, 430 (1951).
57. A. Simpson and R. Tredgold, Proc. Phys. Soc. B67, 38 (1954).
58. J. Grangl, Phil. Mag. 46, 499 (1955).
59. K. P. Belov and A. N. Goryaga, Izv. Akad. Nauk SSSR (Ser. Fiz.) 21, 1038 (1957).
60. A. Kussman and A. Schulze, Physik. Z. 38, 42 (1937).
61. D. I. Volkov and V. I Chechernikov, Zhur. Éksp. i Teor. Fiz. 27, 208 (1954).
62. S. V. Vonsovskii, Doklady Akad. Nauk SSSR 27, 650 (1940).
63. K. P. Belov, Elastic, Thermal, and Electrical Phenomena in Ferromagnetic Substances [in Russian], 2nd edition, Gostekhizdat (1957).
64. M. I. Zakharov and N. A. Khatanova, Kristallografiya 3, 378 (1958).
65. A. P. Komar and I. I. Portnyagin, Doklady Akad. Nauk SSSR 60, 569 (1948). R. G. Annaev, Magnetoelectric Phenomena in Ferromagnetic Metals [in Russian], Acad. Sci. Turkmen. SSR Press (1952).
66. E. Lapp, Ann. de Phys. 10, 422 (1929).
67. H. Klinghardt, Ann. Physik 84, 167 (1927).
68. R. Bozorth, Ferromagnetism, D. Van Nostrand Co., New York (1951).
69. L. Pal and T. Tarnotsi, Izv. Akad. Nauk SSSR (Ser. Fiz.) 21, 1055 (1957).
70. C. Guillaud, J. Phys. Radium 12, 223 (1951).
71. M. V. Dekhtyar, Fiz. Met. i Metalloved. 3, 55 (1956).
72. D. Smith, Phys. Rev. 102, No. 4, 959 (1956).
73. H. Ebert and A. Kussmann, Physik. Z. 38, 437 (1937).
74. K. P. Belov, Doklady Akad. Nauk SSSR 91, 807 (1948).
75. V. L. Ginzburg, Zhur. Éksp. i Teor. Fiz. 19, 36 (1949); Usp. Fiz. Nauk 38, No. 4 (1949).
76. B. M. Vul and L. F. Vereshchagin, Doklady Akad. Nauk SSSR 48, 662 (1945); G. A. Smolenskii and R. E. Pasynkov, Doklady Akad. Nauk SSSR 79, 431 (1951). L. P. Kholodenko and M. Ya. Shirobokov, Zhur. Éksp. i Teor. Fiz. 21, 1250 (1951). G. I. Skanavi, The Physics of Dielectrics [in Russian], Gostekhizdat (1949). E. V. Sinyakov and I. A. Izhak, Doklady Akad. Nauk SSSR 100, 243 (1955).

77. I. E. Dzyaloshinskii, Zhur. Éksp. i Teor. Fiz. 33, 807 (1957).
78. I. S. Zheludev and L. A. Shuvalov, Kristallografiya 1, No. 6 (1956).
79. R. V. Telesnin and E. F. Kuritsyna, Doklady Akad. Nauk SSSR 65, 797 (1950).
80. K. P. Belov and A. M. Kadomtseva, Vestn. Mosk. Univ., No. 2, 133 (1958).
81. V. V. Parfenov and V. P. Voroshilov, Izv. Akad. Nauk SSSR (Ser. Fiz.) 21, 1334 (1957).
82. I. K. Panina, Candidate's Dissertation, Physics Faculty, Moscow State Universtiy (1957). K. P. Belov and Z. D. Sirota, Zhur. Éksp. i Teor. Fiz. 36, 1058 (1959).
83. G. P. D'yakov, Izv. Akad. Nauk SSSR (Ser. Fiz.) 11, 667 (1947). L. V. Kirenskii and A. Ya. Vlasov, Izv. Akad. Nauk SSSR (Ser. Fiz.), No. 6 (1952). D. I. Volkov, V. I. Chechernikov, and V. B. Tseitlin, Vestn. Mosk. Univ., No. 2, 21 (1956).
84. R. Fowler and P. Kapitza, Proc. Roy. Soc. A124, 1 (1929).
85. S. V. Vonsovskii, Zhur. Éksp. i Teor. Fiz. 10, 761 (1940).
86. A. A. Gusev, Zhur. Éksp. i Teor. Fiz. 29, 181, 895 (1955).
87. L. Patrick, Phys. Rev. 93, 384 (1954).
88. K. P. Belov and G. A. Zaitseva, Fiz. Met. i Metalloved. 1, 404 (1955).
89. K. P. Belov, E. P. Svirina, and Yu. V. Belous, Fiz. Met. i Metalloved. 6, 621 (1958).
90. N. L. Bryukhatov and L. V. Kirenskii, Zhur. Éksp. i Teor. Fiz. 8, 198 (1938).
91. H. Williams and R. Bozorth, Phys. Rev. 56, 837 (1939).
92. L. A. Shubina, Izv. Akad. Nauk SSSR (Ser. Fiz.) 11, 527 (1947). V. I. Drozhzhina and Ya. S. Shur, Izv. Akad. Nauk SSSR (Ser. Fiz.) 11, 539 (1947).
93. R. Bozorth, J. Appl. Phys. 8, 575 (1937).
94. K. Honda, H. Masumoto, and S. Kaya, Sci. Rep. Tokyo Univ. 17, 111 (1928).
95. K. Honda, H. Masumoto, and I. Shirakawa, Sci. Rep. Tokyo Univ. 24, 391 (1935).
96. I. M. Puzei, Izv. Akad. Nauk SSSR (Ser. Fiz.) 21, 1088 (1957).
97. M. Wilkinson and C. Schull, Phys. Rev. 103, 516 (1956).
98. G. V. Spivak and T. N. Dombrovskaya, Doklady Akad. Nauk SSSR 106, 39 (1956). L. V. Kirenskii and I. F. Degtyarev, Zhur. Éksp. i Teor. Fiz. 35, 584 (1958).
99. Ya. Katszer, Izv. Akad. Nauk SSSR (Ser. Fiz.) 21, 1170 (1957).

100. I. A. Yakovlev, T. S. Velichkina, and K. N. Baranskii, Zhur. Éksp. i Teor. Fiz. 32, No. 4 (1957); 32, No. 9 (1957). I. A. Yakovlev and T. S. Velichkina, Usp. Fiz. Nauk 63, 411 (1957).
101. L. D. Landau and E. M. Lifshits, Physik.Z. Sowjetunion 8, 153 (1935).
102. C. Kittel, Phys. Rev. 71, 270 (1947); 73, 155 (1948); 76, 743 (1949).
103. J. Van Vleck, Phys. Rev. 78, 266 (1950).
104. V. K. Arkad'ev, Zhur. Ross. Fiz. Khim. Obshch., chast' fiz. 45, 312 (1913); Physik. Z. 14, 928 (1913).
105. J. Griffiths, Nature 158, 670 (1946).
106. E. K. Zavoiskii, Zhur. Éksp. i Teor. Fiz. 17, 883 (1947).
107. N. Bloembergen, Phys. Rev. 78, 572 (1950).
108. H. Kühlewein, Wiss. Veröf. Siemens-Werke, No. 1, 124 (1932).
109. A. S. Zaimovskii, Byulleten' VEI 2, 1 (1941).
110. F. Fraunberger, Z. Naturforsch. 5a, 129 (1950).
111. D. I. Volkov and V. I. Chechernikov, Izv. Akad. Nauk SSSR (Ser. Fiz.) 21, 1111 (1957).
112. M. Fallot, J. Phys. Radium 5, 153 (1944).
113. G. Gustafsson, Ann. Physik 28, 121 (1937); G. Manders, Ann. phys. 5, 167 (1937).
114. M. Wheeler, Phys. Rev. 56, 1137 (1939).
115. W. Pauli, Z. Physik 41, 81 (1927).
116. L. Néel Ann. phys. 17, 6 (1932); 5, 232 (1936).
117. L. D. Landau, Physik. Z. Sowjetunion 4, 675 (1933).
118. O. N. Trapeznikova and L. V. Shubnikov, Physik. Z. Sowjetunion 6, 66, 255 (1935).
119. S. S. Shalyt, Zhur. Éksp. i Teor. Fiz. 8, 518 (1938); Nature 143, 799 (1939).
120. H. Bizette, C. Squire, and B. Bsai, Compt. Rend. 207, 449 (1938).
121. L. Patrick, Phys. Rev. 93, 370 (1954).
122. A. Meyer and P. Taglang, Compt. Rend. 239, No. 23, 1611 (1954); A. Kussmann and E. Raub, Naturwissenschaften 42, No. 14, 411 (1955).
123. Antiferromagnetism, Collection of papers edited by S.V. Vonsovskii (Russian translations), Foreign Lit. Press, Moscow (1956).
124. J. Van Vleck, J. Chem. Phys. 9, 85 (1941).
125. N. N. Bogolyubov and S. V. Tyablikov, Zhur. Éksp. i Teor. Phys. 19, 256 (1949). S. V. Tyablikov, Fiz. Met. i Metalloved. 2, 193 (1956). A. Ts. Amatuni, Fiz. Met. i Metalloved. 3, 409 (1956).
126. M. I. Kaganov and V. M. Tsukernit, Zhur. Éksp. i Teor. Fiz. 34, 106 (1958).

127. K. B. Vlasov, Izv. Akad. Nauk SSSR (Ser. Fiz.) 18, 339 (1954).
128. A. S. Borovik-Romanov and N. M. Kreines, Zhur. Éksp. i Teor. Fiz. 31, 20 (1956).
129. A. S. Borovik-Romanov and N. M. Kreines, Zhur. Éksp. i Teor. Fiz. 33, 1119 (1957).
130. C. Gorter, Revs. Mod. Phys. 25, 332 (1953).
131. N. Poulis, G. Hardemann, and Bölger, Physica 18, 429 (1952).
132. M. O. Kostryukova, Doklady Akad. Nauk SSSR 96, 959 (1954).
133. J. Hölzl, Z. Physik 151, 220 (1958).
134. I. G. Fakidov and A. Ya. Afanas'ev, Fiz. Met. i Metalloved. 6, 176 (1958).
135. M. Foex, Compt. Rend. 227, 193 (1948).
136. N. Tombs and H. Rooksby, Nature 165, 442 (1950).
137. A. Snow, Revs. Mod. Phys. 25, 127 (1953).
138. Y. Y. Li, Phys. Rev. 100, No. 2,627 (1955).
139. M. Fine, Nature 166, 523 (1950).
140. H. Bizette, J. Phys. Radium 12, 161 (1951).
141. M. Trombe, J. Phys. Radium 12, 170 (1951).
142. C. Gorter, J. Phys. Radium 12, 275 (1951).
143. N. P. Grazhdankina, Zhur. Éksp. i Teor. Fiz. 33, 1524 (1957).
144. L. Maxwell and T. McGuire, Revs. Mod. Phys. 25, 279 (1953).
145. C. Kittel, Phys. Rev. 82, 565 (1951).
146. J. Ubbink, J. Poulis, A. Gerritsen, and C. Gorter, Physica 18, 361 (1951).
147. C. Gorter, Revs. Mod. Phys. 25, 332 (1953).
148. C. Shull and S. Smart, Phys. Rev. 75, 1008 (1949).
149. C. Shull, W. Strauser, and E. Wollan, Phys. Rev. 83, 333 (1951). R. P. Ozerov, Usp. Fiz. Nauk 47, 445 (1952). G. Bacon, Neutron Diffraction, Oxford 1955.
150. R. Erickson and C. Shull, Phys. Rev. 83, 208 (1951).
151. L. Néel, Ann. phys. 4, 249 (1949); Revs. Mod. Phys. 25, 58 (1953).
152. A. S. Borovik-Romanov and M. P. Orlova, Zhur. Éksp. i Teor. Fiz. 31, 579 (1956).
153. I. E. Dzyaloshinskii, Zhur. Éksp. i Teor. Fiz. 33, 807 (1957).
154. B. A. Tavger, Kristallografiya 3, 342 (1958).
155. F. Lotgering, Philips Reports 11, No. 3, 190; No. 4, 337 (1956); Usp. Fiz. Nauk 66, 247 (1958).
156. C. Guillaud, Thèse Strasbourg (1943).
157. J. Hastings and L. Corliss, Revs. Mod. Phys. 25, 114 (1953).
158. C. Shull, E. Wollan, and W. Koehler, Phys. Rev. 84, 912 (1951).

159. L. Néel, Ann. phys. 3, 137 (1948).
160. K. B. Vlasov and B. Kh. Ishmukhametov, Zhur. Éksp. i Teor. Fiz. 27, 73 (1954).
161. S. V. Vonsovskii and Yu. M. Seidov, Izv. Akad. Nauk SSSR (Ser. Fiz.) 18, 319 (1954).
162. E. I. Kondorskii, A. S. Pakhomov, and T. Shiklosh, Doklady Akad. Nauk SSSR 109, 931 (1956).
163. S. V. Tyablikov, Fiz. Met. i Metalloved. 3, 3 (1956).
164. J. Jafet and C. Kittel, Phys. Rev. 87, 290 (1952).
165. K. Niessen, Philips Res. Reports 9, 197 (1954).
166. K. P. Belov, K. M. Bol'shova, and T. A. Elkina, Izv. Akad. Nauk SSSR (Ser. Fiz.) 21, 1047 (1957).
167. W. Sücksmith and C. Clark, Proc. Roy. Soc. A225, 147 (1955).
168. C. Guillaud, J. Rech., C.N.R.S. Lab. Bellevue 12, 113 (1950).
169. R. Pauthenet, Ann. phys. 7, 710 (1952).
170. E. W. Gorter, Philips Res. Reports 9, 295-320, 321-365, 403-493 (1954); Usp. Fiz. Nauk 57, 279, 435 (1955).
171. E. W. Gorter and J. A. Schulkes, Phys. Rev. 90, 487 (1953).
172. K. P. Belov, K. M. Bol'shova, T. A. Elkina, and M. A. Zaitseva, Izv. Akad. Nauk SSSR (Ser. Fiz.) 22, 1282 (1958).
173. A. N. Men' and A. N. Orlov, Fiz. Met. i Metalloved 1, 410 (1955).
174. K. M. Bol'shova and T. A. Elkina, Vestnik Mosk. Gos. Univ., No. 4 (1959).
175. A. L. Mikaélyan, Radiotekhn. i élektron. 3, 1323 (1958).
176. J. Dillon, Phys. Rev. 105, No. 2, 759 (1957); B. Calhoun, J. Overmeyer and W. Smith, Phys. Rev. 107, No. 4, 993 (1957); J. Paulevé, Compt. Rend. 244, No. 14, 1908 (1957); 245, No. 19, 1604 (1957).
177. F. Bertaut and F. Forrat, Compt. Rend. 242, 382 (1956).
178. R. Pauthenet, Compt. Rend. 242, 1859 (1956), R. Aléonard, J. Barbier, and R. Pauthenet, Compt. Rend. 242, 2531 (1956); R. Pauthenet, Compt. Rend. 243, 1499 (1956). R. Pauthenet, Compt. Rend. 243, 1737 (1956); L. Néel F. Bertaut, F. Forrat, and R. Pauthenet, Izv. Akad. Nauk SSSR (Ser. Fiz.) 21, 904 (1957).
179. S. Geller and M. Gilleo, Acta Cryst. 10, 239 (1957).
180. J. Nielsen, J. Appl. Phys. 29, No. 3, 390 (1958).
181. L. Néel, Compt. Rend. 239, 8 (1954).
182. A. Harpin et P. Mériel, J. Phys. Radium 18, No. 6, 32 (1957).
183. G. Villers and J. Loriers, Compt. Rend. 245, No. 23, 2033 (1957); R. Pauthenet, J. Appl. Phys. 29, No. 3, 253 (1958); M. Gilleo and S. Geller, J. Appl. Phys. 29, No. 3, 380 (1958).

184. N. P. Grazhdankina and I. G. Fakidov, Doklady Akad. Nauk SSSR 93, 429 (1953); 102, 957 (1955). F. S. Smirnov, Zhur. Tekh. Fiz. 23, 50 (1953).
185. T. Hirone, S. Maeda, and N. Tsuya, J. Phys. Soc. Japan 9, 496 (1954); E. Uchida, J. Phys. Soc. Japan 10, 517 (1955).
186. K. P. Belov, A. V. Zalesskii, and A. S. L'vova, Kristallografiya 1, 696 (1956).
187. R. Benoit, Compt. Rend. 234, 2175 (1952).
188. L. Néel, Proc. Phys. Soc. A65, 869 (1952); Revs. Mod. Phys. 25, 60 (1953).
189. E. Uchida and K. Kondoh, J. Phys. Soc. Japan 10, 357 (1955).
190. K. P. Belov and A. V. Zalesskii, Kristallografiya 3, 388 (1958).
191. D. Healy, Phys. Rev. 86, 1009 (1952).
192. T. Okamura and Y. Kojima, Phys. Rev. 86, 1040 (1952).
193. J. Galt, W. Jeger, and F. Merritt, Phys. Rev. 93, 1119 (1954).
194. J. Dillon, S. Geschwind, and V. Jaccarino, Phys. Rev. 100, 750 (1955).
195. P. Tannenwald, Phys. Rev. 100, No. 6, 1713 (1955).
196. S. Krupička, Czech. Phys. J. 7, 344 (1957)
197. B. Calhoun, J. Overmeyer and W. Smith, Phys. Rev. 107, 993 (1957).
198. J. Van-Wierlingen, Phys. Rev. 90, 488 (1953).
199. J. Paulevé, Compt. Rend. 241, No. 6, 548 (1955).
200. L. A. Fomenko, Usp. Fiz. Nauk 64, 669 (1958).
201. G. A. Smolenskii, Izv. Akad. Nauk SSSR (Ser. Fiz.) 16, 728 (1952).
202. A. S. Mil'ner and O. P. Kirichenko, Doklady Akad. Nauk Ukr. SSR No. 2, 258 (1955).
203. A. N. Goryaga and L. I. Koroleva, Vestnik Mosk. Gos. Univ., No. 3-4 (1955).
204. A. P. Komar and V. V. Klyushin, Izv. Akad. Nauk SSSR (Ser. Fiz.) 18, 400 (1954).
205. K. P. Belov and E. V. Talalaeva, Nauch. Dokl. Vyssh. Shkol., Fiz. Matem. Nauki, No. 2, 220 (1958). K. P. Belov, A. A. Popova, and E. V. Talalaeva, Kristallografiya 3, 733 (1958).
206. Yu. P. Irkhin and E. A. Turov, Fiz. Met. i Metalloved. 4, 7 (1957).
207. A. A. Yudin, Zhur. Éksp. i Teor. Fiz. 33, 873 (1957).
208. Yu. P. Irkhin, Candidate's Dissertation, Ural Branch, Academy of Sciences (1958).
209. N. P. Grazhdankina and I. G. Fakidov, Izv. Akad. Nauk SSSR (Ser. Fiz.) 21, 1116 (1957).
210. J. Volger, Physica 20, 49 (1954).

211. K. P. Belov and E. V. Talalaeva, Zhur. Éksp. i Teor. Fiz. 33, 1517 (1957).
212. L. Bochirol, Compt. Rend, 232, 1474 (1951).
213. S. A. Varchen'ya and Ya. G. Dorfman, Radiotekhnika i Élektronika, No. 3, 345 (1957).
214. L. Weil, Compt. Rend. 231, 122 (1950).
215. J. L. Snoek, New Developments in Ferromagnetic Materials. Elsevier Publ. Co., Amsterdam (1947).
216. P. A. Khalileev, Phys. Z. Sowjetunion 7, 108 (1935).
217. B. Calhoun, Phys. Rev. 94, No. 6 (1954).
218. M. Fine and N. Kenney, Phys. Rev. 94, No. 6, 1573 (1954).
219. S. Abrahams and B. Calhoun, Acta Cryst. 6, 105 (1953). H. Rooksby and B. Willis, Acta Cryst. 6, 565 (1953).
220. L. Bickford, Revs. Mod. Phys. 25, No. 1 (1953).
221. Ching Hgien Li, Phys. Rev. 40, 1002 (1932).
222. H. Williams, R. Bozorth, and M. Goertz, Phys. Rev. 91, 1107 (1953).
223. N. L. Bryukhatov, Izv. Akad. Nauk SSSR (Ser. Fiz.) 21, 1268 (1957). N. P. Narovskaya, Kristallografiya 3, 346 (1958).
224. N. S. Korolevskaya and A. S. Mil'ner, Fiz. Met. i Metalloved. 3, 186 (1956).
225. E. Verwey and M. Heilmann, J. Chem. Phys. 15, 174 (1947).
226. E. Verwey, P. Haaymann and F. Romeijn, J. Chem. Phys. 15, 181 (1947).
227. C. Guillaud and H. Creveaux, Compt. Rend. 230, 1256 (1950).
228. T. Okamura and J. Simoizaka, Phys. Rev. 83, 664 (1951).
229. D. Gibbons, J. Appl. Phys. 28, 810 (1957).
230. M. Fallot, J. Phys. Radium 12, 256 (1951).
231. M. Fallot and P. Maroni, J. Phys. Radium 12, 256 (1956).
232. R. Aleonard, J. Cloube Barbier, and R. Pauthenet, Compt. Rend. 242, No. 21, 2531 (1956).
233. D. I. Volkov and V. I. Chechernikov, Nauch. Dokl. Vyssh. Shkol., Fiz. Matem. Nauki, No. 2, 210 (1958); Vestnik Mosk. Gos. Univ. No. 2, 101 (1959).
234. K. P. Belov, Uchen. Zap. Mosk. Gos. Univ. 162, 21 (1952).
235. K. P. Belov and V. V. Shmidt, Zhur. Tekh. Fiz. 23, 44 (1953). A. V. Zalesskii, Pribory i Tekh. Éksper., No. 4, 71 (1958).
236. L. S. Levin, Izmerit. Tekh., No. 5 (1956).
237. G. I. Kataev, Zavodsk. Labor., No. 10, 1258 (1958).
238. F. Forster, Industrie Anzeiger 77, No. 64 (1955).

239. N. V. Vol'kenshtein and G. V. Fedorov, Fiz. Met. i Metalloved. 2, 377 (1956).
240. K. P. Belov, G. I. Kataev, and R. Z. Levitin, Zhur. Éksp. i Teor. Fiz. 37, 938 (1959).
241. V. M. Shmatov, Fiz. Met. i Metalloved., Nos. 3 and 5 (1959).
242. E. A. Turov, Zhur. Éksp. i Teor. Fiz. 36, 1254 (1959).
243. K. P. Belov, M. A. Zaitseva, and A. V. Ped'ko, Zhur. Éksp. i Teor. Fiz. 36, 1672 (1959).
244. K. P. Belov and E. P. Svirina, Zhur. Éksp. i Teor. Fiz. 37, No. 11 (1959).